STRUCTURE I

NEW YORK · CHICAGO

Readings for

THE
GOLDEN ECHO

Sister Mary Rosenda

O.S.F., Ph.D.
ALVERNO COLLEGE
MILWAUKEE, WISCONSIN

W. H. SADLIER, INC.

ACKNOWLEDGMENTS

Grateful acknowledgment is made to the following publishers for permission to reprint material in copyright:

Golden Press, Inc., New York: THE ILIAD and THE ODYSSEY, Homer, text reprinted by permission from THE ILIAD AND THE ODYSSEY as told by Jane Werner Watson, illustrated by Alice and Martin Provenson. Copyright © 1956 by Golden Press, Inc.

J. B. Lippincott Company, Philadelphia: MORTE D'ARTHUR, Sir Thomas Malory, from BOOK OF KING ARTHUR AND HIS NOBLE KNIGHTS, adapted by Mary McLeod. Reprinted by permission of the publisher, J. B. Lippincott Company.

TABLE OF CONTENTS

THE MINSTREL AND HIS WORLD

One day, a little less than three thousand years ago, a brightly painted ship came sailing into a harbor of the land that is now called Greece.

On the ship's deck crouched a man with a rough goat's wool cloak wrapped around him. Under the cloak he held a finely carved lyre. This was the most precious thing the man owned, for he was a wandering minstrel. He traveled from place to place, singing songs that told the tales of great heroes and brave deeds.

News of the minstrel spread quickly. First to hear about him were the fishermen mending their nets on the shore. They sent a boy hurrying up the path to the towns back in the hills. He called out to the lookouts on the stone walls around the towns.

"A minstrel is here!" he said. "He has just this moment arrived on a swift ship from Smyrna!"

The lookouts shouted down the news to the crowded streets. Before the doorways of their stone huts, workers in leather and metal smiled as they used their needles and hammers. They passed on the word to the traders and visiting farmers at the open market place in the center of town.

Gathered in the market place that day, to decide upon some laws, were the town leaders—the men who owned land. They, too, heard of the minstrel. Eagerly they turned to the king of the town, who sat on his carved stone bench.

Before long, the king announced that he would give a banquet at the palace on the hilltop. Everyone was welcome to take part in the feast, and to hear the singing of the minstrel.

The food for the banquet was prepared by slaves. They were

the people of captured towns, or the wives and children of enemy warriors killed in battle. They roasted meat on turning spits, heaped baskets with bread, mixed wine with water and spice.

When all was ready, the minstrel was given a place of honor —a seat draped with a soft, thick rug. And after the feasting, he tuned the strings of his lyre and began his songs. They were really long stories that were sung instead of told—stories of men and gods, of wars and adventure, of strange and wonderful happenings in history and legend.

Even then, the stories were already old. They had never been written down, for there were no books in those days. But one minstrel learned the stories from another, and so they were kept alive for hundreds of years.

Gods were just as important as men in these stories. The people of ancient times lived close to nature, and they believed that everything in nature was the work of gods in human form. Trees, streams, the winds, the seas, even the earth itself—all had their gods.

The gods were ruled by Zeus, the god of the sky. He was the father of the gods, and spoke in the thunder. In his palace on cloud-encircled Mount Olympus the gods gathered for their banquets, just as the people of a town gathered at the palace of their king.

Zeus had a jealous wife, Hera, and many children. Among them were young Apollo, the sun god, and his shy twin sister, Artemis, goddess of the moon. Both could strike down people by shooting them with arrows of sickness. Some other gods were Athena, wisest and greatest of the goddesses; clever and crippled Hephaestus; Demeter, goddess of the earth; and Poseidon, god of the seas.

The gods could never die. They could fly through the air, change their forms, and even make themselves invisible. But, just as nature is changeable, so were the gods. A god might help a man one day, and turn against him the next. And so the people built shrines and temples in every town, and prayed and made sacrifices to the gods. And the minstrels never failed to tell of the doings of the gods in their stories.

Each minstrel told his tales in his own way—and the greatest minstrel was Homer. He was one of the master storytellers of all time, and the first whose name has come down in history.

Countless people of many nations have enjoyed Homer's tales. Reading the ILIAD, which tells of the Trojan war, they heard the clang of armor, tasted the dust of the battlefield, and saw great warriors fight each other to the death. Reading the ODYSSEY, they shared the adventures of Odysseus, a brave and powerful man who boldly faced the terrors he met on land and sea.

Today, centuries after Homer sang to his lyre, the ILIAD and the ODYSSEY are still two of the greatest and most wonderful stories ever told.

WHY THE TROJAN WAR CAME ABOUT

Hundreds and hundreds of years ago—perhaps 3,500 years —there was a proud trading city called Ilium or Troy.

Now across the Aegean, on the mainland we call Greece, and on many of the islands dotted about that small sea, were other cities and rugged towns whose men also traded by sea. There was rivalry between these cities and Troy for many years. At last there was a long and terrible war. This is how, according to old legends, that war came about.

King Priam of Troy and his wife Queen Hecuba had many sons and daughters. But when one of these babies was about to be born, the queen dreamed that he would grow up to be a flaming torch and would destroy the city. In those days people believed strongly in dreams; so the sad father and mother, when a fine baby son arrived, decided that he must be left on the slopes of nearby Mount Ida to die to save the city they loved.

They entrusted the sad task to a shepherd. But the shepherd was a kindly man, and had no children. So he kept the baby and raised him as his own.

The boy was named Paris, and he grew up a strong, handsome shepherd lad with no thought that he was the son of a king. But your fate, so people thought in those days, was something you could not escape. And so young Paris' destiny caught up with him at last.

Up on Mount Olympus, where men's fates were often decided by the immortal gods, three goddesses quarreled one day. The three were Hera, queen of the gods, Athena, the goddess of wisdom, and Aphrodite, goddess of beauty. They quarreled as to which of them was the most beautiful, and they decided to put the choice to a mortal man.

Down went the three to the slopes of Mount Ida, and whom should they find there but Paris, quietly tending his sheep. The goddesses asked him to choose between them; but then, quite unfairly it seems to us, they began to offer him gifts. Hera offered him the greatest of powers over armies and men, if he would only choose her; Athena offered him all knowledge; but Aphrodite offered him the most beautiful woman in the world for his wife if he would choose her, so he did.

Now Paris was no longer satisfied with his quiet life on the mountainside. Down into the city of Troy he went to seek the fortune the goddess had promised him. There his charm of face and manner and his skill at games soon brought him to the court of the king. It was not long before his story came out, and his happy parents, pushing aside their fears, welcomed back their long-lost son. Soon Paris was sent off with a fleet of his own to trade and see the world.

That was where the trouble came in. Paris had not forgotten the promise the goddess had made, and wherever he went he looked for the beautiful woman who had been promised to him.

He soon heard of a woman who was famed far and wide as the most beautiful in the world. She was Helen of Sparta. So to Sparta he went, and he found that the stories were true. Paris fell in love with Helen at once, and when he sailed away he took her with him, home to Troy to be his wife.

Now this would all have been very well, but for the fact that Helen was married already. Her husband was the red-haired Spartan king, Menelaus by name. And he was as angry as you can imagine when his wife sailed away to Troy.

Menelaus went at once to his brother, Agamemnon, king of golden Mycenae. Together the two planned their revenge. From island to island, from town to town they sailed, visiting every city-state of Greece, building up an army and a fleet of ships to win back Helen and to punish Troy.

They beached their boats at last on the Trojan shore. Then, in a sweeping curve around their boats, they threw up a great wall of earth as a shelter for their camp. Behind this wall, close to the high-prowed boats, they built themselves huts, and built them well. And those huts were to be their homes through ten long, weary years of war.

First one side, then the other had victories through the years. But the Trojans could never burn the Greek boats, or force them out to sea. And the Greeks could never break through the city walls to win back Helen from Troy.

So it is at the end of the ninth long year of war that Homer's story begins.

THE
ILIAD

THE ILIAD

The Quarrel

This is the story of one man's anger, of all the troubles it brought to the Greeks, and of all the warriors it sent down to Hades in death.

Achilles was the man, and his anger rose when he quarreled with the great King Agamemnon. It happened that the Greeks took as prisoner Chryseis, the daughter of a priest of Apollo, and she was given to King Agamemnon. Her father offered rich ransom for her, but Agamemnon rudely sent him away.

The old man went, but when he reached the shore of the sea, he lifted his hands in prayer to Apollo and asked a curse on the Greeks.

Down from Olympus charged Apollo, bow in hand, quiver of arrows on his back. Into the Greek camp he sent arrows of sickness, until day and night fires burned for the dead.

"Apollo is angry," said the Greeks' seer, "because the daughter of his priest was not returned home. He will not stop shooting his arrows of sickness until she is returned and proper offerings are made."

Now Agamemnon leaped up in anger. "Let the girl be returned, for the safety of the army. But I will not be done out of my prize. Let something of equal value be found for me, or I shall send men to Odysseus' tent, or to Ajax's, or Achilles', and take one of their prizes for my own."

"You greedy schemer," Achilles sneered. "I will take my

ships and sail back home rather than stay here to be insulted and pile up riches for you."

"Go home with your ships and men," replied Agamemnon. "I will not beg you to stay. But now, to show you who is the stronger, I shall send to your tents and take the girl Briseis, who is your prize. Then others will know enough not to cross me this way."

This stabbed proud Achilles to the heart. He turned on Agamemnon with searing words.

"You good-for-nothing, with the eyes of a dog and the heart of a frightened deer! Listen now, while I take a solemn oath. As surely as this staff I hold will never grow again, never again put forth twigs and leaves—just as surely the day will come when all you Greeks will miss Achilles. And as your men fall by hundreds before Hector of Troy, you will beat your breasts in sorrow for having trampled on the best man of all."

With these words Achilles flung down his gold-studded staff and sat down in his place, while Agamemnon glared at him.

After this the assembly was dismissed, and Achilles, followed by his men, went off to his ships and huts.

Agamemnon promptly sent Chryseis home by a ship under Odysseus' command. But he did not forget his quarrel with Achilles. He sent two unwilling heralds to the hut of Achilles, to bring Briseis to him.

When the men had led the weeping Briseis away, Achilles, sad at heart, walked down beside the sea. And he cried out to his mother, the sea-nymph Thetis, as she sat beside her father, the god of the sea. Up she came, rising like a gray mist from the water. Sitting down beside her son, she gently stroked his hand.

"My son," she said, "tell me why you weep, so that I may sorrow with you."

So, although as a goddess she knew everything, Achilles told her all that had happened that day.

"Go to Zeus," he begged when he had finished his story. "Clasp his knees and persuade him, if you can, to help the Trojans—to fling back the Greeks to their ships with heavy slaughter. That would show Agamemnon how foolish he was to insult his best warrior."

Thetis went at once to the sky. There, finding the father of the gods seated by himself on the highest peak of Olympus, she sank down at his feet and clasped his knees.

"Father Zeus," she begged, "if ever I have done anything for you, grant me this boon: honor my son, who is fated to die so young, and who now has been insulted by Agamemnon. Favor the Trojans until the Greeks pay Achilles the honor which is due him."

Zeus sighed unhappily. "This is a troublesome thing," he said. "It is sure to get me into a quarrel with my wife, Hera, who already fusses because she says I favor the Trojans too much. Do go away before Hera sees you. But first, to show that I grant your plea, I will nod my head."

And as Zeus swung forward his great head in a lordly nod, all of cloud-crowned Olympus shook.

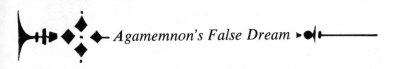 *Agamemnon's False Dream*

In keeping with his plan to destroy many Greeks on the battlefield for the glory of Achilles, it seemed best to Zeus to send a false dream to King Agamemnon. So he called to him from the house of Sleep one of the Evil Dreams, and sent it to tell King Agamemnon that victory was at hand.

Away went the dream with all speed to the camp. It sought out Agamemnon, asleep in his tent.

"Asleep?" it said to him. "This is no time to sleep, when the immortals have at last decided to let you capture Troy with its broad streets."

Then the dream slipped away, and Agamemnon awoke with its voice still in his ears. He sat up quickly. He put on a fine new tunic, flung his cloak over his shoulders, laced up his sandals, and slung his sword over his shoulder. With his royal sceptre in his hand, he set out among the ships.

First he called a meeting of his leaders, torn from sleep, to give them the false good news. They in turn called the soldiers to assembly. Like a vast swarm of bees the men rushed out from their huts on the sands. So great was the roar that it took nine heralds, shouting loud, to quiet them enough to listen to their leaders' words.

When at last they were all seated, Agamemnon arose, leaning on his royal sceptre.

"My friends, heroes of Greece, warriors all!" he greeted them. "Soon the city of King Priam will bow her head, captured and sacked by the hands of the Greeks. There will not be another day's delay. But first, men, dismiss, have a good meal and make ready for battle.

"Sharpen your spears, adjust your shields, feed your horses well, and see that your chariots are ready for action.

"For this will be a long day. We shall fight without pause, until your shield straps are stuck to your breasts with sweat and your hands are heavy on the spears. As for any shirker who lingers by the ships, he shall be food for the vultures and the dogs!"

The Greeks welcomed this speech with loud cheers, like the roar of the sea breaking on a rocky coast. Then the assembly broke up, and the men scattered among the ships, to build their fires and prepare their meal. Each man made an offering to his favorite god, and prayed that he might be alive when the battle ended that night.

Agamemnon, too, made his sacrifice, a fine five-year-old bull, to Zeus. And he prayed that Troy might fall in flames that day, and its hero Hector and his friends roll in the dust.

Zeus accepted the sacrifice. But he did not grant the prayer, for he planned death and suffering that day for the Greeks.

When the meal was finished, Agamemnon sent out his clear-voiced heralds to sound the battle cry. At once the men poured out from the ships and huts, clan after clan in battle array. Captains brought their companies into battle order, there on the river Scamander's plain. And Zeus made Agamemnon stand out from the rest as one great bull in a herd of cattle.

Out marched the men, with a dazzle of bronze that shone like a forest fire on the mountains. And the earth shook beneath their tramping feet.

Meanwhile, Zeus had sent swift Iris, goddess of the rainbow, to Troy in the form of a Trojan scout. She found the leaders gathered at the city gates, and there she addressed King Priam and his son, Prince Hector.

"Sir, you still go on talking here," she said to Priam, "as if we were back in the days of peace. But a death struggle is upon us, for a force is at this moment rolling over the plain, in numbers like the leaves of the forest or the sands of the sea. Hector, I beg you, have your allies draw up their men in companies and go forth to battle!"

Hector recognized the goddess's voice in this warning. He dismissed the meeting swiftly and sounded the call to arms. Soon with a great din the Trojan army and its allies were pouring through the city gates to a mound in the plain.

 *The Duel*

Now the two armies approached each other, the Trojans shouting like a huge flock of cranes, the Greeks in grim silence. About their feet the dust rose, thick as mist in the mountains when a man can see no farther than a stone's throw.

As the forces came close enough to do battle, out from the Trojan ranks stepped Prince Paris. He offered to meet any Greek in a duel, man to man. With a panther skin flung over his back, a curved bow and sword hanging from his shoulders, and two sharp, bronze-headed spears in his hand, he made a fine, godlike figure.

When Menelaus saw that it was Paris, he was filled with joy, like a hungry lion sighting its prey. Now was his chance for revenge on the man who had wronged him! So down he leaped from his chariot, with all his armor clanking.

Paris saw Menelaus come forward, and his heart failed him. He stepped back, like a man who sees a snake in the woods.

Then Hector turned on his brother with scorn.

"Paris, you handsome weakling, I wish you had never been born. Or I wish you had died before you found a wife. What a joke you must seem to the Greeks, with nothing to you but good looks. Can you be the man who sailed the seas and brought home with you the beautiful queen of a warlike land? And now you are too cowardly to stand up to the brave man you wronged. We Trojans should have stoned you long ago for all the trouble you have caused."

"All you say is true enough, Hector," Paris replied. "If you insist on my fighting this duel, have all the troops sit down, and I will fight him between the armies. Let us fight for Helen and her wealth. The one who wins gets both lady and goods, and the rest can have peace at last."

This pleased Hector well enough. He stepped forward through the Trojan lines and made this proposal to all.

"One of us must die, it is certain," said Menelaus, "and it is well that the rest should have peace. Let Priam come then, to make solemn sacrifices to the Earth and Sun, and swear an oath to give Helen to the winner, that afterward there may be peace."

Greeks and Trojans were all delighted by a chance to end the war. They arranged the chariots in order and unyoked the horses. Then, between the heaps of armor they had put down, they cleared a space for the duel.

Hector sent heralds back to the city for King Priam. But meanwhile Iris disguised herself as a daughter of Priam and brought Helen the news. She found Helen in her palace, weaving a great web of purple, double width, in which she was picturing battle scenes from the great war fought for her sake.

When Helen heard the news of the duel, a longing swept over her—a longing for her parents, for her home and child, and for the husband she had left. Putting a white veil over her head, she ran, with tears glistening in her eyes, to the tower above the Scaean Gate, from which the fighting could be seen.

There Priam sat with the old men who could no longer fight. They chirped together like grasshoppers in the sun, and as they saw Helen walking toward them, one said to another, "It is no wonder the Greeks and Trojans have fought all these years for this woman's sake. Her beauty is like that of the immortal gods. Yet it would be better for her to sail away than to stay and bring ruin on our children and our homes."

Priam called her to him kindly, for he did not blame her. He asked her to point out to him Agamemnon and Odysseus. Helen also pointed out old Nestor, towering Ajax, and other leaders of the Greeks. Then the heralds came from Hector to say that Priam was wanted to offer the sacrifice for the duel.

Priam sighed when he heard the news. He feared for the safety of his son. But he set out in his chariot, made the sacrifices, and swore the most solemn oaths for peace. Then he rode back into the city, for he could not bear to watch the duel.

Now Hector and Odysseus measured off the ground. Then into a helmet they put two lots, made of pieces of broken pottery. One lot was marked for Menelaus, one for Paris. The helmet would be shaken, and the lot that leaped out would show which man would cast the first spear.

The watching armies lifted up their hands and prayed. One prayer served them both, for it was a prayer of peace.

Then Hector shook the helmet, looking away, until one lot leaped out. It was marked for Paris.

The troops sat down in rows, and Paris put on his armor—splendid greaves with silver ankle clips on his legs, a breastplate on his chest. Over his shoulders went a silver-studded sword and a great tough shield. On his head he set a helmet finely made, with a nodding horsehair plume. And in his hands he grasped a spear well suited to his grip. Meanwhile, Menelaus armed himself in the very same way.

Clanking their weapons and glaring fiercely, the two stepped out onto the cleared ground. It was Paris who had won the first cast. His long spear shot out and landed squarely on Menelaus' shield, but did not pierce it; the strong point bent.

Menelaus raised his spear and offered a prayer for revenge to Zeus. His spear went straight through Paris' shield, through the breastplate on his breast, through his tunic—but he swerved aside, and so was saved from death.

Then Menelaus drew his silver-set sword and brought it down with a mighty crash on Paris' helmet. But the blade broke to splinters and fell from his hand.

"O Zeus! How spiteful you are!" cried Menelaus. He hurled himself upon the stunned Paris, dragging him by the chin strap of his helmet back toward the Greek lines. That would have been the end of Paris, but Aphrodite was watching over her favorite. She caused the strap to break, and Menelaus got only an empty helmet. He threw it back to his friends and went after Paris with a spear. But Aphrodite carried Paris off to his own bedroom in Troy. And while Menelaus stormed, searching through the ranks, Paris rested safely there.

At last Agamemnon spoke to the Trojans. "It is clear," he said, "that Menelaus is the conqueror. Now it is up to you to return Helen and her goods."

At this the Greeks applauded loudly. And had Zeus willed it, the Trojan war might have ended then.

The Fatal Arrow

Now, the gods had gathered in the golden-floored palace of Zeus. And while they drank nectar from their golden goblets, they looked down to see what was going on in Troy.

Zeus stroked his beard and smiled to himself as he thought of a way to tease Queen Hera.

"I know we have here two supporters of the Greeks," he said, "in the Lady Hera and Athena. But they sit calmly by while Aphrodite has saved her favorite, Paris, from certain death. Still, there is no doubt that Menelaus has won the duel, so if you approve he will take his Helen home, and the city of Priam will stand."

These words angered Hera and Athena, who were set on having Troy destroyed. Athena held her tongue, but Hera could not.

"Zeus," she cried, "how can you suggest such a thing? Have I gone to all that trouble for nothing, getting myself and my horses in a sweat from rushing around Greece, gathering the armies? And now you say Troy is to escape! Do as you like, but don't expect me to approve."

Now Zeus was angry too. "What harm have Priam and his sons ever done to you that you should be so determined to ruin their lovely town? It happens that of all the cities of the world, Troy is the dearest to my heart."

"All I ask," said Hera, "is that you let Athena go down to the battlefield and arrange for the Trojans to break the truce. Surely I deserve that much consideration, as a goddess and your wife."

To this Zeus agreed, since it was also his wish.

Down to earth Athena swooped like a shooting star. The watching men on the plain below knew she brought a message from the gods. But what would it be—peace or war?

Athena knew the answer. She put on the disguise of a Trojan warrior and sought out Pandarus, a fine archer.

"Pandarus, why not win the thanks of all the Trojans," she suggested, 'by making an end of Menelaus with a single arrow from your bow? Paris will surely give you a very handsome gift. Come, fit an arrow to the strings, pray to Apollo, the god of archers, and the deed is done."

Foolish Pandarus let himself be persuaded. He took down his great bow, sixteen hands long, made of the horns of an ibex. He strung the bow, then laid it down. Hiding behind his companions' shields, he took from his quiver a new feathered arrow and fitted it to the string.

With a prayer to Apollo, he drew back arrow and string until the string was near his breast. When the bow was bent in a great circle, he let the arrow go, with a twang of the bow and a singing of the string.

Through the crush of men, straight to Menelaus, the arrow found its way. Through the golden buckle of his belt, through the folds of his corselet, even through the tunic it went. But

Athena had not forgotten Menelaus. She turned aside the arrow's point so that, though the purple blood gushed out, no vital spot was hit.

Agamemnon shuddered when he saw the dark blood flow. For how could he go home to Argos without his brother at his side?

But Menelaus comforted him. "The wound is nothing," he insisted, "and will soon be cured."

So Agamemnon sent for the surgeon Machaon, who took out the arrow, undid belt and corselet, and sucked out the blood from the wound. Then he applied some healing ointments.

While Machaon was attending to Menelaus, the Trojans began to advance under arms. So the Greeks once more put on their armor, and with gray-eyed Athena to help them, they again turned their thoughts to war.

No one could make light of that battle. Many a warrior went down to darkness, and the Trojans and Greeks fought like wolves for the armor of the fallen men. Many were the Greeks and Trojans who lay in the dust side by side that day, paying with their lives for the broken truce.

Hector the Brave

The treachery of Pandarus put new fury into the Greek fighters. The Trojans were about to be forced back into their city, defeated and disgraced. But Helenus, a son of Priam and the best prophet in Troy, sought out Hector at this moment.

"It is up to you to make a stand," he said. "You are the best of all our leaders. Keep the men away from the gates, or they will go running in to the women and give our enemies the victory. Once you have the ranks in order, we will stand and fight, weary though we are, for we can do nothing else.

"Then go to our mother, Queen Hecuba, and ask her to offer to Athena the largest, finest robe she has. And let her promise the goddess twelve young heifers if she will spare our wives and children and have pity on our town."

Hector at once leaped down from his chariot. Swinging his spears, he moved among the men. He put such new heart into their fighting that the Greeks thought some god must be fighting for Troy, and many of them turned away.

Then Hector walked back into the city, with the rim of his black shield slung behind him, tapping at his ankles and neck. When he reached the great oak tree at the Scaean gates, Trojan wives and daughters swarmed about him, pleading for news of their men. "Pray to the gods," he told them all, for the news he had for many was sad.

On he went to Priam's handsome palace, with its doorways and columns of polished stone. Here his mother came out to meet him, and clasped his hand.

"Why have you left the battle?" she asked. "The Greeks must be pressing you hard. Come, make your sacrifice to Zeus, and have some refreshment for yourself."

"No, mother," said Hector, "I cannot offer a sacrifice with the blood and grime of battle on my hands. But you and the older women go to Athena. Offer her the finest robe you have. Lay it on her knees, and promise her twelve young heifers if she will spare our wives and children and hold off the Greeks from Troy."

The queen made the sacrifice and placed on Athena's knees a great robe of the finest needlework, shining like a star. But Athena refused her prayers.

Then Hector left and went to his own house.

"My place is with the army," he said to himself. "But first I must go home for one look at my wife and little boy. For I cannot tell whether I shall ever see them again."

Andromache, his wife, was not at home. From the maids he learned that she had gone off to the wall, upset by the news that the battle was going badly for Troy.

So Hector hurried back through the streets until he reached the Scaean gates. There his dear wife came running to meet him.

The nurse followed with their little boy in her arms—a merry little boy, his father's darling and the hope of Troy. Hector smiled when he saw his son, but Andromache burst into tears.

"My dear, can you do nothing but fight?" she cried. "Have you no thought for your little boy, or for your unhappy wife, who will be a widow soon? If I lose you, I do not want to live, for I have no one but you. You are father and mother and brother to me, as well as my dearly loved husband."

"I have not forgotten that, dear wife," said Hector, "but I could not show my face in Troy if I hid like a coward from danger."

As he spoke, Hector reached his arms out for his son, little Astyanax. But the boy was frightened by the gleaming metal helmet with its fiercely nodding horsehair crest, and he shrank back against his nurse. Both his father and mother laughed at that, and Hector took off his helmet and laid it on the ground. Then he kissed his son and swung him in his arms. "O Zeus and all you gods," he prayed, "grant th.t this son of mine shall one day be king of Troy."

Then he gave the boy back to his mother, who pressed him to her breast, smiling through her tears. When her husband saw this, he stroked her with his hand.

He said, "My dearest, do not grieve too much. We cannot escape our fate, but no one will send me down to Hades before my appointed time."

Then Hector took up his helmet and spear, and Andromache went on her way home, turning again and again to look back, while her tears flowed fast.

The Scales of Victory

Now Zeus had the horses harnessed to his chariot, swift, bronze-hoofed horses with manes of gold. Robed all in gold, and flicking his golden whip, Zeus mounted the chariot and flew away to Mount Ida. There he hid his horses in a cloud and sat himself down near his altar on the hilltop, looking down at the city and the ships.

As the day wore on, with men clashing and dying, Zeus laid out his golden scales. Into each pan he put the sentence of death, one for the Greeks and one for the Trojans. Then he raised the balance at the middle. Down sank the beam on the side of the Greeks, spelling a day of doom. Up to the sky went the Trojan side. Then Zeus thundered loud from Mount Ida, and sent a flash of lightning down among the Greeks, which struck terror into every man.

Now neither Odysseus nor Agamemnon could stand his ground, nor could the two Ajaxes, great warriors though they were. Even old Nestor, King of Pylos, was in danger, when Paris struck one of his chariot horses, throwing the team into confusion. The old man would have lost his life had not Diomedes, another hero, seen him and gone to his rescue.

As Diomedes and Nestor raced back toward the ships, Hector cried out to his men:

"Trojans! Now is the time to prove your valor. Zeus has granted us a great victory, and a great disaster for our foes. Look at the wretched wall they have raised—it will be no defense. And as for their ditch, our horses will jump it. Then on to the ships, and let the watchword be Fire! I want to burn the ships and kill the men as they stagger in the smoke."

Zeus gave the Trojans such courage that they drove the

Greeks straight back to their trench, with Hector leading the way. He hung on the heels of the Greeks, striking down whoever was in the rear as they ran. At last the troops crossed both ditch and fence, though many fell along the way. Closed in among the ships, they lifted their hands and prayed to heaven. And Hector, relentless, wheeled his horses back and forth, glaring like the god of war.

Now the bright sun set in the ocean, drawing darkness behind it across the earth. The Trojans were sorry to see the light go, but to the Greeks it brought more-than-welcome relief.

With darkness, Hector had to draw back his troops from the ships. They found an open space near the river which was clear of corpses. There they held an assembly, climbing down from their chariots to hear what their prince would say.

"Trojans and allies," Hector began, "I had hoped we could destroy those ships before we returned to the city. But darkness saved them, so we shall camp here, and at the first ray of dawn we shall renew our attack.

"Bring out oxen and fat sheep from the town, and bread and wine for our evening meal. Bring firewood, too. We must keep fires blazing, lest the enemy try to slip away by night. I wish I were as sure of immortality as that tomorrow will bring ruin to the Greeks!"

The Trojans answered with applause. Then they unyoked their horses and tethered them to the chariots, and brought wood and food out from the city.

Soon, between the river and the ships, watch fires twinkled on the plain, as many as the stars in heaven seen on a windless night. And around each fire sat fifty men, while their horses stood by the chariots, munching the good grain.

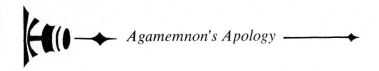

➤ While the Trojans kept their watch on the plain, panic gripped the men in the camp of the Greeks. Agamemnon wandered about, crushed by pain and grief. When his leaders met in a gloomy assembly, he faced them with tears running down his cheeks.

"My friends, Zeus has been most cruel to me. He once promised that I should bring down the walls of Troy. But now he has managed it so that I must go home defeated to Argos, after losing so many lives. Well, if this is the will of the gods, let us be off on our ships while we can, for surely Troy will never fall to us."

The soldiers listened in downcast silence, until Diomedes rose to speak.

"My lord," he said, "I must tell you in public assembly that your advice is foolish. You may run away if you wish. There is the sea, there are the ships—the whole great fleet you brought from Mycenae. But the rest of the Greeks will stay here till we sack Troy. And even if the rest wish to go, my charioteer and I will stay to work out the will of heaven!"

Everyone cheered Diomedes, and Nestor rose up to make the peace.

"Good advice is what we need most," he said, "that and a good meal. Let us eat, for we have stores in plenty, and then let us make our plans."

When they had all eaten, Nestor spoke to Agamemnon.

"My lord, there is something you could do. Even at this late hour you could make peace with Achilles, in whom the gods delight. By giving in to your proud temper, you drove him away. You could win him back with soft words and gifts."

"Yes, you speak the truth," Agamemnon agreed. "I was mad

indeed, I do not deny. And now it is my wish to make peace with him. This is what I will offer Achilles now: seven new tripods, ten ingots of gold, twenty fine cauldrons, twelve splendid race horses, and seven women skilled in handwork whom we captured in Lesbos. I will return to him the girl Briseis, and if we capture the city of Troy, he shall have his pick of the spoils.

"All this I will do if he will only serve with me again. For surely one man whom the gods love so much is worth an army of others."

Nestor spoke again. "Lord Agamemnon, such gifts as yours surely no one could despise. Now let us choose envoys to take them. Let us send great Ajax and wise Odysseus."

This choice was approved by all.

As they walked together beside the sounding sea, Ajax and Odysseus offered many a prayer to Poseidon, god of the earth-circling waters, that they might successfully persuade the strong-willed one.

When they reached the huts of the Myrmidons, they found Achilles playing on a beautiful lyre with a silver bridge. He was singing songs of great heroes for his friend Patroclus and himself.

As the two envoys approached, Odysseus in the lead, Achilles sprang to his feet. He greeted them warmly, and led them to purple-covered chairs in his hut.

"Now, Patroclus," he cried, "bring out bigger bowls and better wine, for of all the Greeks these are my two best friends."

Patroclus did as his friend bade him. And on a big bench in the firelight he laid out good meat, too, and spitted it, and laid it over the coals. When it was nicely browned, he handed around baskets of bread, while Achilles himself served the meat.

After they had all had enough, Odysseus spoke.

"Your health, Achilles!" he began. "Surely we have never had a better feast at the board of Agamemnon himself. But tonight our business is not feasting, but life and death for all our troops. Unless you will come back to fight with us, we stand no more than an even chance of coming off with our lives. The Trojans are at this very moment camped by their watch fires on the plain, planning tomorrow to burn our ships and slaughter us beside them. So rise up now, I beg you, if you wish to save your people.

"Remember your father, when you left home, warned you against quarrels and pride of heart. It is not too late to change, for we come from Agamemnon to offer you the richest gifts, if you will forgive him." And then Odysseus listed the gifts, the gold and the horses, the women skilled in handwork, and all the rest.

But Achilles was not moved by such promises.

"I must tell you two exactly how I feel," he said. "I hate this man with all my heart. I am tired of sleepless nights and days of battle, all for his profit and his sake. Why must the Greeks make war on the Trojans? For Helen? Are Agamemnon and Menelaus the only men here who love their wives? Does not every right-minded man love his wife? And are not the Trojans, too, fighting only for their homes and womenfolk?

"Not if he offered me all the riches in the treasure houses of Delphi or Thebes would Agamemnon move me. For to me life is worth more than all the world's wealth. You may capture cattle, and buy gold and horses, but to win back a man's life, once the breath has passed from his lips, that no one can do.

"My mother Thetis offered me two roads—either to stay here at Troy and die, winning deathless fame, or to live out a long, quiet life at home. Now that is what I shall do. What is more, I advise you to go, too. For Zeus holds this city under his loving hand, and you will never find your way into Troy's hilly streets.

"No, go back and take this message to your princes, and let them find some better plan than this, if they wish to save their ships and men."

When Achilles had finished, the envoys each offered wine to the gods from a two-handled cup. Then they made their way back along the line of ships, with Odysseus in the lead.

When they reached Agamemnon's quarters, everyone sprang to his feet, toasting them from golden cups, then asked for the news.

"Your majesty," Odysseus said, "Achilles refuses all your gifts. He is further than ever from giving in. He threatens to put to sea at dawn, and advises us to do the same."

A long silence followed this heavy blow. But at last Diomedes broke it, as before.

"Let him go, to stay or sail as he likes. But for our part, let us have a good night's sleep, and at the first light of dawn let us lead our men into battle, and by our example inspire them to noble deeds!"

Everyone applauded this heartily, and so they went off to sleep.

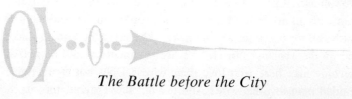

The Battle before the City

As Dawn arose from her bed to bring light to men and gods, Zeus sent down the Spirit of Battle to the ships of the Greeks. She stood on the black hull of Odysseus' ship and uttered a loud and dreadful cry. It could be heard to the ends of the camp and filled the men with bravery.

Agamemnon himself shouted the call to arms. Then he buckled on his own fine greaves, and put on his breast the corselet which had been sent him by the King of Cyprus when he heard of the expedition to Troy. Over his shoulder he slung his great sword, knobbed with gold on the end, and cased in a silver sheath. His huge shield was made of ten circles of bronze, studded with knobs of white tin. On his head he put a two-horned helmet with a dreadful, nodding horsehair plume. With two spears of glittering bronze in his hands, the King of Golden Mycenae started off to war.

The two hosts were like lines of reapers before whom the rich grain falls. So the Trojans and Greeks leaped at each other, cutting down men in swaths. All through the morning, while the sun was climbing, the arrows flew from both sides and the men fell evenly. But, about the time when a woodsman in the mountains tires of felling trees and wants a bite to eat, about then the Greeks broke through the enemy ranks with a triumphant shout.

In the thickest of the fighting was Agamemnon, with his men backing him up. Now foot soldiers fell on foot soldiers, charioteers on charioteers, while the thundering hooves of the horses kicked up a great cloud of dust. Agamemnon slew and slew, like a forest fire blown on by the wind. As the trees topple over before the flames, so the Trojans fell before the king.

Past the ancient tomb of Ilos, past the wild fig tree which marked the middle of the plain, on toward the city, Agamemnon pushed the Trojans, with his hands dripping blood. When they came near the Scaean gates and the great oak, both armies made a stand. And the Trojans would have been pushed to their very walls, had not Zeus sent a message down to Hector by Iris, goddess of the rainbow.

"Tell Hector that as long as Agamemnon is dealing out death at the head of his army, he is to keep away himself. But when Agamemnon, wounded by some spear or arrow, mounts his chariot to retreat, I will give Hector the victory, to drive them to their ships until darkness falls."

So spoke Zeus to Iris.

As soon as Iris had delivered the message and sped swiftly away, Hector leaped down from his chariot. He rallied his men with a great rattling of spears. But he avoided Agamemnon, as Zeus had warned.

Agamemnon, as always, was at the front. And when he was pulling his spear from the throat of a Trojan victim, another warrior of Troy stabbed him broadside, below the elbow, straight through the flesh of the arm. Agamemnon shuddered at the blow, but fought sternly on.

As long as the blood flowed from his wound, Agamemnon could still fight. But when it began to dry, the stabbing pains came strongly, and Agamemnon mounted his chariot, crying to his friends to carry on. Then he told the driver to hurry to the ships, for he was in great pain.

Hector saw that Agamemnon was retreating, wounded, and shouted for all to hear:

"Trojans, allies! He is gone, their best man! Zeus has given us the victory, so drive straight for the ships!"

Thus Hector, son of Priam, like the war god himself spurred the Trojans on. And he flung himself into the battle like a whirlwind from the upper air sweeping down on the sea. Who fell first and last to the mighty Hector? There were too many to name.

Now complete disaster threatened the Greeks, who were being pushed back against their ships. For all their leaders were hard hit. Diomedes was caught square in the foot with an arrow from Paris' bow. A Trojan spear pierced the shield of Odysseus, pierced his belt, and tore away the flesh from his flank. Mighty Ajax, too, at last had to make a stubborn retreat to the ships.

As a final blow from the gods, one of Paris' arrows put Machaon, the great surgeon, out of the fight. Nestor saw him wounded, and went to his rescue at once. Soon Nestor's horses, sweating and steaming, brought the two to the camp beside the hollow ships.

Achilles was standing on the high stern of his ship, watching the rout of the Greeks. When he saw Nestor's chariot come in, he called Patroclus, his good friend, to him.

"Now at last I shall have the Greeks on their knees before me," he said, "for they are in a bad way. Go to Nestor and ask who is the wounded man he has just brought in. He looked to me like Machaon, but I could not clearly see his face. I want to know, for a surgeon who can heal an arrow wound is worth many fighting men."

Patroclus set off at a run through the huts and ships. By this time Nestor's chariot had reached his hut. The two men got out and, after standing on the beach to dry their sweaty tunics, they went inside.

Just then Patroclus appeared in the doorway. Nestor rose to invite him to join them, but Patroclus declined.

"Achilles asked me to find out who the wounded man was. Now that I see it is the honorable Machaon, I must hurry to tell him, for you know how hot-tempered he is!"

"I cannot see why Achilles is so concerned over one wounded man," said Nestor, "when our whole army is in such distress.

Our best men are wounded—Agamemnon, Diomedes, Odysseus. Yet Achilles is not concerned about that, brave fighter that he is! Is he waiting for our ships to go up in flames?

"You should remember, Patroclus, what your own father said, when he sent you off to the war. 'My son,' he said, 'Achilles is of nobler blood than you, and also is stronger. But you are older. You must give him good advice and set him a noble example.' That was your father's bidding. Have you forgotten?

"You are Achilles' great friend. Perhaps you can still persuade him. Or perhaps he will give you his Myrmidons, and his own armor to wear. Then the Trojans, seeing fresh troops in the field, and thinking Achilles is leading them, may fall back and give our weary men a rest."

Patroclus was moved by Nestor's words, and as he hurried back to the hut of Achilles, his mind was busy with sober thoughts all the while.

Hector at the Ships

Now the fighting had reached the trench and the wall about the Greeks' camp. When the Greeks had built this thick wall, they forgot to offer sacrifices to the gods, so it was destined not to stand for long. But at this time it still stood firm, while the battle raged around it and spears rattled against its stones and wooden towers.

While the Greeks were penned against their ships by fear, Hector ranged up and down his lines, urging his men to cross the moat. The horses would not go, whinnying in terror at the wide ditch. And it was not an easy one to cross, for in both overhanging banks were set rows of sharp-pointed stakes.

"Why not leave our horses alongside the moat?" a Trojan

suggested to Hector. "Then we shall follow you and bring death to the Greeks, if it is the will of the gods!"

This seemed to Hector excellent advice. He leaped down at once from his chariot, in full armor. The other charioteers followed his lead, drawing themselves up in companies. And when brave Hector led the way, his men followed with roaring cheers.

Trusting to Hector's friendship with the gods and to his mighty strength, they rushed across the ditch and at the wall. They tore out stones, pulled up stakes, and dragged out the buttresses supporting the walls, hoping the walls themselves would come down.

But the Greeks would not give way. They filled the holes with oxhide screens and poured volley after volley of arrows and stones down on those who tried to climb the walls.

There the battle hung in the balance, until Zeus at last gave a fresh spurt of power to Hector and let him be the first to enter the Greek camp.

"Up we go, Trojans!" he shouted to his followers. "Down with the wall, and let us see flames rising from the ships!"

Every Trojan heard the cry, and charged the walls with spear in hand. But Hector did more. Near the gate he picked up a huge pointed rock, thick as a barrel at the end. Two men could scarcely have raised it into a cart with a lever. But Zeus made the rock light in Hector's hands, and he smashed it against the wings of the gate, which were bolted together at the center.

The panels smashed to splinters, the hinges collapsed, and the great gate groaned as it gave way.

Into the camp strode Hector, with a face like night. He held two spears, and his armor flashed with bronze. Only a god could have stopped him then, as he turned into the camp of the Greeks and bade his men follow him. Over the wall, through the gate they came. And as the Greeks fled among the ships, the uproar rose to the skies.

Now Nestor, leaving his hut, met the wounded kings Diomedes, Odysseus, and Agamemnon, coming up from their ships on the seashore, a long way from the fighting. For the beach, wide as it was, stretching from headland to headland, was not large enough to hold all the ships, so they had been drawn up in rows. The kings, then, to get a view of the battle, had to walk inland, leaning heavily on their spears, in gloomy frame of mind.

When they saw the wall knocked down, and the Trojans within the camp, Agamemnon was disheartened. "Let us launch the ships closest to the sea and anchor them offshore," he said. "Then by night we can draw down the other ships."

"This is nonsense," said Odysseus. "You had better be still, or the men may get wind of this idea, and then all will really be lost. You should have an army of cowards to command, if this is how you plan."

"Harsh words, Odysseus, but you are right," Agamemnon admitted. "I will not ask the men to launch the ships. But if anyone has a better idea, let us hear it."

"I say let us go to the battlefield," said brave Diomedes. "We must keep out of range, wounded as we are, but we can encourage the others."

So on they went, but when they arrived Apollo himself was holding the cloak of victory over Hector as he led his men among the ships' high sterns. Hector caught hold of one fine ship, and rallied the battle around him there, more violently than before. Only great Ajax astride the deck kept him from setting it afire.

While this battle was raging around the ships, Patroclus came to his friend Achilles with tears pouring down his cheeks.

"My dear Patroclus," said Achilles, "why are you crying? You look like a little girl running to her mother, plucking at her skirt and crying, begging to be picked up. What is it, man? Bad news from home, or are you weeping for the Greeks? They are suffering for their own faults, after all."

"Oh, Achilles," sighed Patroclus, "don't be angry with me. Our people are suffering such terrible misfortunes, with all their best men wounded. If you are still so cruel and cold that you will not give up your grudge, at least let me take the Myrmidons and wear your armor on my shoulders, to see if that may help."

So he begged, foolish one, for his own death! And proud Achilles was moved by his words.

"Perhaps you are right and I should not hold this grudge forever. I did think I would wait until the flames and battle reached my own ships. But you go ahead. Wear my armor and lead our brave Myrmidons into the battle, now that the Trojans are sweeping over the ships like a black cloud and our people are trapped with their backs to the sea.

"Go on and beat them, Patroclus. Save our ships and bring honor to me. But when you have pushed the Trojans away from the ships, come back at once. Even if Zeus offers you a chance for victory, you must not fight on and steal my glory. Don't go as far as the city walls, or the archer-god Apollo, who dearly loves Troy, may step in. Just save the ships and come straight back!"

Now while Achilles and Patroclus were talking, Ajax, guarding his tall ship, had come at last to the end of his strength. His helmet rang from the blows upon it. His left shoulder was tired from holding up his shield. His breath came in gasps, and sweat poured from him. Weary as he was, and almost alone among the leaders, he had still been standing off the Trojans. But now, as Ajax gave way at last, fire came to the ships.

Hector's great sword sliced through Ajax's spear, and the useless blade clattered to the ground, leaving the handle in his hand. Then Ajax knew that Zeus was against him. There was nothing more he could do. He retreated, while the Trojans hurled their firebrands. The flames licked first along the stern, and after a moment fire blazed up all over his ship.

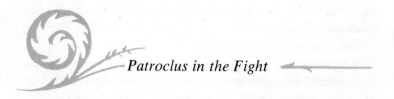

Patroclus in the Fight

Seeing flames among the ships, Achilles slapped his thighs and shouted to Patroclus, "Hurry into the armor while I call the men. I see fire at the ships. We must not let them cut off our retreat."

So Patroclus hurried into Achilles' armor—the leg greaves with silver anklets, the star-shining corselet, the great, silver-knobbed sword and strong shield. Setting on his head the proud plumed helmet, he took up two lances. He took all but the spear of Achilles, which no other man could lift.

The immortal horses of Achilles were harnessed, and Achilles brought the Myrmidons from their camp, under arms and eager as wolves for the hunt. Led by Patroclus, they closed their ranks firmly, helmet to helmet, shield to shield, man to man, and moved out to battle.

Behind them Achilles offered a sacrifice to Zeus, with a prayer for their success and for Patroclus' safe return. Zeus heard him, and granted half the prayer. But half he did not grant.

Patroclus and his men marched on until they found the Trojans. Then they fell upon them like a swarm of wasps, and the ships echoed back their shouts. The Trojans, seeing Patroclus in his shining armor at the head of the Myrmidons, believed that it was Achilles back in the fighting, and every man looked for escape. They fell back from the burning ships, and the Myrmidons quickly put out the fire.

Then Patroclus and the Greeks behind him set upon the Trojans, who forgot that they had ever been brave and remembered only how to run.

Patroclus circled the fleeing army, driving them toward the ships. He kept them from reaching the safety of their city, herding them there in the space between the river and the ships and the tall city walls. Again and again he charged and struck, until there were many dead.

Now Zeus was debating Patroclus' fate. Should he let Hector kill him there, and strip Achilles' armor from his shoulders? At last he decided to let Patroclus push the Trojans back to their city walls, killing as he went.

The first step was to make Hector's courage fail. When Zeus himself had sapped his spirit, Hector climbed into his chariot. He called for a retreat, for he knew that in the sacred scales of Zeus, Troy had lost the day. Seeing him, all the Trojans fled.

Now Patroclus, blinded by victory, ignored Achilles' orders

and commanded his charioteers to drive him after the Trojans. If he had gone back, as Achilles had told him to do, he might have escaped black death. But such was not the will of Zeus.

For a while, it seemed that Patroclus might even take Troy! Three times he set his foot on the wall. But Apollo pushed him back, telling him sternly that the city was not to fall to him nor even to Achilles.

Now, Hector had paused at the Scaean gates. He was told by Apollo, disguised as a young man of Troy, to go out after Patroclus. So Hector left the others behind and drove straight toward the Greek. Patroclus had just killed another of Priam's sons with a big stone, and pounced upon him, when Hector leaped from his chariot to meet him. There they fought over the body of the prince, and, though Patroclus did not know it, the end of his life was in sight.

For Apollo, hidden in a mist so that Patroclus could not see him, struck him between the shoulders with the flat of his hand. Down rolled the proud helmet of Achilles, in the dust of the battlefield. And Patroclus staggered dizzily, while blackness swam before his eyes. Then a spearman struck him between the shoulders, but even that did not finish him. As Patroclus tried to find shelter among the Myrmidons, Hector struck him hard in the stomach, and with that his body crashed to the ground.

Now Hector exulted over fallen Patroclus.

"Boast if you will," said Patroclus feebly, "but I tell you, Hector, you have not long to live. Death at the hands of the great Achillés is drawing close to you."

As he spoke, death stopped Patroclus' words. And his soul went off to Hades, bewailing its youth that was lost forever.

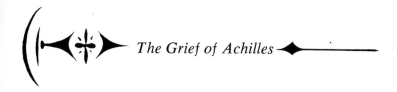

The Grief of Achilles

While the battle went on, Antilochus, son of King Nestor, ran to the ships with the news. He found Achilles in front of his hut, already anxious in his heart. But when he heard the dreadful news Antilochus gave him with tears streaming down his face, black despair overcame Achilles. With both hands he poured dust over his hair and over his handsome face. He tore his hair and fell flat on the earth, like a fallen statue of a god, while the women he and Patroclus had captured beat their breasts and wailed. Antilochus, still weeping himself, held Achilles' hands, for fear he might cut his own throat.

Then Achilles gave a terrible cry, which his mother heard in the depths of the sea where she sat with her sisters, the nymphs. She cried out, hearing her son's grief, and all the nymphs of the sea wailed with their sorrowing sister, and joined in her lament.

"Hear, my sisters, the sorrow of my heart," she said. "I am the mother of a hero of all heroes. I brought him up gently, like a tender plant, and sent him off to fight at Troy, because he had chosen a short and glorious life. But even that short life is darkened now by sorrow, and I must go to him to see what its cause may be."

She left the sea cave then, and all the nymphs went with her, up through the sea to the darkened beach where the ships of the Myrmidons lay. There Thetis found her son Achilles as he sat and mourned.

Taking his dear head in her hands, she asked, "My child, why are you weeping? What is the trouble now, since Zeus has given you your way in everything, driving the Greeks back to huddle at their ships?"

"Yes," replied Achilles with a groan, "Zeus has done all this for me. But what does it matter, now that Patroclus is dead? For I do not wish to live unless I can kill Hector with my spear."

"Ah, my child," Thetis wept, "that brings your death close. For soon after Hector, you die."

"Then let death come quickly," Achilles said, "for I am going now to find Hector, and make him pay with his life. Though you love me, do not try to make me change my mind."

"But my child," said Thetis, "the Trojans have your armor. Hector now is wearing it proudly himself. Do not go into the battle until tomorrow, for by then I shall bring you a new set, from the god Hephaestus himself."

With that she sped off to Olympus to ask Hephaestus, the great craftsman, to make armor for her son.

She found him hard at work at his bellows and forge.

"My dear Thetis, what an honor for our simple home!" he greeted her. "Tell me what you wish, and if I can do it, I shall be glad to serve you."

Then Thetis answered him through her tears, and told him of Achilles' plight.

"Do not worry," the famed Hephaestus reassured her. "He shall have armor which will be a marvel to everyone who sees it. I only wish it were as easy to shield him from death when it comes."

At once he went back to his forge and bellows. He put brass and tin, gold and silver over the fires to melt. Then he set up a great anvil stone, and with hammer and tongs went to work with a will.

First he made a great, strong shield five oxhides thick, adorned all over with shining metals and decorated wondrously. On it he showed the Earth, the Sky and the Sea, the Sun and the Moon and the Stars. There were cities at peace, with the people dancing and singing, and cities besieged by war. There were vineyards ripe for harvest and fields under the plow, and cattle standing by a river bank. And around the outermost edge of the shield the river of Ocean ran.

When the shield was finished, he made a corselet that gleamed like fire itself. He made a golden-crested helmet and greaves of well-fitting tin. All this Hephaestus gave to Thetis, and swift as a hawk in its downward flight, she swooped from Olympus to her son. When Dawn in her yellow robe rose from the ocean to bring light to men and gods, Thetis was back at the Greek camp with the armor for Achilles.

She found him still weeping, holding the body of Patroclus in his arms. But when he and his Myrmidons saw her gift of armor, they all were struck with awe. Now a flame flashed in Achilles' eyes, and he felt a battle passion rising in his heart.

"Mother, this is armor of the gods indeed," he cried. "I shall go off to battle at once!"

"First make your peace with Agamemnon," Thetis answered. "Then you may arm yourself with all your strength."

Achilles obediently strode along the shore of the sea, calling all the Greeks to an assembly. Diomedes and Odysseus came, still limping from their wounds, and Agamemnon still troubled by his. How the cries rose up from the host of the Greeks when Achilles declared the feud at an end! Again Agamemnon offered his gifts, but Achilles lusted for battle and did not want to wait for them.

"Give us a little time, Achilles," Odysseus urged, "for the men must have food and drink. No one fights well on an empty stomach, but with plenty of food a man can fight all day."

Reluctantly, Achilles agreed.

First Odysseus sent men to Agamemnon's quarters, to bring the promised treasures before the assembly, including the lady Briseis. She wept when she saw Patroclus' body, for he had been kind to her. Then Agamemnon slew a boar for a sacrifice to Zeus. Next the Greek soldiers had their meal. Only Achilles would not eat, nor be comforted in his sorrow.

But he put on the armor of Hephaestus, which shone in that place like a moon and star. It seemed to lift him up like wings. When he had taken up his father's spear, which no other man in the host could handle, he stepped into his chariot, armed for war and shining like the god of the sun himself.

The Gods Join the Battle

As the Trojans took battle positions on the plain, awaiting the attack of Achilles and the Greeks, Zeus ordered all the gods to Olympus, and they came—down to every river sprite and nymph. When they had taken their places in the galleries of the palace of Zeus, Poseidon, god of the earthquakes, rose up and spoke for them.

"Why have you called us here, Lord of the Lightning?" he asked. "Are you worried about the Trojans and Greeks, who are about to fight again?"

"You are right, Earthshaker," said Father Zeus. "I am concerned about them. Nevertheless, I shall stay on Olympus to watch from some shady glen. The rest of you, though, may take sides as you wish. For if Achilles is left to himself, he may take the city before its time."

The gods lost no time in making their way to the battlefield after this! To the Greek camp went Hera, Athena, Poseidon, Hermes, the god of luck, and Hephaestus. To the Trojans went Ares, god of war, Apollo, Artemis his huntress sister, Leto their mother, the river Xanthus, and beautiful, laughing Aphrodite.

Before the gods came down to the battle, the Greeks had swept everything before them. But now, when Athena raised her war cry, she was answered by Ares, raging like a storm at sea.

Up on high Father Zeus crashed out his thunder. Down below Poseidon shook the earth and mountaintops. Troy and the Greek ships trembled alike, and in the underworld the King of the Dead leaped from his throne in fear! Now Hera was faced by Apollo's sister, Leto by Hermes, and Hephaestus by the river Xanthus. Thus the gods went to war.

Achilles, meanwhile, hurried through the ranks with a word for every man. And as he went among the Greeks, Hector was stirring up the Trojan warriors, promising them to stop Achilles himself.

Apollo warned him against attempting that. "Do not seek out Achilles," he said, "or he will fell you with his spear and sword."

This warning sent Hector back into the crowd, until he saw Achilles down Polydoros with his spear. Polydoros was the youngest and favorite child of old King Priam, and the swiftest runner of them all. His father had forbidden him to fight, because he was still a boy. But this day his youthful vanity made him run back and forth among the fighters. Now death, in the form of the swift Achilles, caught up with him. As he ran by, Achilles caught him in the back with his spear, through the gold clasps of his belt.

When Hector saw his beloved young brother sink to the earth, clutching his wound, tears dimmed his eyes. He could stay away from Achilles no longer. Like a flash of fire he rushed at him, brandishing his spear.

Achilles sprang to meet him, shouting, "Here is the man who killed my dearest friend! We have finished now with dodging one another among the battle lines. Come quickly and meet your end!"

Hector answered him quite calmly.

"You cannot frighten me with words, Achilles. I know you are the better man, and stronger. But these things lie in the lap of the gods. They may let me take your life with my spear, which has a sharp point, too."

With that he hurled his spear, and hurled it well. But Athena was watching over Achilles. She turned the spear aside with a puff of wind so that it lost all its force and fell at Hector's feet.

Achilles rushed forward, charging with his spear, but Apollo caught Hector up in a dust cloud and carried him away. Three times Achilles charged that dust cloud. Three times his bronze spear point struck only air.

"Once more you have escaped me, dog!" cried Achilles, whirling his spear through the dust again. "Next time I shall have a god at my side, too, and then I shall finish you. For the present I shall find someone else."

With these words, Achilles went raging through the troops like a driving wind that whirls the forest fire's flames over a mountain's slopes. Across the battlefield he swept like a fury, until the earth ran dark with a river of blood.

Meanwhile, the feud between the gods broke out with violence. They fell upon each other with a great din that made the heavens ring. Zeus on Mount Ida heard the noise and turned to watch. He laughed in delight as Athena, in revenge for Ares' insults, hit him in the neck with a huge stone. Down he went, with his head in the dust. When Aphrodite tried to lead him away, Athena struck her a blow with her fist that sent her tumbling down.

White-armed Hera smiled. But when she heard Artemis chiding Apollo for not fighting old Poseidon, she snatched away Artemis' bows and arrows and boxed her ears with them. Poor Artemis went off in tears to the arms of her father Zeus, and her mother Leto picked up her bows and arrows to bring them back to her.

Then one by one the gods drifted home, tiring of the battle. Only Apollo stayed. He went into the city of Troy, fearing that in spite of fate Achilles might take it that day.

Old King Priam on the city walls watched the great Achilles sweep the Trojans before him in terrified defeat. Groaning aloud, he came down to the gates. He ordered the watchmen to throw them open until the fleeing men were safe inside.

The open gates offered the only chance of saving the troops. Apollo rushed out to meet them as, parched and dusty, they made for the city with Achilles raging at their heels.

Then Apollo led Achilles away from the city, by taking the shape of Hector and running along, just out of reach, toward the river Scamander.

Meanwhile, the mob of Trojans swept into the city. There they huddled like frightened deer, quenching their thirst and leaning against the walls. They had not even spirit enough left to see who was still alive and who had fallen.

But Fate, for her own dark purposes, kept Hector outside the walls, in front of the Scaean gate.

The Death of Hector

Hector had taken his stand at the gate, resolved to fight Achilles there. But it was King Priam who first saw Achilles come running over the plain, his armor flashing like the Dog Star at harvest time, brightest of all in the sky. And old Priam groaned, stretching out his arms to Hector in a last appeal.

"Come in, I beg you," cried the king, "and save our city. Remember me, your old father—old, but not too old to grieve if my sons are killed, my city destroyed, my house looted, my daughters dragged off into slavery before my eyes. For it will be last of all that someone will strike me down and leave my body for the dogs."

As the old man spoke, he tore his white hair, but Hector still stood firm. His mother, too, pleaded and wailed and wept. But Hector, though he was deeply moved and indeed feared his own fate, would not retreat. Resting his shield against the wall, he watched the dreadful Achilles come on.

"This is no time for retreat or for bargaining," he told his heart sternly. "Better to get to work and see whom the gods have chosen as victor."

So he thought, while Achilles, like the war god himself, drew near, his burnished armor shining like a flame.

Hector looked up and, seeing him close before him, trembled and lost heart. He could no longer stand and wait. He ran from the gate in terror.

Achilles was after him in a flash, as a hawk pursues a dove. Under the walls of Troy they ran, past the lookout, past the fig tree, keeping on the cart road there, until they came to Scamander's springs.

On went the chase, a good man in front but a far stronger at his heels. They ran hard, for this was no common race—the life of Hector was the prize. Three times around the walls they ran, with all the gods watching from above. Zeus grieved for Hector and would have saved him, but Athena would have none of that.

"This man is mortal, and his day of fate has come," she cried. "How could you save him from death?"

It was like a race in a dream, where both run and run, yet neither can escape nor catch the other. Then, as they came to the fountains the fourth time, Apollo, who had been helping Hector run, left his side at last. And Athena appeared at Hector's right hand, in the shape of one of his brothers, treacherously offering help.

"Brother, you are worn out from this chase," said Athena in the voice of a Trojan prince. "Let us make a stand and face Achilles here."

Heartened by this help, and by the brave show of friendship, Hector turned and spoke as Achilles drew near.

"I shall run from you no longer, Achilles," he said. "Let us fight and kill or be killed. But first let us make a promise by the gods. If Zeus grants me the victory, I will not harm your body, but will give it to your friends for burial, once I have stripped it of its armor. Promise me you will do the same."

Achilles glared as he replied, "There can be no bargains between us. Lions do not come to terms with men, nor wolves with lambs. Between you and me there can be nothing but hatred. Now call up your courage and your skill, for I intend to pay you back for all the pain and grief you have caused."

At this, Achilles hurled his long spear. But Hector crouched down so that it sailed past his shoulder, and stuck in the earth behind. Athena pulled it out and returned it to Achilles, but Hector did not see this.

Hector poised his own spear and cast it. It hit the shield squarely, but the god's workmanship sent it bouncing off. Hector was angry that his fine cast had failed. He called to his brother for a second spear, but no brother was in sight. Then Hector knew that the gods had fooled him and he was facing death.

"At least let me face it bravely!" he said.

Then, brandishing his long, heavy sword, he swooped down

on Achilles like an eagle pouncing on a lamb. Achilles rushed to meet him, full of savage anger, searching for an opening in his armor. He found a spot on the neck, by the collar bone, and there he stabbed with his spear.

Down went Hector in the dust, and Achilles roared his triumph over him.

"No doubt you thought that you were safe when you downed Patroclus, o fool! But a better warrior by far was waiting at the ships, I who have laid you low. Now Patroclus shall be buried with honor while you are eaten by the dogs!"

Once Hector spoke, from the gates of death.

"Remember before you do this thing that the gods may bear it in mind. For you, too, will fall at the Scaean gate to Paris and Apollo."

Then death cut short his words, and his soul went off to Hades, bewailing its lost youth.

Now Achilles stripped the armor from the body, and the other Greeks gathered round, marveling at his size and good looks. But each in turn stuck his spear into the corpse, for it was safer to come near Hector now than when he had been burning the ships.

Next Achilles did a shameful thing. He cut the tendons of Hector's feet, threaded them through with leather thongs, and fastened the thongs to his chariot. Mounting his chariot, he drove across the plain, dragging the body of Hector behind him with his black hair streaming out, and the once handsome face bumping over stones and trailing in the dust.

The people in Troy had all they could do to keep King Priam from rushing out the gate.

And the weeping and wailing reached the room where Hector's wife sat at her loom, weaving flowers on a wide purple web. The shuttle dropped from her quivering hand, and she ran from the house like a mad woman, with two servants to support her.

When she came to the wall, she climbed to the tower, where a crowd had gathered. Searching the plain, she saw her husband being dragged before the town. Then the blackness of night came before her eyes, and she fell, fainting, to the dusty ground.

The women of Troy gathered around her. When she could

speak again, she cried out, "O Hector, I am left a widow in our once happy home. And our baby son, Astyanax, as they call him because you were the hope of Troy—fatherless. What will become of him? His lot will be one of sorrow."

So she spoke and wept, and the women wept with her, sorrowing for the lost hope of Troy.

The Ransom of Hector

▶Achilles went on grieving for his friend Patroclus. Each day at dawn, after a sleepless night, he would harness his horses to his chariot, drag Hector's body three times around Patroclus' burial mound, then leave it face-down in the dust.

Through all this mistreatment, Apollo kept Hector's body from harm, and many of the gods felt pity for him. Only Hera and Athena would not forgive Troy and Priam's family for the fatal choice that Paris had made.

As the twelfth day came on, Apollo angrily insisted that something must be done.

So Zeus sent word to Achilles, through his mother Thetis, that he was to accept a ransom for Hector's body when King Priam should offer it.

Zeus meanwhile sent Iris, goddess of the rainbow, off to Priam in Troy. When Priam heard the whisper of the goddess at his ear, he trembled with fear. But he did not hesitate. At once he gave orders to his sons to make ready a mule cart with a wicker body on it. Meanwhile, he went to the high-roofed room lined with cedar where he kept his richest ornaments.

From this storeroom he took twelve handsome robes, twelve cloaks, with mantles and tunics for all. He took out ten great lumps of gold, two shining tripods, four cauldrons, and a magnificent cup.

Then he hustled his sons into loading the ransom goods into the wagon they had prepared.

When everything was almost ready, Queen Hecuba, in great distress, brought out a golden goblet of wine, for a drink offering to Zeus. In response, Zeus sent an eagle, a bird of good omen.

Cheered by this sign, King Priam mounted his cart and drove out through the gateway and across the plain. When he stopped to give the mules a drink at the river, Zeus sent Hermes, disguised as a young prince, who guided him, unseen, past the Greek sentries and straight to Achilles' hut.

Then back to Olympus went Hermes, while Priam opened the door and, still unseen, walked into the hut where Achilles sat with two servants.

Priam at once clasped Achilles about the knees and kissed the hands that had slaughtered so many of his sons. Achilles and his men stared in amazement at this.

Then Priam made his plea. He reminded Achilles of his own father, until Achilles' heart ached with longing. Gently he pushed the old man from him, and they both burst into tears. Priam, crouching at Achilles' feet, wept for Hector. Achilles wept for his father, and then for Patroclus again.

When they could speak, Achilles, out of pity, took Priam by the arm and raised him from the floor.

"Ah, poor man, you have suffered many sorrows. And what strength of heart you have, to come alone to the camp of the Greeks! I shall let you take Hector back with you."

Achilles sent men out to unload the cart and bring the ransom in. He also called out women to wash Hector's body, anoint it with oil, and wrap it securely for the journey home. Then he returned to the hut and spoke to Priam.

"Your son has been set free as you asked, and is now lying on your cart. At daybreak you may see him yourself as you take him away. But now let us two have something to eat. Time enough to weep for your son when you have him back in Troy."

Then Achilles killed a white lamb, which his men flayed and chopped up, spitting small pieces and roasting them well. They laid the meat on the table, set out bread in handsome baskets, and Achilles served the meal.

Presently old Priam said, "I must ask to retire now, for since my son lost his life my eyelids have not closed. Neither had I eaten until your food and sparkling wine passed down my throat."

Achilles gave orders at once for a bed to be made up outside his hut, with rugs of purple, and blankets above them, and a woolen sleeping robe. The women took torches and went to work.

"And now," said Achilles, "will you tell me how many days you will need for Prince Hector's funeral? I will keep the army from fighting for that time."

"If we may have a proper funeral, we shall be deeply grateful," the old king replied. "We would mourn him nine days. On the tenth day we would bury him, and hold the funeral feast. On the eleventh we would build him a mound. And on the twelfth we shall fight again if we must."

"It shall be as you wish," Achilles promised, clasping his hand at the wrist. Then he led Priam to his bed on the porch.

While everyone else was fast asleep, both in heaven and on earth, Hermes came to Priam to warn him to be up and away before daylight broke. Priam roused himself at once, and drove toward the city while Dawn spread her pale robe over the earth.

His daughter Cassandra was the first to see him coming. She had climbed to the top of the tallest tower, and from there saw her father standing in the cart, and the body of Hector on a bier.

"Men and women of Troy," she cried, "all you who once welcomed Hector home from battle, come and see him now."

Soon not a man or a woman was left in the city. They all crowded out to meet their king and the dead hero beyond the gates.

Then home to his palace they brought him, and laid him on a wooden bed, with mourners posted to sing their dirges while the women wailed in chorus.

Andromache, holding his head in her hands, led the lament— for her husband, dead so young, for herself a widow, and for their little son who would never grow to manhood now that his father no longer guarded the city.

Then Hecuba lamented for her dearest son. And Helen mourned Hector, too, as the only man in Troy, except fatherly Priam, who had never spoken a word of blame for the sorrow she had caused. And as they mourned, the whole city lamented.

Then old Priam gave orders to the people. They hitched mules and oxen to their wagons, and for nine days they hauled down from the mountains great quantities of wood. At dawn on the tenth day they carried the body of brave Hector to the funeral pyre and set it on fire.

When Dawn came again, the people gathered once more at the pyre. They quenched the last of the flames with wine. Then Hector's brothers and his comrades collected his white bones, wrapped them in soft purple cloths, and put them in a golden chest. This they laid in a hollow grave, and over it raised a great mound of close-set stones.

As they worked, they kept lookouts against an attack. And when the work was done they went back to the city, where a great funeral feast was held in the palace of Priam the king.

Such were the funeral rites for Hector.

The Fall of the City

Now the Greeks, with the help of the goddess Athena, built a gigantic horse with sides of fresh-cut pine. They pretended it was an offering to the gods for their safe return to Greece. But secretly, under cover of night, they hid the pick of their warriors, fully armed, inside the wooden horse.

Now, not far from the shore, within sight of Troy, lay an island, Tenedos by name. There the Greeks sailed, and hid their ships on its lonely beaches. All the while, the Trojans thought they had fled and were running before the wind back to Mycenae.

In Troy all the long sorrow turned to joy. The gates which had so long been barred were flung open. How pleasant it was to be able to wander freely through the deserted camp of the

Greeks, seeing the empty places where their ships had stood, and the long, deserted shore.

The Trojans stood amazed when they saw the horse, a deadly offering to the goddess Athena, and marveled at its tremendous size. Then one man urged that it be taken into the city and set up in the inner fortress itself. Whether the voice of treachery spoke through him, or whether the fate of Troy had already been decreed, who can say?

At word of this plan, down from the highest point of the city came running the priest Laocoön, with his heart aflame. "My ill-fated countrymen," he cried when he was still far off, "what madness is this? Do you trust the enemy really to have left? Do you think it safe to accept any gifts from the Greeks? In this wood Greeks may be hidden—or perhaps it is an engine of war planned to ram down our walls or invade our houses from above. There is some trick about it, mark my words! Men of Troy, do not trust this horse!"

With these words he hurled his heavy spear against the monster's side. And had not the will of Heaven been against it, the men of Troy would have joined him in hacking the Greek horse to bits with their good steel—and Troy might still be standing today.

For the gods sent a terrible sign. As Laocoön, priest of Poseidon, stood beside his accustomed altar, ready to slay a sacrificial bull, up from the sea came two dreadful serpent-dragons. Seizing upon Laocoön and his sons, they devoured them all!

Now a horrid dread filled every heart. The word went around that Laocoön had suffered for striking the holy wood with his spear. So with one voice the men cried out that the horse should be dragged into the holy place of the city, and prayers offered to the goddess there.

The walls had to be cut, and the town laid open. But everyone set to work. Wheels were placed under the base of the horse, ropes were stretched about its neck. And while boys and maidens chanted sacred songs, it rolled onward, upward, into the city.

Four times on the threshold it halted. And four times the clank of armor could be heard within. But heedless and blind, the Trojans pressed on. They set the accursed thing in the city's holiest place, while the temples were hung with garlands as if for a feast.

Meanwhile, Night rushed down over Ocean, and soon the Trojans lay deep in quiet sleep. Now the Greek fleet was moving in orderly array from Tenedos, through the silent moonbeams, back toward the familiar beach.

At a signal from the royal galley, a Greek lad stealthily unbarred the pine horse and released the Greek warriors hidden inside.

They rushed upon the sleeping city, slew the sentinels, and welcomed their comrades through the wide-flung gates. Then, with a braying of trumpets and shouting of men, they rushed through the city with sword and flame.

So fell the ancient city, a queenly city for long years. And the bodies of her children lay scattered in great numbers in the streets and houses—even in the very temples themselves.

Reading, Writing, and Discussion of the ILIAD

1. Perhaps you have the Golden Press edition of THE ILIAD AND THE ODYSSEY. Examine the ILIAD. Pay special attention to the front and back endpapers. Notice the Greek soldiers, the chariot, the women, the statue of Athena. From what you already know about Greek life and mythology, what do these figures suggest? **2.** Notice the names around the border of the endpapers. Identify the characters named. **3.** On the title page, notice the drawings of the ship and the city. What is the significance of these two in Greek life? **4.** Study the pictures throughout the book. Make a list of subject matter from the illustrations throughout the ILIAD. What subjects occur most frequently? Do the gods play an important part in the story? **5.** What do the illustrations tell you about Greek methods of warfare? Is there any way of identifying the hero of the ILIAD? his troops? the enemy? the gods? **6.** From the map on page 6, notice **-a** the position of Greece's allies and friends **-b** the position of Troy's allies and friends **-c** the position of the following places. Identify them.

Troy	Thessaly	Pylos
Greece	Mycenae	Ithaca
Mount Olympus	Sparta	Cyprus

7. Study the text, list and identify the gods. **8.** Which characters of the ILIAD have been met previously in your study of folk tales? Make a list of these and the stories in which they appear.

THE QUARREL

1. What characters are introduced? Identify each character. Who tells the story? Do you feel the presence of the narrator at any point? **2.** What starts the quarrel between Agamemnon and Achilles? What are some important features of Achilles' character? of Agamemnon's? **3.** List the verbs that show Achilles in action. What conclusions can you draw? **4.** What do you think of Achilles' request of his mother? **5.** Is Thetis a necessary part of the action of the story? Take special note of the intervention of the gods. **6.** What do you find out about Achilles from his conversation with Agamemnon? **7.** Although this translation is in prose, quite different from the original in poetry, the translator has used some of the devices of poetry to retain the flavor of the original. Well phrased sentences add rhythm to the work; figures of speech add color. Find a few paragraphs that are particularly beautiful in rhythm. Read aloud in class. Notice the author's use of images. Point out a few.

AGAMEMNON'S FALSE DREAM

1. Why does Homer introduce a dream to deceive Agamemnon? Could this deception have been accomplished in any other way? **2.** Reread Agamemnon's speech to his men. Is this an effective rallying speech? Take note of the intervention of the gods.

THE DUEL

1. In this section we see Paris and Menelaus at close range. Why is it fitting that Paris should fight Menelaus? What is the result of the duel? **2.** Where is Achilles, the hero, during this duel? **3.** What is the significance of having Helen stand above the battle and identify the warriors? For how much of the Trojan War is Helen responsible? Can she be considered a main character? **4.** How do the gods intervene? If the gods had not intervened, the Trojan War would have come to an end with the return of Helen to her husband. According to the first plan of the story, why would this not be the proper place to end the ILIAD? Why is the gods' interference necessary?

THE FATAL ARROW

1. Who steps in to move the story along? **2.** This section is particularly vivid with sounds and sights of war. Read aloud the sentences which give such impressions of the battle. **3.** Does the author comment on this scene anywhere in this section?

HECTOR THE BRAVE

1. What kind of character is Hector? List some of his outstanding qualities as discovered thus far in the story. **2.** What part does he play in the carrying out of the plot? What makes the reader sympathize with Hector? **3.** What incident so far in the story is responsible for Hector's eagerness to enter the battle? **4.** Discuss the character of Hector's wife, Andromache.

THE SCALES OF VICTORY

1. Discuss the pictorial nature of the description of the battle. In the original poetic version this description took the form of long accumulative lists and impressive enumerations of battle gear and the warriors. What reasons might the poet have had for making such accumulative lists? What is the effect in this adaptation? **2.** Reread Hector's speech before battle. Does this tell anything about him? Does it tell us anything about the future action in the story? **3.** Make a list of images used by the poet to describe the setting of the battle.

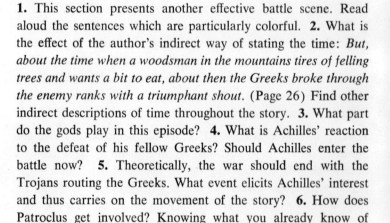

1. What event causes Agamemnon to regret his actions? What is his proposal to regain Greek losses? What part do the gods play in this apology of Agamemnon? How do they prompt the action he takes? **2.** Note that Odysseus is introduced here. Since Odysseus is the hero of the ODYSSEY, which you will read soon, you will want to know him and the part he played in the Trojan War. Try to find out as much as you can about him. **3.** What is the choice given to Achilles by his mother? What reasons does he give for his refusal? What do you think of Achilles as a hero up to this point? What is the result of Achilles' refusal?

THE BATTLE BEFORE THE CITY

1. This section presents another effective battle scene. Read aloud the sentences which are particularly colorful. **2.** What is the effect of the author's indirect way of stating the time: *But, about the time when a woodsman in the mountains tires of felling trees and wants a bit to eat, about then the Greeks broke through the enemy ranks with a triumphant shout.* (Page 26) Find other indirect descriptions of time throughout the story. **3.** What part do the gods play in this episode? **4.** What is Achilles' reaction to the defeat of his fellow Greeks? Should Achilles enter the battle now? **5.** Theoretically, the war should end with the Trojans routing the Greeks. What event elicits Achilles' interest and thus carries on the movement of the story? **6.** How does Patroclus get involved? Knowing what you already know of Achilles, can you foretell what may happen as the result of Patroclus' entry into the battle? **7.** Can you gather any idea of the Greek concept of hero from the comments of the men?

HECTOR AT THE SHIPS

1. How much of the burning of the ships could have been accomplished without the intervention of the gods? **2.** Note the part Odysseus plays in this section. What element of humor enters the scene here? **3.** Notice the comment of the narrator. What does the comment add to the movement of the story? **4.** What is Achilles' reason for acting? What direction does Achilles give to Patroclus? Is this significant?

1. In this section we learn much about the hero from a description of his armor, his horses, his men. Achilles has not shown himself to be a hero yet, but what tells us that he is one? **2.** The narrator tells us that Zeus granted half the prayer of Achilles. *But half he did not grant.* How does this comment add to the movement of the story? **3.** Refer to an encyclopedia for the origin of the Myrmidons. Retell the story to the class. **4.** Zeus allowed Patroclus to push back the Trojans to the city. What result does this temporary victory have in the story? What effect might this have had on the hearers of the story? **5.** How is Hector able to overcome Patroclus? Does this tell you anything about Hector as a warrior? Does it tell you anything about the sympathies of the narrator? **6.** What is the effect of Patroclus' warning to Hector?

THE GRIEF OF ACHILLES

1. Is the greatness of Achilles' grief consistent with Achilles' heroic character? **2.** The death of Patroclus is the cause of Achilles' personal entry into the war. Why is this delayed until this point in the narrative? In the original version this incident occurs after three-fourths of the narrative has been related. Discuss the reason for this climactic action occurring at this point. **3.** What part does Thetis, Achilles' mother, play in this section of the story? She is present at the beginning, she interferes here at the climax, and she will appear again at the end. Is she necessary to the movement of the story? **4.** Read aloud the description of Achilles' armor. Note the color and splendor of it, as if the armor itself were something more than human creation. Is there a reason for this? **5.** Notice how Achilles is endowed by the gods so generously with favors that mark him as a hero. Though the modern reader may sympathize with Hector, the ancient Greeks who listened to the story would have sympathized with one who enjoyed the favor of the gods. Make a list of the gods and goddesses who help and advise Achilles in any way. Compare this with a list of the gods and goddesses who favor Hector.

THE GODS JOIN THE BATTLE ━━━━━━━◆━◀━◆▶━━

1. Up to this point in the story the gods have been taking sides in the battle only indirectly. Now Zeus orders all to take an active part. The scene, as described in this section, adds color and sound and massiveness to the Greek-Trojan conflict, and to the personal conflict of Achilles and Hector. Why does Homer wait until the end of the story to show this general chaos? **2.** We have never seen Achilles prepare for battle before. What one thing does he do that shows his leadership? **3.** The battle between Achilles and Hector is paralleled by the conflict of the gods. Compare and/or contrast these two battles.

THE DEATH OF HECTOR ━━━━━━━◆▶━◀◆▶━◆━━

1. Which warrior does Homer favor? Prove your answer. **2.** What part do the gods play in the death of Hector? Do Achilles and Hector recognize the role of the gods? **3.** Compare Achilles' killing of Hector with Hector's killing of Patroclus. **4.** Study the dialogue between Achilles and Hector as they fight. What do you learn about both men from what they say when fighting? **5.** The narrator says, *Then Achilles did a shameful thing* . . . Would the audience think Achilles' deed a shameful thing? Why? **6.** Refer to the death of Patroclus on page 34. Why does the author use almost the same words to describe Hector's last moments? Keep in mind the oral nature of the original epic.

THE RANSOM OF HECTOR ━◆━━━━━━━◆━━◆▶━◆

1. Is Achilles' revenge heroic? How can you explain his cruelty? In killing Hector, Achilles is carrying out the judgment of the gods against the house of Priam. What is Achilles' personal reason for killing Hector? Is Achilles conscious of his role in carrying out the will of the gods? **2.** It was Paris who caused the anger of the gods. Why does Hector suffer? Has Paris suffered at all for his fatal choice? Would Paris make a better adversary for Achilles? **3.** Is the humiliation of Priam a necessary part of the story? Is it fitting that Priam, an old man, should debase himself before Achilles, a younger man? **4.** Is Achilles' pity a fitting attribute for a hero?

THE
ODYSSEY

THE ODYSSEY

The Land of the Lotus-eaters

From Ilium, as Troy is sometimes called, the winds carried Odysseus, his twelve stout ships and their crews, to Ismarus. There, being a warrior of that time, he thought it only right to plunder the town and kill the men. The women and cattle and goods he saved and divided among his men.

Then wise Odysseus warned his men to pick up their heels and be off. But they, in their foolishness, would not obey. They loitered on the beach, beside the great fires, feasting and drinking wine, until the men from the neighboring towns came down. And in the great battle that followed, several men from each ship were killed.

From that shore the rest sailed away, sick at heart. But their troubles had only begun.

Zeus the Cloud-Gatherer called up the North Wind. And he sent a terrible tempest against the ships, covering land and sea with clouds. Then night came rushing down from the sky. In the blackness the ships plunged along, their sails ripped to shreds by the wind.

When they had recovered from the gale, Ithaca was not far off. But the sea and the current and the north-west wind caught the ships as they doubled Cape Malea, and drove them adrift past Cythera.

When they reached land again, after being beaten about by bitter winds for nine days, they were in the country of the lotus-eaters. These people proved to be friendly enough. They offered Odysseus' men some of their food. But alas, whoever tasted that honey sweetness thought no more of his ships or his home. He wanted only to stay with the lotus-eaters, idly feeding with them on the luscious fruit.

Odysseus had to tie his men and drag them back to the ships by force, while they wept and protested all the way. And before any more could taste of the lotus, he had them bending to their oars, and the ships went scudding across the gray sea.

In the Cave of the One-eyed Giant

As they sailed along, none too merrily, Odysseus and his men came to the land of the one-eyed giants, the Cyclops, a wild and lawless tribe. Trusting to the kindness of the gods, the Cyclops neither planted nor plowed. Everything grew for them without effort—wheat and barley and grapes in great bunches grew all by themselves. They built no ships with crimson sails, nor even boats to row from town to town. Each one lived on a mountain in his own hollow cave. And he laid down the law for his own wife and children, with no thought for anyone else.

Now a tree-covered island lay not far from their harbor, given over to wild goats. It was not a bad place, having soft, well-watered meadows, rich soil and a fair harbor where ships could be run up on the beach. Still better, at the head of the harbor was a spring of fine water gushing out of a cave, with poplar trees around it.

This was where providence guided the ships of Odysseus, through the moonless mists of night. He had not so much as glimpsed the island, nor even heard the breakers rolling toward a beach, before his ships had run up on the sand.

When the ships were beached, the men lowered the sails. Then they stepped over their ships' sides and slept soundly on the beach until dawn.

In the morning they roamed about, exploring the island. And the nymphs sent down wild goats from the hills so that, putting their curved bows and spears into play, the men soon had enough game for a good meal. So all day long they feasted, with plenty of meat and good red wine.

Looking across to the land of the Cyclops, not far away, they could see the smoke of the cooking fires, and hear the voices of sheep and goats. So, after another night on the beach, Odysseus decided to explore.

Calling the men together, Odysseus spoke to them.

"Good fellows, the rest of you stay here," he told them, "while I take my ship and crew to visit this land and see what sort of people live there."

Then he climbed aboard, his men followed, and soon they were rowing across the gray sea. When they came to the land, which was not far off, they saw a cave's mouth on a headland, where flocks of sheep and goats were kept. Outside the cave was a high-walled enclosure made of stones and the trunks of tall oaks and pines. This was the shelter of a giant man, more like a wooded mountain peak than the home of a mere man who lives by bread. But this they had still to learn.

Now Odysseus bade the crew stay with the ship, all but twelve picked men who were to go with him. They took with them a goatskin of fine wine and a bag of meal, for Odysseus had a feeling in his heart that they would find no hearty welcome here.

When they came to the cave, they found no one at home. The master of the place was out shepherding his fat flocks in the pasture. So they entered the cave for a look around.

There were baskets full of cheeses, pens crowded with lambs and kids. There were great pots swimming with fresh milk and with whey.

"Let us take the cheeses and be off," said the men, not liking the place. "Let us take the lambs and kids and sail away."

How much better it would have been for them if Odysseus had listened to their pleas! But no, he wished to see the giant himself, and to claim the gift which in those days anyone was expected to give to a stranger who stopped with him.

So they lit a fire, made a thank-offering to their gods, and settled down with a meal of cheeses to wait for the giant to come home.

At last he came, carrying a great load of firewood with which to cook his supper. He tossed down the wood with a crash that sent the men into hiding. Then he drove his milking flocks into the cave, leaving the rams and billy-goats outside in the high-walled pen. Before he milked, he rolled a great stone across the door—a rock that a score of four-wheeled carts pulling together could not have moved.

As he was finishing his work with the flock, he spied the hiding men.

"Who are you?" he called out. "And why are you here? Are you traders or adventurers or troublesome pirates?"

At his words and the sound of his terrible voice, the hearts of the men cracked with terror. But Odysseus spoke to him firmly enough, saying that they were warriors who had lost their way sailing home from Troy.

"We come as strangers, on our knees before you," he said. "Pray remember, most noble sir, that Zeus himself walks beside a stranger to see that no harm comes to him."

But the giant broke in with a heartless roar.

"You are mad if you think we care for gods here," he sneered. "We are stronger than they."

With that he reached out and seized two of the men. Dashing their brains out against the rocky floor, he cut them into pieces and prepared them for his supper.

The others groaned aloud and raised their hands to Zeus, seeing this dreadful deed. But there was nothing they could do.

When the Cyclops had finished his meal of human flesh and washed it down with milk, he lay down to sleep among his sheep. Then Odysseus considered driving his sharp sword into the monster's breast. But a second thought held back his eager hand. For how could he and the others escape, with that great rock barring the door?

When dawn came, the giant lit his fire, milked his flocks, and seized two more men for his morning meal. When he had finished, he pushed aside the stone, drove out his flocks, and replaced the stone as neat as the cork in a bottle.

With a whoop he led his fat flocks away to the hills. He left Odysseus behind him, seething with plans to have his revenge and make his escape.

Now this was the plan which seemed the best. The Cyclops had left behind him in the cave a sapling of green olive wood he planned to carry as a club. It was tall as the mast of a twenty-oared ship. But Odysseus cut off a six-foot length and had his men smooth it down well while he sharpened up one end. This end he charred in the ashes of the fire. Then he hid the pole in the rubbish on the floor.

"Now draw lots," he told the men, "to see who shall help me drive the sharpened point into the great Cyclops' single eye when he is fast asleep."

Four men were soon chosen, and they were four of the best. With Odysseus that made five.

In the evening, back the Cyclops came, driving in his flocks, both sheep and rams. He made fast the door with the great rock, and milked all his flocks. Then he made his dreadful meal on two more of Odysseus' men.

Now Odysseus stood beside him with a great ivy-wood cup filled with red wine.

"Have a drink," he offered, "after that nice meal of man's meat."

The Cyclops took the cup and swallowed down the wine. Delighted, he begged for more, promising fine gifts in return.

Again Odysseus filled the great cup—and a third time as well. The heavy wine, which the Greeks drank mixed with several parts of water, the Cyclops swallowed down in gulps. It soon went to his head.

"What is your name?" he asked Odysseus.

"No Man," Odysseus replied.

"No Man shall be the last to be eaten," the cruel monster replied. "That is my gift to you."

As he spoke he slipped to the ground, fast asleep. Odysseus

brought out his stake from hiding and put the pointed end into the fire. When it was about to burst into flame, he and his helpers thrust it into the giant's eye. They turned the pointed pole round and round, while it sizzled and smoked.

The Cyclops raised up with a terrible roar that rang fearfully from the rocks. Maddened with pain, he pulled out the stake. He flung it from him, calling to his neighbors in their caves among the windswept peaks.

The other Cyclops heard the cry, and they came from all around.

"What is the matter?" they shouted through the rock. "Why have you awakened us?"

"No Man is killing me stealthily," the Cyclops roared.

"If no man is killing you, it must be the gods who have sent you stealthy pains," his neighbors answered. "Say your prayers to your father Poseidon!" And they went away.

Odysseus laughed within himself as he heard how his cunningly chosen name had fooled them. But the Cyclops, groaning in his pain, had lifted the rock away from the door. He sat at the opening of the cave with hands outspread for anyone who might try to escape with the flocks.

Now Odysseus had been thinking over all kinds of schemes, and this seemed best to him. He tied together rams in threes, with one of his men tied under the middle one of the three. For himself he chose the biggest ram of all, the finest of the flock. He curled up beneath this ram's shaggy belly, clinging with both hands to the wonderful fleece. Thus they waited for the dawn.

When morning came, the flocks surged out to pasture, their master feeling the back of each sheep. But he could not feel the men tied under the rams' bellies, so they went safely by.

When the great ram came out last of all, the giant laid his hands on him, saying, "Dear ram, you who are always first are the last today. Perhaps you are sorrowing for your master, whom No Man blinded when his wits were thick with wine. Ah, if you could only speak and tell me where he is, how I would beat his head on the ground! Then I might feel a bit better for all I have suffered at the hands of this No Man!"

At last he let the great ram go. Just a short way from the

cave, Odysseus let himself drop to the ground. He loosed his companions, too.

Then, driving the flocks as fast as they could, with many a backward glance, they hurried back to the ship.

The rest of the crew gave a joyful welcome to those who were left alive. But they grieved so loudly for the dead that Odysseus at last, with a fearful frown, cried, "Enough of this! Load these fat sheep quickly on board, and let us sail away!"

Soon the ship was under way. But when it was as far out as a man could shout, Odysseus put his hands to his mouth and called out to the Cyclops:

"This is your punishment from Zeus for eating the guests who were in your house!"

In his anger the Cyclops wrenched off the peak of a hill and flung it into the sea. The sea heaved up, and a giant wave flung the ship back on shore.

Odysseus wasted no time pushing it off, and he bade his men row for their lives. But when they were somewhat farther away, they could not stop him from shouting once more:

"If anyone asks who put out your eye, it was Odysseus, son of Laertes of Ithaca!"

At that the Cyclops gave a loud cry. "A soothsayer told me once I should lose my sight at the hands of Odysseus. But I thought he would be a fine, strapping man, not a puny weakling like you! Come back now, Odysseus. Let me ask my father, Poseidon, god of the sea, to give you some rich gift."

Odysseus replied with scorn, and the wounded giant lifted his arms to heaven and prayed to Poseidon:

"Hear me, Poseidon, lord of earth-circling sea! If I am truly your son, grant that Odysseus, son of Laertes of Ithaca, shall never reach his home again! Or if he must see his home and friends again, may he be a long, weary time in coming, and may he come at last in another man's ship, having lost his whole company, to find all in confusion at home!"

This was his prayer, and the god of the dark seas heard it. The Cyclops flung another great rock, but it pushed the ship towards its island goal, and the men were soon back with their companions.

There on the sandy beach they divided the flocks, giving each man a fair share. The great ram was given to Odysseus, who offered him up to Zeus.

Zeus, who is the lord of all, did not accept the sacrifice. He was laying his own plans to destroy all those stout ships with their brave crews.

But the men, unknowing, passed the day in feasting on meat and sweet wine. And when the sun sank and darkness came, they lay down to rest beside the shore. At dawn they rowed away over the sea, sorrowing still for their lost companions, but glad to be alive.

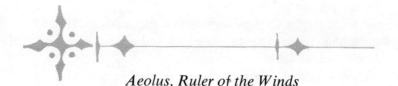

Aeolus, Ruler of the Winds

The next stop was the island of Aeolia. It was a floating island walled with bronze, the home of Aeolus, ruler of the winds, and his happy family.

Odysseus and his men spent a month there as guests, while Odysseus told the king their story, from beginning to end.

When at last it was time to leave, Odysseus asked their host to speed them on their way. Aeolus gave them a bag of oxhide, in which he had bottled up all the winds. For Zeus had made him keeper of the winds, to hold them back or to let them out as he chose.

Aeolus tied the bag with a silver wire, so that not a breath could escape. But the west wind he left free to blow, to speed the ships along. Still, all his caution was of no use. For by their foolishness the men ruined it all.

Nine days and nights they sailed. And on the tenth day their homeland came in sight. They could see men tending watch fires on the shore.

All this time Odysseus had been at the tiller himself, to

ensure the speediest possible trip. But now he was tired, and, with the goal within his sight, he fell into a deep sleep.

Then the men began to whisper together, saying, "What a favorite Odysseus is! Everywhere he goes he is given rich gifts, to say nothing of the treasures he is bringing home from Troy. And we who have traveled the selfsame road come home with empty hands! Now Aeolus, too, has given him gifts. Let us take a look inside this bag, and see how much gold and silver there may be."

A wicked plan, but all agreed. They opened the bag, and out rushed the winds. At once the gale caught up the ships and whirled them off to sea again, far from their native land.

Awakened by the gale Odysseus thought of jumping overboard to perish then and there. But he stiffened his will, and simply lay down, covered his head, and let the wild winds blow.

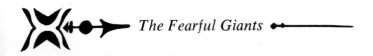 *The Fearful Giants*

For six days and nights Odysseus and his men were blown about. On the seventh day, they at last sailed into a fine harbor, with a narrow mouth between two headlands. They moored all their ships side by side in the calm waters—all but the ship of Odysseus, which was anchored outside, just beyond the point.

Odysseus climbed the cliff nearby for a view of the land. He could see neither field nor garden, but only the smoke of fires. So he sent three picked men down the road to see what kind of people lived here.

The men followed a road wide and level enough for carts, and as they were coming near the town, they met a giant of a girl who had come out to draw water from a clear spring. When they asked her who the king might be, she led them to her father's high-roofed hall.

There a terrible welcome awaited them. For her father at once snatched up one of the men and used him for his supper. The other two raced back to their ships. But from every direction fearful giants came, showering stones which smashed the ships, and spearing the men like fish.

Only Odysseus' ship, moored outside the harbor, escaped this dreadful fate. For Odysseus, seeing the horror from the cliff, slashed the ship's mooring. He ordered his men to the oars, and they sped away from those towering cliffs—one shipload left of twelve.

Circe, the Enchantress

On they sailed, glad to be alive, but sorrowing for their brave companions. It was then they came to the island of Circe, a goddess with beautiful hair, who spoke in the simple words of men.

Guided by a god, they silently brought their ship into the shelter of a harbor. There they went ashore, and for two days and nights gave themselves up to their sorrow.

On the third day, when the fair-haired Dawn came bringing light, Odysseus took his spear and sword and climbed a hill to look around to see if there was anyone about. From a rocky hilltop he saw smoke rising from a house hidden away in a thick grove of trees. Odysseus decided it would be best to go back to the ships on the shore, give his men their noonday meal, and send some of them to make a search.

When they had finished eating, Odysseus gathered the men together and said to them:

"My friends, this morning I climbed that high hill there and took a look around. I found we are on an island washed by the endless sea. And in the midst of the flatness of the island, I saw smoke arising from the middle of a grove of trees."

At these words, a sadness crushed their hearts. They thought of the dreadful giants they had just escaped, and of the violent Cyclops. They wept aloud, but what good are tears?

Sturdy Odysseus then divided his company into two bands. He himself was in command of one, while the other was under a fine warrior named Eurylochus. They shook lots in a helmet, and out leaped the lot of Eurylochus. He started off, with all his men grumbling. And the rest, left behind, grumbled too.

In the midst of the grove they found the house, which belonged to Circe. It was well built of polished stones and set in a fine clearing. All around the house roamed wolves and lions —really men Circe had bewitched. They did not attack the newcomers, but jumped upon them like friendly dogs hoping for a treat.

At the outer door of the house of the goddess, they stopped. They heard fair-haired Circe inside, singing in a sweet voice as she worked at a loom strung with wondrous fabric such as goddesses make.

Then Polites, a fine, trustworthy leader, said, "Friends, I hear someone singing sweetly at a loom. Be she goddess or woman, let us go in and speak to her."

At his signal, they called out. Circe came at once and opened the shining doors, bidding them all come in. Only Eurylochus stayed behind, for he feared some kind of trick.

She gave them all comfortable seats, and made them a dish of cheese and meal and yellow honey mixed with wine. But with it she also mixed harmful drugs to make them forget their native land. When they had swallowed the strange brew, she tapped each man with her wand. In a flash they were turned one and all to pigs. Circe herded them into the pigsty, and threw them nuts, such as most pigs eat.

Now Eurylochus hurried back to the ship to bring news of his companions and their sad fate. When Odysseus heard how his men had vanished into the house in the grove, he buckled on his great bronze sword and slung his bow about him. But Eurylochus clasped him about the knees and pleaded with him to escape while he could with the men who were left.

"You stay, Eurylochus," Odysseus said. "Stay here eating·

and drinking beside the ship. But as for me, I must go on, for something drives me there."

So up he went from the seashore, into the enchanted woods. There he met Hermes, the messenger of the gods, appearing in the likeness of a young man. Hermes took Odysseus by the hand and said, "Where are you going, unhappy man? Your companions are shut up in Circe's pigsty. And you are in danger of landing there yourself, never to return.

"Still, if you insist upon going, I will help you to keep safe. Take this herb, and when you get to Circe's house, drop it into the brew she serves you. It will keep you from an evil fate."

Hermes gave Odysseus an herb he picked from the ground, black of root, white of flower. The gods called it moly and made it difficult for mortal men to find.

This done, Hermes departed toward Olympus. Odysseus went on to Circe's house, with a troubled heart.

At her doorway he stopped and called out loudly. At once the beautiful goddess came and opened the shining doors to him.

Odysseus followed her, and she led him to a fine carved chair with knobs of silver, with a footstool for his feet. She mixed him a brew, dropping in her evil drugs. He drank it off, but was not bewitched. Still she tapped him with her wand and said, "Off to the sty with you, too!"

Then Odysseus drew his sharp sword and leaped at her as if to kill her. But she cried out and threw herself at his knees, saying, "Who are you? Where is your home? There has never been a man who could drink my enchanted brew and not be completely bewitched. Surely you must be Odysseus, the man who is ready for anything! For Hermes has told me you would stop here on your way home from Troy. Come now, put up your sword and let us be true friends."

But Odysseus answered, "How can you ask for my friendship when you have turned my men into pigs? I can never be your friend until you swear by all the gods that you will never harm me."

So Circe swore a long and mighty oath.

Meanwhile, her four maids, the nymphs of springs and woods and sacred rivers, had been at work in her hall. One had spread fine coverings upon the seats, linen and purple cloths. Another drew up silver tables to the chairs, and set golden baskets on them. The third mixed wine in a silver mixer, and set out cups of gold. The fourth brought water and warmed it in a great cauldron over a fire she built.

Circe led Odysseus to a bath and poured warm, pleasant water over his head and shoulders, until his weariness melted away. When she had bathed him and rubbed him with olive oil, she gave him a fine cloak and doublet to wear. Then she led him to the chair made ready, and a handmaid brought him water for his hands in a handsome golden bowl. Others filled the table with delicacies, which Circe bade him eat.

But Odysseus could find no pleasure in the feast, and sat bowed in deep thought.

"Why do you sit there like a stick?" Circe asked. "Why will you not eat and drink? Do you still fear some sort of trick? I have given my solemn oath."

"Oh, Circe," Odysseus answered, "what man worthy of the name could eat and drink before his companions have been freed and brought before his eyes? If you really want me to eat and drink, let me see my friends."

Then Circe took her wand and went to the sty and drove out all the pigs. When they stood before her, she went among them, sprinkling over them another charm. At once they were turned back to men again, but younger and more handsome than before.

When they saw Odysseus, they grasped him by the hand and shouted for joy until the hall rang with the sound.

Even Circe was moved, and she said, "O Odysseus, go to your ship. Draw it safely up on the shore and put all your goods in a cave. Then bring all the rest of your men with you, that I may entertain them as I should."

This Odysseus did. When the men had all had baths and fresh clothing given them in Circe's house, they joined the others feasting merrily in the hall. And when they saw each other face to face again, truly the roof rang!

Then Circe came to Odysseus, and said, "Odysseus, I know how many trials you have suffered on the seas, and how many cruel enemies have attacked you on the land. Stay here now and eat and drink until your spirits have returned. For you are all wasted and downhearted."

So there they stayed a full year, feasting on meat and sweet wine.

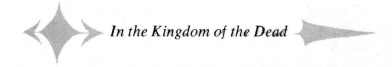

In the Kingdom of the Dead

When a year had passed and the seasons came round again, the long, bright days in their turn, the men were eager to be on their way.

It was then that Circe warned Odysseus of the dangers that lay ahead. And she gave him bitter news. Before he could reach Ithaca, he must make a journey to the Kingdom of the Dead!

This fairly broke Odysseus' great heart. But Circe told him how to set his sails for the groves of Persephone, and what sacrifices to offer there, in the land of the Queen of Death. And she told him that the soothsayer there, wise old Teiresias, would tell them how they might at last reach home.

The men lamented and tore their hair when they heard this awesome news; but weeping does no good. They launched their ship at last, and sailed to the very edge of the world, to the land of the Cimmerians, shrouded in mist and clouds.

There they found the grove and made their sacrifices. Soon the souls of the dead came crowding up, Teiresias with the rest.

This was the word Teiresias had for Odysseus:

"You may still reach home, Odysseus, if, when you come near the island where the herds of the sun god graze, you sail on and do them no harm.

"But if you touch the cattle of Apollo, then I see ruin for your ship and crew. You yourself, Odysseus, will be a long time coming home. You will find your house filled with bold men wooing your faithful wife. You will have to slay them all!"

That was the news Odysseus heard. Then Teiresias moved away. But other ghosts of the dead drifted by, and Odysseus spoke to them all: his mother's ghost and those of all the heroes who had died before the walls of Troy, Achilles among them. For an arrow from Paris' bow had downed that great warrior at last.

He saw Tantalus, too, standing in a lake of water. Whenever Tantalus stooped to drink, the water sucked away. Over his head hung branches heavy with fruit—pears, pomegranates, apples, and figs. But when the old man reached for food, the wind tossed them away.

He saw Sisyphus, forever rolling a monstrous stone up a great hill. Each time he neared the brow of the hill, just as at last he was about to push the stone over the top, the weight of the stone would make him slip. Down the stone would roll to the plain again, and once more Sisyphus had to push and heave.

There were others of the olden days he might have seen, but the crowds of the dead began to set up a great clamor. So Odysseus left that place at last and hurried back to launch his ship again.

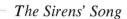 *The Sirens' Song*

After their ship had left the river Oceanus for the open sea, a gentle breeze sped them on their way. All too soon they reached the first of the dangers against which they had been warned. It was the isle of the Sirens, whose songs bewitched all men. There they sat in a meadow on the shore, surrounded by the bones of men they had lured to death. And there it was that the wind died to a breathless calm.

The men rolled up the sail and put it in the hold, and whitened the water with their oars. But wise Odysseus busied himself kneading a lump of wax until it grew warm and soft. He stuffed bits of it into the ears of his men, and had them bind him to the mast. For this was the way in which Circe had told him he might hear the Sirens' song.

When the ship came within shouting distance of land, the Sirens spied it. They sent over the waves the notes of their lovely song:

> Come, great Odysseus,
>   Hero in thy glory,
> Stop, bring your ship to rest
>   And hear our honeyed story.
> Turn that black prow toward shore;
>   Taste the sweet delights
> Waiting here for heroes dear
>   Through magic days and nights.
> We know thy noble past,
>   Know the future's plan.
> Pause with us, then go thy way,
>   A happy, wiser man.

So they sang, and so liquid sweet were their voices that Odysseus was filled with a great yearning to hear more. With shouts and frowns he pleaded with his men to set him free. But they could not hear his shouts any more than they could hear the song, and they would not heed his frowns. They only bent more firmly to their oars, and speeded the ship along.

When they were safely beyond earshot, the men removed the wax from their ears and freed Odysseus from the mast. And they all congratulated themselves on one danger safely passed.

Scylla and Charybdis

As soon as the Sirens' isle had been left behind, clouds of smoke rose up ahead. The sea roared so loudly that the men were afraid and their hands dropped from the oars. The ship trembled on the roughened waters, but Odysseus strode among the men, urging them on, and telling the helmsman how to steer.

Beyond lay two dangers he must choose between—so lovely Circe had said.

The first lay in a sheer cliff, too steep and smooth for mortal man to climb, which had a cave gaping darkly in its side. This was the home of Scylla, a ghastly monster with six long necks. Each neck had a horrible, hungry head reaching down to snatch a victim from any passing ship.

The other cliff was lower, but even more dangerous. It was there that the dreaded Charybdis lived, sucking down the waters three times a day, and three times spewing them forth. Though Scylla would surely snatch six of his men to feed her ghastly heads, still her side would be the safer of the two.

Odysseus said nothing to the crew about Scylla. Circe had warned him that there was no escape from her, and he did not want the men to panic and hide, leaving the ship adrift.

On they sailed then, straight toward Charybdis. Avoiding the moment when she sucked down everything into her troubled depths, they pushed past as she seethed forth, spraying foam to the very tops of the cliffs. The men did not even look toward Scylla's cave. But her six heads snaked forth and snatched six of the best men to their doom.

Crying aloud in their agony, they flailed their arms and legs as they were lifted through the air, and they called Odysseus' name. As a fisherman flings his writhing catch ashore, so the long necks flung the men up to the cave, and there Scylla devoured them.

The Cattle of the Sun God

Still sick at heart from the dreadful sight of their comrades' doom, Odysseus' men soon sighted the fair island where the cattle of the sun god grazed.

Now the words of Teiresias rang in Odysseus' ears. "Let us drive straight on past," he begged his men, "and avoid the dreadful danger here."

But one man spoke for the whole crew.

"Surely you are a man made of iron, Odysseus, so that your limbs never tire. Otherwise you would certainly let your weary men, worn out with hard work, go ashore here and have a good hot meal. You know the dangers of sailing by night. How could we escape, weary as we are, if a boisterous wind should come up? Let us spend the night close by the ships. In the morning we will go on board and sail away once more."

Hearing the cheers with which his men greeted these words, Odysseus knew deep in his heart that some god was planning disaster for them. But still he spoke one last warning solemnly.

"I am one against many. I cannot stop you all from having your way. But give me your most solemn oath that if we come upon cattle or flocks of sheep, you will not harm a single head. Circe has given us food in plenty, and it may save our lives if we keep away from the cattle."

So they all swore, and that night they made their supper with food from the ship and laid them down to sleep.

But in the night Zeus the Cloud-Gatherer stirred up the angry winds into a terrible tempest which shrouded land and sea alike in clouds and seemed to swallow up the whole world.

At the first light of day they dragged their ship up the beach into the shelter of a pleasant cave, the dancing floor of the nymphs.

Once more Odysseus warned his men not to touch the cattle of the sun god. But as the stormy winds continued to blow, he saw their fate draw close. As long as their stocks of grain and wine provided them with food, they held back from the fat cows. But when hunger began to gnaw at them, and they wandered about the island in search of birds or fish, they began to mutter darkly among themselves.

"Why should we die the slow, painful death of hunger," they said, "surrounded here by food? Why not drive off the best of the cattle as a sacrifice to Apollo, god of the sun, and promise him a fine temple when we get home, and many rich gifts as thank offerings to him for saving our lives? Even if he is still angry, and wishes to wreck our ship, surely it is better to go with one gulp of a wave than slowly to starve to death on a desert isle."

So they argued among themselves. And while Odysseus prayed to the gods for a wind to take them safely away, the men killed the first of the sacred cattle. They offered up fine thigh slices wrapped in fat as a worthy sacrifice, then spitted tasty bits for themselves.

When Odysseus came upon this scene, he groaned aloud, for he knew the fate they must meet. And even then there were dreadful signs. The skins of the slain cattle seemed to creep about, and the roasting flesh bellowed aloud on the spits with the voices of cows.

Still the men, unheeding, settled down to their feast and seemed happier for it.

On the seventh day, the storm winds retreated. Odysseus and his men quickly embarked and put out to sea, raising their white sail to the welcome breeze.

But Father Zeus had his plan well laid. No sooner were they out of sight of land than a dark cloud came to hover above the ship, chilling the very sea. Then the West Wind struck with hurricane force, snapping the mast and tumbling it, rigging and all, to the deck. A piece of the mast struck the helmsman, crushing his skull and flinging him like a diver headlong from the deck.

Then Zeus flung his thunderbolt and struck the ship with

lightning. The whole ship reeled, and the doomed men were flung off this way and that. There would be no homecoming for them. Zeus had made sure of that!

Still Odysseus paced through the stricken ship, which the winds drove wildly along, until the waves tore it ribs from keel. At last he lashed two timbers together with an oxhide thong. Clinging to those, he was carried along, drifting helplessly before the wind, for nine long days and nights. On the tenth night the gods washed him up at last on an island, more dead than alive.

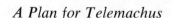

A Plan for Telemachus

The wooded island where Odysseus landed was the home of a fair goddess, the nymph Calypso. She herself came down to the shore to meet him. And she took him back to her comfortable home in a high-arched cave. She treated Odysseus with the most tender kindness, for she longed to have him stay.

Odysseus, for his part, longed for home and for his wife Penelope. Each day he would wander down to the shore to stare out at the empty sea. But not a sail ever passed that way. So at night he would wander back to the cave, where the lovely Calypso sat waiting, singing at her loom, saving her warmest smiles for him. And as the months stretched into years, he felt the sweetness of his life fading slowly away.

All the gods were sorry for him—all but Poseidon, who still raged against Odysseus. It happened, though, that Poseidon went off for a visit to the distant Ethiopians, who live at the ends of the earth. While he enjoyed himself at their feasts, the other gods gathered in the palace of Zeus. There Athena put before them Odysseus' unhappy case.

"Let us send Hermes to tell Calypso she must let Odysseus

leave," the goddess Athena begged. "And I will go to Ithaca, to put a little spirit into Odysseus' son, to get him to take a stand against the mob of suitors wooing his mother and eating up his wealth."

To this the gods agreed. So Athena bound on the golden sandals which carried her with the speed of wind over land and sea. To Ithaca, to the doorway of Odysseus' house, she came, disguised as a traveler. And it was Odysseus' son Telemachus, sitting heavy-hearted among the suitors, who saw and welcomed her first.

Telemachus led the way into a lofty hall, and seated his guest on a handsomely carved chair with a footstool. He had a maid bring water in a golden jug with a silver bowl for the washing of hands. Then he called for a carver, who offered platters of sliced meats, and the housekeeper brought a basket of bread and all kinds of dainty foods. For Telemachus wanted the stranger to enjoy his meal before the noisy suitors came.

They all swaggered in soon enough and flung themselves down on the rows of seats, ready to be waited on and fed.

"Who are all these people?" Athena asked. "Is it a banquet or wedding feast? Surely these men do not behave like very proper guests."

"Sir," said Telemachus, "since you ask, I must tell you that this was once an honorable house. But its master, my father, went off to Troy and has not returned. Nor have we ever heard a word to say he was dead or alive. So all the noblemen of the islands—Dulichium, Same, and Zacynthus as well as rocky Ithaca—are wooing my mother and wasting my goods. As for her, she cannot bear to marry, yet she never quite refuses them. So here they stay and ruin our house—and would like to finish me, too."

"It is surely time your father came home," said Athena, "to deal with these rude men. Or you will have to do it yourself. For you are now the man of the house."

When she had finished dinner, Athena took her leave. But she had planted a seed of daring in Telemachus' heart. And while he sat there, silent among the noisy suitors, he was busy thinking.

As the evening wore on, it happened that the minstrel sang a mournful ballad of the war at Troy. Penelope heard it, in her room above. She could not help coming down the stairway, with a handmaiden at each side. Holding a soft veil over her cheeks, she stood beside a pillar and, in tears, begged the minstrel to choose another song.

But Telemachus broke in upon her. "Do not blame the minstrel," he said. "Odysseus was not the only fine warrior who did not return from Troy. Now you go back to your rooms and to your own work—the loom and the spindle. Leave the talking to men, and especially to me, since I am the master of this house."

He spoke to impress the bold suitors, but Penelope was amazed and secretly pleased by her son's show of strength. And she went quietly back to her room.

That night, when the suitors ceased their merry dancing and song, and went away to their own houses, Telemachus went to his chamber. And all night long, wrapped in woolly fleeces, he thought to himself about the wise words Athena had spoken, and he planned what he should do.

Next morning he called an assembly in the town, to protest against the suitors' bold, high-handed ways. After he had made his speech to them, one of the suitors, Antinous by name, strode to the middle of the assembly and took the speaker's staff into his hands.

"So you would put us to shame, Telemachus, in this spiteful way," he said. "But I tell you the fault lies not in the suitors, but in your own mother, that clever woman. It is more than three years now, well into the fourth, that she has been keeping us all up in the air. She gives hope to all of us, and sends us private messages promising this and that, but all the time she does not mean a word of it.

"Look at her latest trick. She set up a great web on her looms —to weave a shroud for your grandfather, noble old Laertes, she said. And she asked us to wait patiently until it was finished. To this we all agreed. But each day she wove at the web, and each night by torchlight she unraveled her work! For three years she fooled us all with this trick. But when the fourth year began, one of her maids told the secret to us. So we caught her at last at her unraveling! Then she finished the work.

"But now I tell you, we will not leave until she makes her choice among us and marries one of us."

Then the seer of Ithaca, who could look into the future, gave a word of warning to the suitors one and all:

"I see a dark doom rolling toward you," he said. "Remember, I forecast long ago that Odysseus would return, after losing all his men. Now that time has come, and he is not far off, sowing seeds of death for you."

But Eurymachus, another leader of the suitors, stood up to reply.

"Go home and prophesy to your children," he said scornfully. "I can prophesy better than that. I say Odysseus has long since perished. His wealth will be speedily eaten up unless his wife accepts one of her suitors and marries him with a proper wedding feast, which her family should be glad to provide."

Now Telemachus knew that they would not leave. It was he who must make some plan.

The Raft

Zeus the Cloud-Gatherer gave commands at last to end Odysseus' woes. He sent off Hermes, his messenger, to Calypso's isle. On golden sandals, as swift as the wind, Hermes sped over land and sea, straight to the cave of the nymph.

He found her at home, the lovely nymph, with her long hair flowing about her. On the hearth burned a great fire, fragrant of cedar and juniper. And beside it sat Calypso, singing at her loom as she moved her golden shuttle back and forth.

Calypso looked up and knew Hermes at once, for that is the way among the gods. She invited him to sit on a brightly polished chair and set a table beside him with ambrosia ready, and a cup of nectar, too. Then she said straight off:

"Hermes, this is a great honor. I cannot help but wonder what brings you here. Tell me what I may do for you."

"It was Zeus who sent me here," Hermes answered her. "Of that you may be sure, or I never would have come. All that unending stretch of water, with not a city, not a soul to send up a nice sacrifice along the way!

"But Zeus says you have a mortal here who has had much more than his share of troubles since he left the shattered walls of Troy. He says you are to release him now, for he is not fated to finish his days here on this far-off isle. No, he is to see his home again, his own house in his native land."

Calypso trembled at his words.

"I rescued this man from the angry waves, and I cherished him," she said. "I even wanted to give him eternal youth. But no one can quarrel with almighty Zeus. So let him go, let him cross the seas! I have no boats, no sailors to give him. I cannot transport him home. But I will help him as I can, if it is Zeus' will."

"Then send him on his way at once," said Hermes, and disappeared.

As soon as he was gone, Calypso went out in search of Odysseus. She found him sitting on the shore, his eyes wet with weeping as they always were. For this was how he spent each day, grieving for his life which was slipping away.

Now Calypso came and stood beside him.

"Unhappy man, come, do not weep any more," she said. "I am going to help you to leave this place. If you will cut the trees to build yourself a raft, I will stock it with bread and water and wine, anything you ask, so that you will not starve. I will give you warm clothing and a fair wind, so that you may reach home safely if it please the gods."

Odysseus shuddered at her words.

"Surely you have something else in mind," he said, "than a safe trip home for me. This sea crossing is hard enough for a ship, but you want me to go out on a raft! I would have to have your solemn oath that this is no plot, before I could risk that."

Calypso the fair smiled at him then, and stroked him with her hand.

"You are a wicked one, to think of such a thing," she said. "By the Earth and the Sky and the River Styx, I swear—the strongest oath I know!—that my plan is to help you, not to hurt you. For after all, my heart is not made of stone!" And with this she walked quickly away.

The next day, when Dawn touched the East with rosy fingers, Odysseus was up and dressed. And Calypso wrapped herself in a silvery robe, with a golden belt around her waist and a veil over her head. Then she turned her mind to Odysseus' task.

A great ax she gave him, with a double blade of bronze, and a handle of olive wood. Then she gave him a polished adz, and she led him to a grove where the trees grew tall—alders and poplars and firs.

Odysseus set to work. Twenty trees he felled, dry, sapless ones which would float well. With augers Calypso gave him he bored holes, and fastened the logs together to make a good broad floor.

He fitted on ribs, and a deck above, and he made a mast for his boat. A steering oar he made, and a yardarm, and Calypso brought him cloth for a sail. When he had fashioned all the ropes for the rigging, he dragged his craft on rollers into the smooth sea.

At the end of the fourth day all was done. And on the morning of the fifth, Calypso saw him off, bathed and freshly dressed and well supplied with water and wine, meat and bread. A gentle wind, too, she provided, and Odysseus spread his sail with a happy heart.

Then he sat at his steering oar, and when night came he was guided by the trusty stars. For seventeen days he sailed the sea. And on the eighteenth he saw ahead the shadowy hills of the Phaeacians' land, lying like a shield on the sea.

But now Poseidon, the Earthshaker, was homeward bound from Ethiopia. He spied Odysseus sailing along, and his anger bubbled up. He knew that Odysseus was fated to get home, but he could not resist one last blow.

So he gathered the clouds and stirred up the sea with his

three-pronged fork. He sent Night rushing down the sky. And he caused the waves to scatter the timbers of Odysseus' sturdy raft, as a wind might scatter straw.

Then Odysseus cried out: "They were the lucky ones who fell before the walls of Troy! For they at least had burial mounds and proper funeral rites, while I shall die alone, unmourned, here on the raging sea."

But when Athena saw Odysseus clinging to a single beam, spitting out the salty brine as it streamed down his face, she took pity on him. She quieted all the winds but the North, and had it blow him through the heavy seas, toward the distant shore.

On the morning of the third day, he sighted land at last. But even then he was not safe. The shore was lined with craggy rocks which might have broken all his bones. But Athena put it into his mind to swim along outside the surf to the mouth of a swift stream.

Then he prayed to the river to pity him, and it held back its current and made its waters smooth. So Odysseus, swollen and battered and weak, reached the shore at last. He lay among the reeds at the river's mouth, too weak to move or speak. But he bent his face and kissed the earth in gratitude.

Nausicaä

In the palace of the Phaeacian king, the lovely princess Nausicaä awoke from a happy dream. In her mind tingled the memory of the dream of a bridegroom coming, and of all the handsome clothes she and her family would need for that happy day.

So she left her sleeping chamber at once and went through the palace looking for her father and mother.

"Father dear," she asked shyly, when she found them, "could you let me have a big, strong-wheeled cart, so that I may take all our best clothes to the river and give them a washing?" For that was what Athena had suggested to her.

Her father smiled and gave orders to the men. When the mules were yoked to the smooth-running cart, Nausicaä brought out the bright clothes and heaped them up in it. Her mother added a basket of dainty food, and a goatskin bottle of wine. Her mother also gave her olive oil, for a rub after bathing. Then Nausicaä picked up a whip and reins, and flicked the mules to set them off. Away they went with a clatter of hoofs, and the young maids followed along.

They reached the river, with its swirling pools, bubbling enough to wash even the dirtiest clothes. The girls trod the clothes down in these pools, until they were bright and clean. They spread them out in rows on the stony beach, just beyond the tumble of the waves.

When they had bathed and rubbed themselves with oil, they had their meal in the sun, waiting by the river for the clothes to dry. It was after they had eaten, as they were playing with a ball and giving merry shrieks, that Athena awoke Odysseus.

Out he crawled from his sheltering brush, holding up a leafy branch, because he had no clothes. Swollen and grimy and caked with salt, he was a fearsome sight. Frightened, the maids all scampered away, up and down the shore. But the king's daughter stood her ground, for Athena gave her strength.

"Are you some goddess or a mortal woman?" the cunning Odysseus said. "If goddess, surely you must be Artemis. But if you are a mortal, your mother and father are fortunate indeed, and so are your brothers, too. And happiest of all shall be your bridegroom, for such beauty I have never seen.

"Now I hope you will pity me, tossed up on this shore after nineteen days at sea. Please give me some clothing and direct me to the town, for I do not even know where I am."

Then Nausicaä of the white arms said, "Sir, I can tell you are not a bad man. You shall not lack for anything here. For this is the country of the Phaeacians, and I am the daughter of Alcinoüs the king."

Then she called to her maids to bring the stranger clothing. And when he had bathed in a sheltered place and dressed himself in the clean clothes, Athena shed her grace upon him, so that he looked handsome indeed.

"Oh," thought Nausicaä when she saw him now, "how I wish he might decide to stay among us and make his home in our land. For it is just such a man I should like for my bridegroom."

She called to her maids to give him both food and drink. And after he had eaten, the laundered clothes were piled once more in the cart, folded for the journey home. Nausicaä told Odysseus he might follow along with the maids behind the cart.

"But when we get to the city," she said, "near to the assembly place, you must stop and rest in a poplar grove you will find. For I do not wish men to see us together and think that perhaps I am bringing you home to be my bridegroom!

"Then, when you think we have had time to reach the palace, come into the city. Ask for the king's house, and walk straight through the courtyard to the great hall. There you will find my mother at the hearth, twisting yarn of the deep sea purple by the light of the fire. Fall at her knees. If she is kindly disposed toward you, she will soon see to it that my father sends you safely home."

She flicked the mules with her whip, and they soon left the river behind. Before the sun set, they reached the poplar grove where Odysseus sat down to wait.

When he thought enough time had passed, he went on to the palace of Alcinoüs. And Athena wrapped him in a mist, so that no one saw him on his way.

As he approached the mansion, he stopped for a moment to look about him before he set foot on the bronze threshold. For there was a brightness about the place like the light of the sun or moon.

In the great hall were seats ranging down both sides, spread with light coverings of lovely fabrics made by the palace women. And light for the banqueting came from flaming torches held up by golden boys.

Odysseus stepped into the great hall. Still guarded by Athena's mist, he made his way to the thrones of the king and the queen. And it was only when he clasped the knees of Queen Arete that the mist fell away. The people saw him there and fell silent at the sight.

"Queen Arete," said Odysseus, "after much suffering I fall at your knees and ask refuge with you and your lord. May the gods grant happiness to you and yours, if you will arrange passage for me to my country, so that I may at last see my friends again."

Then he sat down in the ashes at the hearth. And silence filled the room. But King Alcinoüs took Odysseus by the hand, and led him from the hearth to a banquet seat which his favorite son now gave up. A maid came in with water in a golden pitcher and poured it into a silver bowl so that he could wash his hands. The table beside him was heaped with good things, and Odysseus ate and drank his fill.

Meanwhile the king ordered wine poured out so that all the company could make an offering to Zeus, the god of wanderers. And only after that did Arete ask the questions which had been in her mind ever since she had recognized the clothes he wore as some she had made herself.

"Who are you, sir? Where are you from? And who gave you these clothes, if I may ask?"

So Odysseus started in directly, saying, "I am Odysseus, son of Laertes, from mountainous Ithaca." And while the Phaeacians sat spellbound, he told the full story of his adventures.

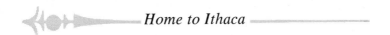 *Home to Ithaca*

After hearing the story of his long adventures, it pleased King Alcinoüs to send Odysseus off the next day at sunset. The king gave him not only a ship and crew to see him safely home, but also clothing, golden ornaments, and other rich gifts— enough to fill a great wooden strong-box.

All these gifts King Alcinoüs himself stowed away under the ship's benches. Then they had a farewell banquet, and listened to the minstrel.

Odysseus was glad to see the sun go down, for he was eager to be off. On the beach he said his farewells, with a proper drink offering to the gods, and a prayer for his host and hostess.

As Odysseus at last stepped on board, Queen Arete sent serving maids, one to lay a blanket and sheet on the deck for him, one with a fresh robe and tunic for his homecoming, a third with his bread and wine. Odysseus lay down, while his crew came aboard, took their places, and cast off. And by the time their blades struck the water, a sweet, deep sleep had sealed his eyes.

Now as a team of stallions leaps under the lash, so that ship bounded over the purple waves, across the roaring sea. And when the bright dawn star arose, the ship drew into harbor at Ithaca.

The Phaeacians knew that harbor well. And so strongly did they row their ship that it ran half its length up on the beach. The men carried Odysseus, still deep in sleep, and laid him in his blanket on the sand. His rich gifts they piled up carefully, well back from the path beneath an olive tree, lest anyone happen by while Odysseus still slept. Then they started for home again.

When Odysseus awoke, Athena spread a mist over the land, so that he did not recognize anything he saw.

"Alas! Where am I now?" he cried. "Why did the Phaeacians not take me to Ithaca, as they promised, instead of putting me down in this strange place? What shall I do now? Where shall I go? And where can I leave my goods?"

It was then that Athena appeared on the scene, disguised as a handsome young shepherd lad. Odysseus was glad to see her, and spoke at once, asking where in the world he might be.

Athena's eyes sparkled as she answered him:

"You must be rather stupid, sir, or very far from home, not to know this place. It's true that it is not very broad, and perhaps too rough for horses and a cart. But it grows a lot of corn, and grapes for good wine, and has rains and pasturage.

The fame of this island of Ithaca has spread, they say, as far away as Troy!"

Odysseus' long-suffering heart leaped up, as he heard that he had reached his home at last. But still he dared not admit who he was, so he told a long tale of being from Crete—a murderer, outcast and shipwrecked here.

At this wild story, Athena smiled and called him by name. Taking Odysseus by the hand, she laid aside her disguise and swept away the mist. Now Odysseus could recognize the place and the goddess as well.

First they hid away in a cave all the gifts of the Phaeacians— the gold and the sturdy copper and the fine-woven fabrics they had given him. Athena closed the entrance to the cave with a stone. Seating herself beneath an olive tree, she motioned to Odysseus to sit beside her, and told him how things stood.

"You must plan, o royal son of Laertes, how you will deal with this bold crew which has been lording it in your halls, eating up your wealth and trying to persuade your wife to marry one of them. She has been pining for your return, holding them off with seeming promises, but longing in her heart for you."

"Alas!" cried Odysseus, "without your warning I would have died on my return home. Now stand beside me, and show me what to do, for with your help I can overcome them all."

"I will help you, of course," said Athena. "I think those suitors will soon be spattering your floors with their blood. But first I am going to change you so that no one will recognize you.

"Then you go straight to the loyal old fellow who is in charge of your pigs. He is faithful to you still, and to your son and Penelope as well. You seek him out and let him talk, while I send your son Telemachus to you."

As she spoke, Athena touched Odysseus with her wand. At her touch his smooth skin withered, his crop of bright brown hair faded, his eyes lost their sparkle in the dimness of age. His clothes she changed to ragged, filthy garments, stained and reeking of smoke. Over his back she threw a worn old deerskin, and she gave him a stick and a tattered old sack with a cord to carry it by.

And that was how, after so many years, Odysseus came home.

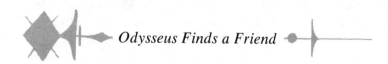

Odysseus Finds a Friend

Athena hurried off toward the palace, and Odysseus started up the rough path through the wooded hills to the spot where she had told him he would find the loyal old swineherd.

Odysseus found him there, in the doorway of the house he had built in a wide clearing. All by himself he had built it of rough stone, with a row of thorns on top. All around was a big courtyard surrounded with stout oaken stakes. In this yard were twelve big sties for the swine—of which there were not so many any more, for the suitors had been feasting on them for years.

There sat the old swineherd, trimming a piece of good brown oxhide into sandals to fit his feet. His fierce dogs caught sight of Odysseus and started for him, yelping loudly. Odysseus knew their ways. He sat down at once and dropped his staff. Even so, they might have harmed him, had not the old swineherd dropped the leather and come running. He shouted at the dogs and drove them away with stones. He led the stranger to his cabin, welcoming him to a seat on a heap of brushwood covered with a shaggy wild goatskin.

Odysseus was well pleased with this welcome. And he was even more pleased when the swineherd tucked up his tunic in his belt and went out to the pens, where he killed two young pigs, cut them up, and spitted the pieces for roasting. When they were done, still piping hot, he set them before Odysseus, sprinkled with barley meal. And in a bowl of ivy wood he mixed him mellow wine.

"Eat, stranger," he said, taking a seat facing Odysseus. "It is only the suckling pigs we can offer you. The fat porkers go down to the suitors of my lady, who have no respect for god or man. I can't help thinking the suitors have somehow learned that my master, who went off to fight at Troy, has met with disaster somewhere. And that may be why they do not woo my lady properly, and then go home if they fail. Instead, they all stay on, wasting my master's wealth, slaughtering his beasts and drinking up the good red wine."

"Who was this wealthy master of yours?" asked Odysseus. "Perhaps I have met him somewhere."

"Oh no, old man," the swineherd said, "you cannot come here with a tale of having seen Odysseus and convince his wife and son. They have been hearing that for years, from every tramp who comes to Ithaca."

"Friend," said Odysseus, "I will do more than say I have seen him. I swear to you that he will be back, within this change of the moon, and will have his revenge for all that has gone on in his home."

"Old man," said the swineherd Eumaeus, with a shake of his head, "Odysseus will never come home again. But now, how about you? Who are you, and what was your family? What ship brought you here?"

Odysseus spun a cunning tale. He told of a home in Crete, of fighting at Troy, of adventures in far-off Egypt on the Nile, of bravery and hardship, shipwreck and treachery.

Now with dusk the weather had turned wild. Rain fell, and the west wind blew, and thick clouds hid the moon. Eumaeus made a bed for his guest close to the fire and thickly spread with skins both of sheep and of goats. Odysseus lay down and Eumaeus covered him with a thick cloak he kept on hand for especially stormy days.

But Eumaeus, good steward that he was, went out to sleep close by the hogs. Armed with a javelin and sword, covered with a fleece, he spent the night where the great porkers slept, sheltered by an overhanging rock.

Telemachus Finds a Father

Athena visited Telemachus as he lay wakeful in the night, and told him to go to the swineherd's hut before the day was old. Telemachus took her words to heart. At dawn he fastened on his sandals and set out at a good pace toward the house where his loyal swineherd lived.

By then Odysseus and the swineherd were busy preparing their breakfast in the hut, the herdsmen having taken the pigs off to pasture. At Telemachus' approach, the noisy dogs did not let out one bark, but jumped about him with wagging tails.

Odysseus heard the footsteps and saw the dogs fawning. He called to his companion, saying, "Here is someone you know well, I am sure, for the dogs are wagging their tails."

Before he had finished, his own son stood in the doorway. The good swineherd sprang up, letting fall the cups in which he had been mixing wine. He greeted his young master as fondly as a son, almost sobbing with joy.

Telemachus gladly accepted a seat in the hut. He joined the two older men at their meal of roast meat left from the day before, served on heaping platters, with baskets of bread and sweet wine mixed in an ivy-wood bowl.

When they had had enough, Telemachus said to the swineherd, "Where does your guest come from? What ship brought him? For surely he did not walk to Ithaca."

"My child," said Eumaeus, "he says he is an outcast from Crete. I put him in your hands now."

"Eumaeus, this embarrasses me," said young Telemachus. "How can I take this stranger to the palace, to have him insulted by those brutal suitors? It is hard for one man to make a stand against that crowd."

"I hope I may put in a word," said Odysseus. "Surely you

do not let this outrageous conduct go on—you a gentleman, and in your own house? Ah, how I wish I had my youth again! If I were Odysseus' son—or Odysseus himself come back from his travels, as I still believe he may!—I should make those suitors rue the day they came!"

"Well," said Telemachus, "the outcome is in the lap of the gods."

Eumaeus soon picked up his sandals and bound them on his feet. He set out for town to do some errands.

Athena watched him leave the farm. Now, she decided, it was time for Odysseus to make himself known to Telemachus. So she spoke silently to Odysseus, saying, "Let Telemachus into the secret. Then the pair of you can plot the suitors' doom."

Athena touched him with her golden wand, and his cloak and tunic shone like new. He filled out to his own height and muscular form, firm-cheeked, full-bearded, and with a fine head of hair. Telemachus saw the change and quickly looked away again, filled with fear that this might be a god.

But Odysseus assured him, "I am no god, but your own father, for whom you have suffered so much. Athena has brought us together here to plan how we two shall deal with our enemies."

"We two!" cried Telemachus. "Father, I have always heard of your warrior's skill. But this is too much. There are not just ten or twenty of these suitors, but more than a hundred, and strong young men, too! You had better think of someone to help us if you can."

"We have Athena and Father Zeus," said stout Odysseus. "They will be at our side in the battle. And I think they will be enough.

"But for the present you must go home and mingle with the suitors as usual. I will have the swineherd lead me in later, dressed as a beggar again. But let no one, not even Penelope and Laertes, know who I am!"

To all this Telemachus agreed. Then, since Eumaeus was returning from the town, Athena touched Odysseus once more, turning him back again into an old beggar man. Telemachus acted as if nothing had happened, and all three sat down to supper together. Soon after, they were fast asleep.

Battle Preparations

Dawn saw Telemachus strapping on his sandals for the journey to town. With his spear in hand, he stepped rapidly along, his thoughts on the fight ahead. Reaching the big house, he leaned his spear against a pillar and stepped across the threshold of stone.

The suitors were amusing themselves with games and contests in the courtyard of the great house. But when the call to dinner came, they hurried into the house in a crowd, flinging down their cloaks upon the chairs, ready for another feast.

Meanwhile Odysseus, clad in rags, with his tattered sack slung over his shoulder by a strap, arrived at the palace door with the faithful swineherd Eumaeus.

Eumaeus went on into the house, where he found himself a stool. He placed it beside Telemachus and sat down to eat.

Close behind him Odysseus went in, entering his own home at last like an old beggar. He went the rounds of the company, stretching out his hands as if he had been a beggar all his years. Many of the suitors pitied his ragged appearance, and gave him bread and meat until his ragged knapsack bulged. But Antinous, who had led the suitors—even to plotting against Telemachus— would have none of this. Picking up a footstool, he threw it hard, and hit Odysseus under the right shoulder.

Odysseus stood firm under the blow. He only shook his head in silence, thinking his own black thoughts. Then he went back to his seat in the doorway. Sitting there with his knapsack beside him, he put a heavy curse on Antinous.

His words made the other suitors uneasy. They feared the beggar might be a god in disguise, who would punish them all.

Amphinomus, one of the best of the suitors, offered Odysseus a toast from a golden cup. And Odysseus countered with a warning for him:

"You, Amphinomus, seem a decent man. You are the son of a fine father, I know. I hope the gods may send you safely home before Odysseus brings down vengeance under his own roof!"

He poured out an offering of wine as he spoke. Then he drank from the cup and handed it back. But a dark cloud hung over Amphinomus' spirits as he went back to his seat. And rightly so, for Athena had decided that he was not to escape, but was to perish at the hands of Telemachus, and at the point of his spear.

When the suitors had at last left for the night, each to his own lodging, Odysseus and Telemachus were left alone in the great hall.

"Let us hide all these weapons," said Odysseus.

He and his son went straight to work, carrying off the helmets and sharp spears, the shields and javelins. Then Telemachus went along the torchlit hall to his own room. But Odysseus, left alone, brooded in the darkness over the vengeance he would seek.

Soon Penelope came from her chamber, as beautiful as a goddess, holding her shimmering veil before her face. Her own chair was placed close by the fire for her, a finely carved piece inlaid with ivory and silver and having a footrest attached to it, covered with soft fleece. There Penelope sat down, while the maids cleared away the dishes and tables from the banqueting. They emptied the ashes from all the burners and heaped them with fresh wood for light and warmth.

Turning to the housekeeper, Penelope said, "Bring up a chair and spread it with a rug, so my guest can sit down for a talk."

When this had been done, Odysseus sat down at his wife's feet and gathered his wits about him.

"Stranger," said Penelope, "I will begin by asking at once who you are and where you came from."

"Ah, my lady," said Odysseus, "do not ask that, I pray. For the thought of home and family fills my heart with such sorrow that I would find myself in tears the whole night long."

"I understand," said Penelope, "for I too am in great distress. Men from all the islands around wish to have me for their wife, and until I decide to accept one of them, they are eating up my house. Still I cannot face a hateful marriage, with Odysseus still in my heart."

Tears poured from Penelope's eyes like mountain streams in flood when the east wind melts the snows. But Odysseus, though his heart was touched, sternly held back his tears.

Instead he told her another tall tale, of having entertained Odysseus and his men in Crete long years before. And he described Odysseus and his clothes—his purple cloak with its turned-back edges, his shining-smooth tunic, and great golden brooch of marvelous workmanship.

Now Penelope's tears flowed more freely than before. For she recognized the garments as the very ones she had taken from her storerooms for Odysseus when he left home for the wars. So when the stranger swore her husband would return before the new moon grew round, her weary heart was forced to rejoice in spite of the long, dreary years.

"I must tell you one thing more," she said. "If Odysseus does not return, I intend very soon to hold a contest among the suitors, and to marry the winner. Odysseus, you must know, used to set up twelve axes in a row, like supports for the keel of a ship. Then for sport he would stand a good way off and shoot an arrow through them all. Now I will ask the suitors to do this, using the same twelve axes, and stringing Odysseus' own bow. And with the winner I shall go, and leave these lovely halls forever, where I came as a happy bride."

"Noble lady," said Odysseus, "do not put off this contest another day. And I promise you that before the bow is strung, Odysseus will return."

On that word they parted for the night, Odysseus to sleep in the gallery of the hall, Penelope to her own chamber and her bed of tears.

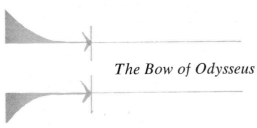

The Bow of Odysseus

Next morning Odysseus went out into the courtyard and lifted his hands to Zeus in prayer. For, although Athena had appeared to him in the night and promised success, his heart was uneasy at the thought of the uneven fight ahead.

The swineherd soon came up, driving three fine hogs, with a kind word for Odysseus. The chief herdsman, too, bringing fatted goats, paused to greet the old beggar with a handshake and a word of cheer.

The sheep and fat goats, as well as porkers and a heifer, were soon slaughtered. And the roasted meat, with baskets of bread and some wine, provided good eating for all the suitors gathered around.

Telemachus found a seat for Odysseus just inside the doorway and served him there, loudly promising him protection from all insults.

But Athena would not let the meal go quietly. The suitors laughed at Odysseus, and cruelly ridiculed him. Telemachus, however, scarcely listened to them now. He was watching his father for the signal to attack.

Strangely enough, it was Penelope who made the next move. She came to the doorway of the great hall and stood beside a pillar there, holding a soft veil before her face. Behind her came her attendants, carrying the master's bow, a quiver of arrows, and the dozen ax heads she planned to use in the contest for her hand.

"Listen now, you men who have wooed me as an excuse for a round of banquets year in, year out, in this house. Here is the great bow of Odysseus. Whoever can string this bow most easily and shoot an arrow through all these ax heads, with him I will go, and I will leave this house of all my happy memories."

At this Telemachus spoke up. "To prove that I am a man, and can manage things if my mother marries and moves away, I will try to string this bow."

Then he stood up, flinging off his purple cloak and sword. He dug a trench for all the axes, set them up in line, and stamped down the earth firmly around them.

Then he tried the bow. Three times he bent over it until it quivered. But he could not pull the string into place, and at last Odysseus signaled him to give up.

"Well," Telemachus said, "perhaps I shall always be a weakling. Let us see you stronger, older men step up and string this bow."

First came soft-faced Leodes, whose favorite seat was close beside the wine bowl. His delicate hands could not even bend the bow, and he soon stepped back.

"This bow can break the spirit of a better man than I!" he said. "Many a man here may have hoped to wed Penelope. But when he has tried this bow, he will go off to woo some other woman, of that I am sure."

"What nonsense!" cried Antinoüs. "Just because you are a weakling! Let us have a good fire lit here in the hall, and put a fleece-covered seat beside it. Then bring in a good big chunk of lard, and we'll warm that bow and grease it well and soon finish this game!"

The fire was lighted, the seat set in place beside it, and the chunk of lard brought out. The young men took their turns warming the bow and having a try, but not one could bend it. At last only Antinoüs and Eurymachus, the leaders of the group, still had their turns to come.

Meanwhile the swineherd and the good herdsman had gone out together, and Odysseus, who had been waiting his chance, followed them.

"What if Odysseus should return?" he asked them. "Would you side with him or with these suitors?"

The herdsman answered without delay. "O Father Zeus, send him home! Then you should see the strength of my hand and arm!" And the swineherd said the same.

Sure of their loyalty now, Odysseus said, "Here I am, good

friends, back in my own house after twenty years. You may see by this scar I had from a boar tusk that it is really I. Now if you really wish to help, wait until I ask for a chance at the bow. The suitors are certain to refuse. Then you, Eumaeus, give it to me. And if the gods grant that we destroy these men, I shall set you both up in good homes of your own, with wives to look after you."

The two loyal fellows burst into tears and flung themselves upon Odysseus. But he sent them off quickly to lock the outer gates and get the women to their rooms. Then back he went into the great hall. Eurymachus was taking his turn, warming the great bow all around at the fire. But still he could not bend it.

"Woe is me!" he groaned. "Not that I care about losing Penelope—there are plenty of women left. But for all of us to be weaker than Odysseus makes a sorry tale."

"That is nonsense," said Antinoüs. "Today is a holiday. Let us celebrate and put the bow aside. We can leave the axes here and finish our game tomorrow."

All were glad to agree to this. But Odysseus spoke up.

"May I beg your permission to try the bow, to see if my muscles still have the strength they once had?"

His words made all the suitors angry, mostly because they were afraid that this old fellow might indeed be able to bend the bow. They scoffed at him until Telemachus spoke up.

"I shall let anyone try that I wish," he said, "for I am master in this house."

In spite of the suitors' jeers, the swineherd took Odysseus the bow. Odysseus turned it around in his hands, to make certain that worms had not harmed it during his years away.

"Well," the suitors whispered to each other, "he seems to know how to handle a bow!"

Odysseus balanced the great bow neatly. As easily as a skilled musician stringing up a new cord on the pegs, he strung the bow, then twanged the string so that it sang under his hand with a good clear note.

The suitors paled with amazement, and Zeus overhead sent a clap of thunder as a good omen.

Odysseus picked up one sharp arrow and laid it against the

bow. Then he drew back notched arrow and string together and, without rising from his chair, he aimed straight ahead and shot. Through every ax handle in the row the arrow sped cleanly, and out the far end.

Turning to his son, Odysseus said, "Telemachus, the stranger has not disgraced you. My strength is still what it was. Now come, let us prepare a treat for all these guests, while the daylight lasts."

At the awaited signal, Telemachus slung on his sharp sword, grasped his spear, and stepped forward fully armed to his father's side.

Doom of the Suitors

Now Odysseus stripped off his rags and sprang to the doorsill, brandishing the quiver of arrows and his bow.

"So the game is over at last!" he cried. "And now for a new target, one which no man has ever hit."

With that he let fly a deadly arrow straight at Antinoüs, who had just lifted a great two-handled goblet and was about to drink from it. The arrow struck him in the throat and sent him tumbling among the bread and meat.

Then what an angry uproar arose, when the suitors saw their leader fall! They looked about the walls for weapons, but not one was in sight.

Odysseus frowned blackly on them and cried, "You dogs, you thought I would never come home from Troy. You thought you could use my household as you wished, and woo my wife by wasting my wealth. You had no fear of men or gods. But now death has fastened itself upon you all!"

The men paled with fear. Of them all, only Eurymachus could speak. "If you are really Odysseus, you are right," he said. "But it has all been Antinoüs' fault. It was he who wanted to kill your son and rule in your place. Now he is dead. So spare the rest of us and we shall go through the countryside gathering flocks and herds and gold to repay you for all that has been destroyed."

"Eurymachus," said Odysseus, "not if you all turned over your whole estates to me could I be stopped from killing until you all have paid the price. So fight, I say, or run if you can."

When the suitors heard this, their hearts all trembled.

"Turn up the tables to serve as shields!" cried Eurymachus. "And draw your swords, my friends. Together we shall push him from the door and soon get help from the town."

He leaped at Odysseus with his sword, but Odysseus let fly another arrow which caught him in the chest. Down fell his sword from his hand, and his brow struck the ground as death clouded his eyes.

Next Amphinomus ran at Odysseus. Telemachus struck him from behind, his long spear going straight through the man, and he fell to the ground.

Telemachus did not dare take time to remove the spear. He raced to the storeroom for shields, spears and helmets for himself and his father. And he brought weapons for their two staunch servants, the herdsman and the swineherd as well.

When he returned, the dead lay about—one for each of Odysseus' arrows. Odysseus leaned the bow against a pillar, put on his shield and helmet, and picked up a pair of spears. Then he and the three supporters fell upon the suitors, hacking them down until the floor ran with blood.

Not one was spared but the minstrel, who had played and sung for the suitors against his will, and Medon the herald, who had long been a friend of Telemachus. These two Telemachus persuaded his father to let live. Odysseus smiled upon them and sent them into the courtyard to wait, away from the slaughter.

At last all the suitors were dead. Odysseus looked around the hall to make certain that no one else was hiding from death. Then he ordered servants to carry out the dead bodies, and to clean the tables and the seats and the floor.

After sulphur was burned to purify the air, Odysseus sent his old nurse to tell Penelope that her husband was home.

Peace at Last

Roused from deep sleep, Penelope would not believe the news at first, for she had hoped too long. But as she listened, tears rolled down her cheeks, and her hope began to grow.

She stepped over the sill into the great hall, where she seated herself in her chair by the fire, across from Odysseus. He sat in silence, with his eyes on the ground, waiting to see what she would do. For some time Penelope could not speak. But her eyes were busy, seeking to find the husband she had known in the ragged stranger before her.

Telemachus became impatient. "What a hard heart you have!" he cried. "Why don't you come right over to Father and speak to him?"

"My boy," said Penelope, "my heart is numbed, so that I cannot find words to say. But if this is really Odysseus, we two shall know each other soon enough, for there are secrets between us no one else knows."

At these words Odysseus smiled. "Let your mother be, Telemachus. Let her put me to the test. You start thinking about what is to be done to make the peace, now that you and I have killed all the best young men of Ithaca."

"That is for you to decide," said Telemachus. "We shall follow your lead."

As always, Odysseus had a plan. "Wash now, and change your clothes, and have all the ladies-in-waiting dress up too. Then have the minstrel take his harp and play a cheerful tune. Fill the house with the sound of singing and dancing, so that the neighbors will think there is a wedding. We must not let out word of these deaths until we can get away to the farms. Then we shall see what ideas the gods put into our minds."

This plan of Odysseus' was put into action at once. The men

put on fresh tunics, and the women dressed in their best. The minstrel took up his harp and soon had them in the mood for merry dancing and song.

Outside the great hall on the street, the people passing by lingered and said to themselves, "Well, one of the lads is marrying our queen at last."

By now Odysseus had been bathed and rubbed down with oil by his old nurse, and had put on a handsome tunic and cloak. Athena, too, had done her part. She made him look taller and handsomer than ever, curling the locks that sprang from his head and touching all his features with new beauty. Looking more like a god than a man, he took his place once more beside the fire, opposite his wife.

"Strange woman!" he said to her. "Surely the gods have given you a heart of iron. Ah, well, Nurse, make a bed for me, for I shall sleep alone."

"Yes, Eurycleia," said Penelope. "Set up his own big bedstead outside the room he built himself, and fit it up with fresh linens and fleeces."

This was her way of testing her husband. But he was much displeased.

"Who has moved my bed, I should like to know?" he cried. "And how did they do it, short of a miracle? I built a living olive tree growing through the house into one post of the bed, trimming off the branches and smoothing the trunk down as neatly as you please! That was our secret, between us two. And now if someone has cut that olive tree and moved my bed, I should like to know about it at once!"

Penelope's knees began to tremble at his words, and her heart melted away. Bursting into tears, she ran to her husband and threw herself into his arms.

"Do not be angry with me, Odysseus, you who were always the most understanding of men. There has always been a cold fear in my heart that some man might come and bewitch me with his talk. There are so many impostors about! But only you could tell me the secret of the bed. You have convinced my hard heart!"

Penelope's words stirred Odysseus' heart, too. He wept as

he held her in his arms. While they clung together, the house-keeper and the nurse made up their bed by the light of torches. Telemachus and the other dancers brought their feet to rest. And the silence of sleep settled down at last over the darkened hall.

But Penelope and Odysseus still had much to say to one another. She told him all she had suffered at her suitors' hands. And Odysseus in his turn told her all his adventures and misfortunes.

Dawn would have overtaken his telling, had not Athena made Dawn wait, with her swift horses champing at Ocean's edge.

When at last Odysseus arose from his bed, he said to his wife, "I am going now to pay a visit to my father, who is worried on my account. When the people of the town hear about the men I killed, be sure you stay safe in your rooms and do not see anyone."

He put on his armor, then wakened Telemachus and the two herdsmen, and they did the same. They all left the palace by the main gate. But Athena kept shadowy darkness around them until they were out of the town.

They soon reached the well-kept farm of Laertes. And while the others went on to the house to prepare the midday meal, Odysseus found his father out in the vineyards, digging about the plants.

When Odysseus saw how wasted and worn his father looked, both with grief and age, he paused beneath a pear tree, and tears came to his eyes. Then he stepped forward and spoke.

"Old man," he said, "you keep your garden in fine order. Not a plant looks neglected. But I hope you will not mind if I say that you do not look so well cared for yourself."

"I grieve for my son, Odysseus, King of Ithaca," said Laertes, with tears in his eyes. And he scraped up dust from the earth and poured it over his head.

Now Odysseus' heart was wrung. "I am he, Father," he cried, "the son you are weeping for! See the scar here I got in hunting a boar, if you doubt my word. But come, we have no time for tears. For I have killed all that crowd of suitors, and I think the whole island will be upon us soon."

So the two set out for the house, where Telemachus and the herdsmen were carving meat for their dinner.

As they sat there over their meal, news of the death of the suitors spread with the speed of flame through the town. Soon a crowd of mourners gathered at Odysseus' gate. With much wailing and lamenting, each family took away its dead. The dead suitors from abroad they sent off on ships, each to his own far-off home and grieving family.

Then the old men trooped off to the market place and called a meeting of the assembly there. The father of Antinoüs was the first to rise and speak.

"Friends, this man Odysseus is an enemy of all our people here," he declared. "Think of the fine crews who sailed away with him. Where are they today? Those he did not lose on his journeys—and their good ships as well—he has slain now on his return. Let us avenge these deaths!"

Now the minstrel and Medon the herald, whom Odysseus had spared, appeared in the market place.

"Listen," said Medon, "we saw what happened, and we can tell you the immortal gods were at Odysseus' side in all he did."

And the seer of Ithaca, who could see the past and the future as well, rose up to speak. "Your own wickedness and that of your sons has caused this doom to fall upon them," he said. "You would not listen to any urgings that you check your sons in their reckless wasting of Odysseus' wealth."

Now the people grumbled, and some jumped to their feet to protest, for they did not like to hear this blunt truth. They snatched up their weapons and marched in a body toward Laertes' house.

But up in the clouds, almighty Zeus had tired of fighting and of blood.

"Have them make peace," he said to Athena. "Let good will be restored."

So Athena appeared, just at the moment when Odysseus and his friends had lined up on the road before Laertes' house to face the ranks of the foe. Laertes had already lifted his long spear for a thrust. But Athena, disguised as Mentor, a wise old leader of Ithaca, raised a great cry:

"Ithacans, stop this tragic fight before more blood is shed!"

At the sound of the goddess' voice, the men of Ithaca threw down their arms and trembled in fear. Then Zeus cast a thunderbolt at their feet. And Athena spoke to Odysseus too, saying, "Bring this war to an end, or you will feel the wrath of Zeus!"

Odysseus obeyed this command of the gods with a happy heart. Then Athena, still in the person of Mentor, established peace between the two forces, and thus brought happiness at last to Ithaca and to Odysseus its king, after so many anxious years.

Reading, Writing, and Discussion of the ODYSSEY

THE LAND OF THE LOTUS-EATERS

1. How does Odysseus get to Ismarus? **2.** Notice the important part the sea and sky, the wind and the weather play in the ODYSSEY. **3.** Start to follow the journey of Odysseus as it is influenced **-a** by weather, **-b** by gods, **-c** by other mortals. **4.** Begin a list of Odysseus' heroic characteristics. Does he show any in this first section? **5.** Do you feel the presence of the narrator at any point?

IN THE CAVE OF THE ONE-EYED GIANT

1. The fantastic is introduced into the ODYSSEY. How does it add interest and movement to the story? **2.** Odysseus causes misfortune in this episode. What long-standing evil results from Odysseus' curiosity? **3.** How is Poseidon drawn into the narrative? **4.** Among the Greeks, Odysseus was famous for his wit. What proof is there that his reputation for wit is not ill founded? **5.** In several instances the author uses foreshadowing and delayed action to create suspense in the story. Find examples of these. **6.** Anger is one of Achilles' faults. What is a fault of Odysseus? In this adaptation the author focuses attention on the wanderings of Odysseus. What is the initiating incident of the Greek hero's wandering?

AEOLUS, RULER OF THE WINDS

1. Notice throughout the story the relationship between Odysseus and his men. What is Odysseus' way of treating them? What do they think of him? **2.** What causes Odysseus' misfortune in this section? Does Odysseus show his heroic nature here? **3.** Keep account of the time of Odysseus' wanderings.

THE FEARFUL GIANTS

1. What coincidence saves Odysseus? **2.** What characteristic of a good soldier does Odysseus show in this section?

CIRCE, THE ENCHANTRESS

1. What part do the gods play in this section? Does the author enter the story to comment? **2.** How does Odysseus avoid enchantment? **3.** Is the detailed description of the appearance and the furniture of Circe's house necessary? **4.** Discuss the personality of Circe. What makes her change her mind toward the strangers? Trace the genealogy of Circe. **5.** Keep charting the passage of time. Why does Odysseus remain so long on the island of Circe?

THE KINGDOM OF THE DEAD

1. What is the effect of Circe's warning on the structure of the story? Note warnings in other places. **2.** The author uses certain stock phrases to pass comment on action; e.g.,

> *sorrowing for lost companions but glad to be alive.*
> *But weeping does no good.*

What function does such a device have in oral poetry? What function does it have in written poetry? **3.** How does the author link the ILIAD to the ODYSSEY in this section? **4.** What characters from mythology appear in *The Kingdom of the Dead*?

THE SIRENS' SONG

1. What precautions does Odysseus take against the Sirens' song? **2.** What is particularly intriguing about the Sirens? What do they offer Odysseus?

SCYLLA AND CHARYBDIS

1. Could Odysseus have used any other strategy to avoid either danger? **2.** How does the author link these separate episodes to each other? How does he create curiosity concerning the outcome?

THE CATTLE OF THE SUN GOD

1. Note Odysseus' relation to his men. What heroic qualities does Odysseus exhibit here? **2.** What part do the gods play in saving Odysseus?

A PLAN FOR TELEMACHUS

1. This section and the two following really precede the wanderings of Odysseus. It is only after he leaves Calypso's island that he comes to the kingdom of King Alcinoüs and tells of his wanderings. Why does the placement of these three sections at this point fit into the episodic structure of the ODYSSEY? **2.** Why do the gods have the council without Poseidon? **3.** Take note of domestic scenes in the ODYSSEY. Compare with domestic scenes in the ILIAD. **4.** Is Telemachus necessary to the furthering of action of the story? **5.** Is the presence of the suitors necessary to any action in the story? Does the author individualize the suitors in any way? How? Examine the dialogue. **6.** How is interest in the following chapters created in this section?

THE RAFT

1. Compare Circe and Calypso. What part does each play in the action? **2.** Continue to keep record of the time. Why does the author make reference to time so often in the wanderings of Odysseus? **3.** Odysseus finally reaches Ithaca. Upon what decision does his return depend?

NAUSICAÄ

1. Athena plays a great part in the working out of the story from here. She personally aids Odysseus in many ways. List what she has done to return him safely to Ithaca. **2.** Can you give a reason for the frequent descriptions of eating and drinking which you find in the ODYSSEY? Are these descriptions necessary to the story?

HOME TO ITHACA

1. This section picks up the story after Odysseus has related his wanderings. Is there any reason, dictated by the story, for Athena to spread a mist over the land so that Odysseus could not recognize anything? **2.** Is there a reason for Athena's disguise as a shepherd? How is humor brought into this episode? Why does Athena choose the disguise of an old man for Odysseus?

ODYSSEUS FINDS A FRIEND

1. Why does Odysseus come to the swineherd first? **2.** What evidence is there that hospitality was considered a religious duty by the Greeks? **3.** How does the author use dialogue for purposes of exposition?

TELEMACHUS FINDS A FATHER

1. Why is Telemachus introduced into the main action of the story at this time? **2.** How does Odysseus test Telemachus? **3.** What heroic qualities does Odysseus show here? **4.** How does Eumaeus treat Telemachus? **5.** Make a list of the Ithacans whom Odysseus meets. How is he accepted by them? How does he react to them?

BATTLE PREPARATIONS

1. What function does this scene of the suitors' mistreating of Odysseus have? What does Odysseus do as a result of this? **2.** Why does Odysseus not reveal himself at once to the suitors? **3.** What function does Odysseus' retelling of his own adventures to Penelope have in the story? Why doesn't Penelope recognize Odysseus?

1. Penelope suggests the contest of the bows to end the dispute among the suitors. What makes her decide to do this at this particular point in the narrative? **2.** Note the characterization of the suitors in their approach to the contest. They are set up as a contrast to Odysseus. **3.** How does Odysseus test Eumaeus? What promise does he make to him? What does this tell you about Greek life?

DOOM OF THE SUITORS

1. What shows the real character of the suitors? **2.** Note Odysseus' agility with weapons. Was he noted for this during his wanderings or during the Trojan War? **3.** Is this revenge too cruel for the deed?

PEACE AT LAST

1. How does the author create feeling at the meeting of Odysseus and Penelope? How is suspense created? **2.** What effect does Telemachus' wager have upon the movement of the story? **3.** The movement slows down from this point until the end of the ODYSSEY. What reason can you give for this? What test does Penelope finally give Odysseus? **4.** What virtue much admired by the Greeks prompted Odysseus to go first to his father? **5.** Is the assembly in the market place and the speech of Antinoüs' father anticlimactic? What finally ends the strife?

Overview—Comparison of Storytelling Methods in the ILIAD *and the* ODYSSEY

1. Compare the time element in both stories. How long does each take? Does each follow chronological order? **2.** Compare the movement. Which moves along more quickly? Why? Which is the more complicated story? Which is a simple linear structure? **3.** The grim atmosphere of war and death pervades the ILIAD. How would you distinguish the atmosphere of the ODYSSEY? What element of interest is present in the ODYSSEY but not in the ILIAD? Give examples. **4.** Take a sampling of verbs from any battle scene in the ILIAD. Compare them with a sampling from an adventure in the ODYSSEY. Can you account for the difference? **5.** Compare Achilles and Odysseus. Which is the greater hero? Which do you think appealed more to the Greeks? **6.** Make a list of the gods and goddesses who helped Achilles and those who aided Odysseus. **7.** Draw up a list of the qualities of an epic hero from your study of Achilles and Odysseus. **8.** Compare Penelope and Andromache. What part does each play in the action? Make note of other women in the epics. How are they portrayed? **9.** Identify the force which opposes the hero in each epic. Which is greater? Can the stature of the hero be measured by the force he overcomes? How? **10.** What other characters besides Odysseus appear in both epics? **11.** Trace on a modern map the wanderings of Odysseus. **12.** Even in this prose translation some trace of the aural devices used by the original singer of the poem remains. List these devices and give examples of them. **13.** Create the scene which might immediately have preceded Odysseus' sailing toward Ismarus. Try to recreate the bustle and activity of the scene. **14.** Make a list of adjectives used to describe the sea. Make a list of verbs that show the sea in action. Using your own experience with ships, if possible, create a *seascape* in words. **15.** Create another voyage for Odysseus. Be sure to devise a transition that will make your original journey fit into the ODYSSEY. **16.** Pretend you are one of Odysseus' men. Describe your captain as you see him acting in any one of his adventures. Be original and resourceful in verb choice. **17.** In the land of the fearful giants, Odysseus is led by the king's daughter to the king's *high-roofed hall*. Give her a name and let her relate her impressions of Odysseus. **18.** Gather several of your favorite characters from the ILIAD and the ODYSSEY and prepare a Grecian banquet with all its fine feasting for them.

AN AID TO
THE PRONUNCIATION
OF GREEK NAMES

Achilles	uh-KILL-eez	Demeter	deh-MEE-ter
Aeaea	ee-EE-uh	Diomedes	dy-oh-MEE-deez
Aegean	ee-JEE-uhn	Dulichium	doo-LIK-ee-uhm
Aeolia	ee-OH-lyuh	Elysium	eh-LIZ-yum
Aeolus	EE-oh-luhs	Ethiopia	ee-thee-OH-pyuh
Agamemnon	ag-uh-MEM-nahn	Eumaeus	yoo-MEE-uhs
Ajax	AY-jax	Eurycleia	yoo-rih-KLEE-uh
Alcinoüs	al-SIN-oh-uhs	Eurylochus	yoo-RILL-oh-kuhs
Amphinomus	am-FIN-oh-muhs	Eurymachus	yoo-RIM-uh-kuhs
Andromache	an-DRAHM-uh-kee	Hades	HAY-deez
Antilochus	an-TILL-oh-kuhs	Hector	HEK-ter
Antinoüs	an-TIN-oh-uhs	Hecuba	HEK-yoo-buh
Aphrodite	af-roh-DY-tee	Helenus	HELL-en-uhs
Apollo	uh-PAHL-oh	Hephaestus	heh-FESS-tuhs
Ares	AIR-eez	Hera	HEE-ruh
Arete	AR-eh-tee	Hermes	HER-meez
Argos	AHR-gohs	Ilium	ILL-ee-uhm
Artemis	AHR-teh-miss	Ilos	EYE-lawss
Astyanax	ass-TY-uh-nax	Iris	EYE-riss
Athena	uh-THEE-nuh	Ismarus	ISS-muh-ruhs
Briseis	brih-SEE-iss	Ithaca	ITH-uh-kuh
Calypso	cuh-LIP-soh	Laertes	lay-ER-teez
Cassandra	cuh-SAN-druh	Laocoön	lay-OH-koh-awn
Charybdis	kuh-RIB-diss	Lesbos	LESS-bawss
Chryseis	kry-SEE-iss	Leto	LEE-toh
Circe	SIR-see	Lycia	LISH-yuh
Cyclops	SY-klahps	Malea	muh-Lee-uh
Cyprus	SY-pruhs	Medon	MEE-dohn
Cythera	SIH-thuh-ruh	Menelaus	men-uh-LAY-uhs
Delphi	DEL-fy	Mentor	MEN-ter

Mycenae	my-SEE-nee	Same	SAY-mee
Myrmidons	MER-mih-dahnz	Scaean	SEE-uhn
Nausicaä	noh-SIK-ay-uh	Scamander	skuh-MAN-der
Nestor	NESS-ter	Scylla	SILL-uh
Odysseus	oh-DISS-yoos	Sirens	SY-ruhnz
Ogygia	oh-JIJ-yuh	Sisyphus	SISS-ee-fuhs
Olympus	oh-LIM-puhs	Smyrna	SMER-nuh
Pandarus	PAN-duh-ruhs	Styx	STIX
Patroclus	puh-TROH-kluhs	Tantalus	TAN-tuh-luhs
Penelope	puh-NELL-oh-pee	Thebes	THEEBZ
Persephone	per-SEF-oh-nee	Teiresias	ty-REE-see-uhs
Phaeacia	fee-AY-shyuh	Telemachus	tuh-LEM-uh-kuhs
Polites	poh-LY-teez	Tenedos	TEN-ee-dawss
Polydoros	pah-lee-DAW-ruhs	Thetis	THEE-tiss
Polyphemus	pah-lee-FEE-muhs	Trojans	TROH-juhns
Poseidon	poh-SY-duhn	Xanthus	ZAN-thuhs
Priam	PRY-uhm	Zacynthus	zuh-KIN-thuhs
Pylos	PY-lawss	Zeus	ZYOOS

MORTE
D'ARTHUR

KING ARTHUR

The Marvel of the Sword

When Uther Pendragon, King of England, died, the country for a long while stood in great danger, for every lord that was mighty gathered his forces, and many wished to be king. For King Uther's own son, Prince Arthur, who should have succeeded him, was but a child, and Merlin, the mighty magician had hidden him away.

Now a strange thing had happened at Arthur's birth.

Some time before, Merlin had done Uther a great service, on condition that the king should grant him whatever he wished for. This the king swore a solemn oath to do. Then Merlin made him promise that when his child was born it should be delivered to Merlin to bring up as he chose, for this would be to the child's own great advantage. The king had given his promise so he was obliged to agree. Then Merlin said he knew a very true and faithful man, one of King Uther's lords, by name Sir Ector, who had large possessions in many parts of England and Wales, and that the child should be given to him to bring up.

On the night the baby was born, while it was still unchristened, King Uther commanded two knights and two ladies to take it, wrapped in a cloth of gold, and deliver it to a poor man whom they would find waiting at the postern gate of the Castle. This poor man was Merlin in disguise, although they did not know it.

So the child was delivered unto Merlin and he carried him to Sir Ector, and made a holy man christen him, and named him Arthur; and Sir Ector's wife cherished him as her own child.

Within two years King Uther fell sick of a great malady, and for three days and three nights he was speechless. All the Barons were in sorrow, and asked Merlin what was best to be done.

"There is no remedy," said Merlin, "God will have His Will. But look ye all, Barons, come before King Uther to-morrow, and God will make him speak."

So the next day Merlin and all the Barons came before the king, and Merlin said aloud to King Uther:

"Sir, after your days shall your son Arthur be king of this realm and all that belongs to it?"

Then Uther Pendragon turned and said in hearing of them all: "I give my son Arthur God's blessing and mine, and bid him pray for my soul, and righteously and honourably claim the crown, on forfeiture of my blessing."

And with that, King Uther died.

But Arthur was still only a baby, not two years old, and Merlin knew it would be no use yet to proclaim him king. For there were many powerful nobles in England in those days, who were all trying to get the kingdom for themselves, and perhaps they would kill the little Prince. So there was much strife and debate in the land for a long time.

When several years had passed, Merlin went to the Archbishop of Canterbury and counselled him to send for all the lords of the realm, and all the gentlemen of arms, that they should come to London at Christmas, and for this cause—that a miracle would show who should be rightly king of the realm. So all the lords and gentlemen made themselves ready, and came to London, and long before dawn on Christmas Day they were all gathered in the great church of St. Paul's to pray.

When the first service was over, there was seen in the church-yard a large stone, four-square, like marble, and in the midst of it was like an anvil of steel, a foot high. In this was stuck by the point a beautiful sword, with naked blade, and there were letters written in gold about the sword, which said thus:

> Whoso pulleth this sword out of this stone and anvil
> is rightly King of all England.

Then the people marvelled, and told it to the Archbishop.

"I command," said the Archbishop, "that you keep within the church, and pray unto God still; and that no man touch the sword till the service is over."

So when the prayers in church were over, all the lords went to behold the stone and the sword; and when they read the writing some of them—such as wished to be king—tried to pull the sword out of the anvil. But not one could make it stir.

"The man is not here, that shall achieve the sword," said the Archbishop, "but doubt not God will make him known. But let us provide ten knights, men of good fame, to keep guard over the sword."

So it was ordained, and proclamation was made that every one who wished might try to win the sword. And upon New Year's Day the Barons arranged to have a great tournament, in which all knights who would joust or tourney might take a part. This was ordained to keep together the Lords and Commons, for the Archbishop trusted that it would be made known who should win the sword.

How Arthur Was Crowned King

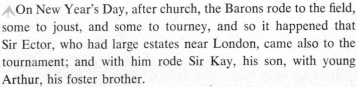

On New Year's Day, after church, the Barons rode to the field, some to joust, and some to tourney, and so it happened that Sir Ector, who had large estates near London, came also to the tournament; and with him rode Sir Kay, his son, with young Arthur, his foster brother.

As they rode, Sir Kay found he had lost his sword, for he

had left it at his father's lodging, so he begged young Arthur to go and fetch it for him.

"That will I, gladly," said Arthur, and he rode fast away.

But when he came to the house, he found no one at home to give him the sword, for everyone had gone to see the jousting. Then Arthur was angry and said to himself:

"I will ride to the churchyard, and take the sword with me that sticketh in the stone, for my brother, Sir Kay, shall not be without a sword this day."

When he came to the churchyard he alighted, and tied his horse to the stile, and went to the tent. But he found there no knights, who should have been guarding the sword, for they were all away at the joust. Seizing the sword by the handle he lightly and fiercely pulled it out of the stone, then took his horse and rode his way, till he came to Sir Kay his brother, to whom he delivered the sword.

As soon as Sir Kay saw it, he knew well it was the sword of the Stone, so he rode to his father Sir Ector, and said:

"Sir, lo, here is the sword of the Stone, wherefore I must be king of this land."

When Sir Ector saw the sword he turned back, and came to the church, and there they all three alighted and went into the church, and he made his son swear truly how he got the sword.

"By my brother Arthur," said Sir Kay, "for he brought it to me."

"How did you get this sword?" said Sir Ector to Arthur.

And the boy told him.

"Now," said Sir Ector, "I understand you must be King of this land."

"Wherefore I?" said Arthur. "And for what cause?"

"Sir," said Ector, "because God will have it so; for never man could draw out this sword but he that shall rightly be king. Now let me see whether you can put the sword there as it was, and pull it out again."

"There is no difficulty," said Arthur, and he put it back into the stone.

Then Sir Ector tried to pull out the sword, and failed; and Sir Kay also pulled with all his might, but it would not move.

"Now you shall try," said Sir Ector to Arthur.

"I will, well," said Arthur, and pulled the sword out easily.

At this Sir Ector and Sir Kay knelt down on the ground.

"Alas," said Arthur, "mine own dear father and brother, why do you kneel to me?"

"Nay, nay, my lord Arthur, it is not so; I was never your father, nor of your blood; but I know well you are of higher blood than I thought you were."

Then Sir Ector told him all, how he had taken him to bring up, and by whose command; and how he had received him from Merlin. And when he understood that Ector was not his father, Arthur was deeply grieved.

"Will you be my good, gracious lord, when you are king?" asked the knight.

"If not, I should be to blame," said Arthur, "for you are the man in the world to whom I am the most beholden, and my good lady and mother your wife, who has fostered and kept me as well as her own children. And if ever it be God's will that I be King, as you say, you shall desire of me what I shall do, and I shall not fail you; God forbid I should fail you."

"Sir," said Sir Ector, "I will ask no more of you but that you will make my son, your foster brother Sir Kay, seneschal of all your lands."

"That shall be done," said Arthur, "and by my faith, never man but he shall have that office while he and I live."

Then they went to the Archbishop and told him how the sword was achieved, and by whom.

On Twelfth Day all the Barons came to the stone in the churchyard, so that anyone who wished might try to win the sword. But not one of them all could take it out, except Arthur. Many of them therefore were very angry, and said it was a great shame to them and to the country to be governed by a boy not of high blood, for as yet none of them knew that he was the son of King Uther Pendragon. So they agreed to delay the decision until Candlemas Day, which falls on the second day of February.

But when Candlemas came, and Arthur once more was the only one who could pull out the sword, they put it off till Easter;

and when Easter came, and Arthur again prevailed in presence of them all, they put it off till the Feast of Pentecost.

Then by Merlin's advice the Archbishop summoned some of the best knights that were to be got—such knights as in his own day King Uther Pendragon had best loved, and trusted most—and these were appointed to attend young Arthur, and never to leave him night or day till the Feast of Pentecost.

When the great day came, all manner of men once more made the attempt, and once more not one of them all could prevail but Arthur. Before all the Lords and Commons there assembled he pulled out the sword, whereupon all the Commons cried out:

"We will have Arthur for our King! We will put him no more in delay, for we all see that it is God's will that he shall be our king, and he who holdeth against it, we will slay him."

And therewith they knelt down all at once, both rich and poor, and besought pardon of Arthur, because they had delayed him so long.

And Arthur forgave them, and took the sword in both his hands, and offered it on the altar where the Archbishop was and so he was made knight by the best man there.

After that, he was crowned at once, and there he swore to his Lords and Commons to be a true king, and to govern with true justice from thenceforth all the days of his life.

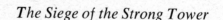

The Siege of the Strong Tower

After Arthur was crowned king many complaints were made to him of great wrongs that had been done since the death of King Uther; many lords, knights, ladies and gentlemen having been deprived of their lands. Thereupon King Arthur caused the lands to be given again to them that owned them. When this was done, and all the districts round London were settled, he made Sir Kay, Seneschal of England, Sir Baldwin, Constable of Britain, and Sir Ulfius, Chamberlain; while Sir Brastias was appointed Warden of the country north of the Trent. Most of this land was then held by the King's enemies, but within a few years Arthur had won all the north.

Some parts of Wales still stood out against him, but in due time he overcame them all, as he did the rest, by the noble prowess of himself, and the Knights of the Round Table.

Then King Arthur went into Wales, and proclaimed a great feast, to be held at Pentecost, after his crowning in the city of Carleon. To this feast came many rich and powerful kings, with great retinues of knights. Arthur was glad of their coming, for he thought that the kings and the knights had come in love, and to do him honour at his feast, wherefore he rejoiced greatly, and sent them rich presents.

The kings, however, would receive none of them, but rebuked the messengers shamefully, saying it gave them no pleasure to receive gifts from a beardless boy of low blood. They sent him word that they would none of his gifts, but they would come and give him gifts with hard swords betwixt the neck and the shoulders. It was for that they came hither, so they told the messengers plainly, for it was a great shame to them all to see such a boy have the rule of so noble a realm as this land.

When the messengers brought this answer to King Arthur, by the advice of his Barons he betook himself with five hundred good men to a strong tower. And all the kings laid siege to him, but King Arthur had plenty of food.

Within fifteen days Merlin, the great magician, came into the city of Carleon. All the kings were very glad to see him, and asked him:

"For what cause is that boy Arthur made your King?"

"Sirs," said Merlin, "I will tell you the cause, because he is King Uther Pendragon's son. And whosoever saith 'Nay,' Arthur shall be King, and overcome all his enemies, and before he dies he shall long have been King of all England, and have under his sway Wales, Ireland, and Scotland, and more realms than I will now relate."

Some of the kings marvelled at Merlin's words, and deemed it well that it should be as he said; and some of them, such as King Lot of Orkney, laughed at him; and others called him a wizard. But they all consented that King Arthur should come out and speak with them, and gave their assurance that he should come safely and should return safely.

So Merlin went to King Arthur, and told him what he had done, and bade him come out boldly and speak with them.

"Spare them not," he said, "but answer them as their King and Chieftain, for ye shall overcome them, whether they will or not."

Then King Arthur came out of his tower, having under his gown a cuirass of double mail; and there went with him the Archbishop of Canterbury and Sir Baldwin, Sir Kay, and Sir Brastias. When he met the Kings there was no meekness, but stout words on both sides, King Arthur ready with an answer to all they said, and declaring that if he lived he would make them bow. They departed therefore in wrath, and King Arthur returned to the tower and armed himself and all his knights.

"What will you do?" said Merlin to the kings; "you had better refrain, for you will not prevail, were you ten times as many."

"Are we well advised to be afraid of a dream-reader?" sneered King Lot.

With that, Merlin vanished away, and came to King Arthur and bade him set on them fiercely. And the magician counselled Arthur not to fight at first with the sword he had got by miracle; but if he found himself getting the worst, then to draw it.

Meanwhile, three hundred of the best men who were with the kings went straight over to Arthur, and this comforted him greatly. All his knights fought gallantly, and the battle raged with fury. King Arthur himself was ever in the foremost of the press, till his horse was slain underneath him. And therewith King Lot smote down King Arthur.

Four of his knights rescued him and set him on horseback. Then he drew forth his sword, and it was so bright in his enemies' eyes that it gave light like thirty torches; and thus he drove back his foes and slew many of them.

Then the citizens of Carleon arose with clubs and stones, and slew many knights. But all the kings banded together with their knights who were alive, and so fled and departed.

And Merlin came to Arthur, and counselled him to follow them no farther.

The Battle of the Kings

After the feast and the tourney, Arthur came to London and called all his Barons to a Council. For Merlin had told him that the six kings who had made war upon him, and whom he had defeated, would hasten to wreak their vengeance on him and his lands. The Barons could give no counsel, but said they were big enough to fight.

"You say well," said Arthur. "I thank you for your good courage; but will all of you who love me speak with Merlin? You know well that he has done much for me, and knows many things and when he is with you I wish that you would beseech him to give you his best advice."

All the Barons said they would gladly hear what Merlin counselled, so the magician was sent for.

"I warn you well," said Merlin, "that your enemies are passing strong for you, and they are as good men of arms as any alive. By this time, too, they have got to themselves four kings more, and a mighty Duke, and unless our King can get more horsemen than are to be found within the bounds of his own realm, if he fight with them in battle he shall be overcome and slain."

"What is best to be done?" asked the Barons.

"I will tell you my advice," said Merlin. "There are two brethren beyond the sea, and they are both kings, and marvellously powerful men. One is called King Ban, of Benwick, and the other King Bors, of Gaul—that is, France. And against these two brothers wars a mighty man, the King Claudas, and strives with them for a castle; and there is great war between them. But because Claudas is very rich he gets many good knights to fight for him, and for the most part puts these two kings to the worse. Now this is my counsel—that our King and Sovereign Lord send to kings Ban and Bors two trusty knights, with letters stating that if they will come and see Arthur and his Court, and help him in his wars, then he will swear to help them in their wars against King Claudas. Now, what do you say?"

"This is well counselled," said the King and the Barons.

So in all haste it was settled.

Ulfius and Brastias were chosen as the messengers, and they rode forth well-horsed and well-armed; and so crossed the sea, and rode towards the city of Benwick. Here in a narrow place they were attacked by eight knights of King Claudas, who tried to kill them or take them prisoners. But Ulfius and Brastias, fighting with them two by two, in turn overcame them all, and left them lying sorely hurt and bruised on the field.

When they came to Benwick it fortunately happened that both the kings, Ban and Bors, were there. As soon as the kings knew they were messengers of Arthur's, they gave them the very heartiest greeting, and when Ban and Bors read the letters, they were made even more welcome than before.

So Ulfius and Brastias had good cheer, and rich gifts, as many as they could carry away, and they took back this answer with them—that the two kings would come to Arthur in all haste.

King Arthur was very glad to get this message, and, when the time came for the kings to arrive, he proclaimed a great feast and went ten miles out of London to meet them. After the feast there was a splendid tournament, in which seven hundred knights took part. Arthur, Ban, and Bors, with the Archbishop of Canterbury, and Sir Ector (Kay's father) sat in a place covered with cloth of gold, like a hall, with ladies and gentlewomen, to behold who did best, and to give judgment thereon. The knights who won the prizes were three of King Arthur's household, Sir Kay, Sir Lucas, and Sir Griflet.

With the help of King Ban and King Bors Arthur utterly defeated and put to rout the eleven kings who were warring against him. When his enemies were scattered, King Ban and King Bors, laden with rich gifts, returned to their own countries. And they made a compact with Arthur that if they had need of him to help them against King Claudas, they would send to him for succour; and on the other hand, if Arthur had need of them, he was to send, and they would not tarry.

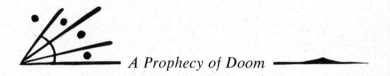 *A Prophecy of Doom*

After the departure of Ban and Bors, King Arthur rode to Carleon. Then there arrived the wife of King Lot of Orkney, one of the kings who had been fighting against him. She came in great state, in the manner of a messenger, but it was really to spy the Court of King Arthur. With her were her four sons, Gawaine, Gaheris, Agrivaine, and Gareth, and many other knights and ladies. Though very cunning and deceitful she was a most beautiful woman; therefore she quite won the heart of King Arthur. He did not know that in reality she was his own half-sister, for she was the daughter of his mother Igraine, who before her marriage with Uther Pendragon had been the wife of a Duke of Cornwall. Another daughter was Morgan le Fay, who was also beautiful, treacherous, and well skilled in magic.

King Lot's wife stayed a month at Carleon, and then went away, and after her departure King Arthur dreamed a marvellous dream, which filled him with great dread. He thought that there came into this land griffins and serpents; and he thought that they burnt and slew all the people in the land, and then he thought he fought with them, and they did him passing great harm, and wounded him sorely, but at the last he slew them.

When the King awoke he was very sorrowful because of his dream, and so to put it out of his thoughts he made ready with many knights to ride hunting. As soon as he was in the forest the King saw a great hart before him, and he rode after it so fast that his poor horse fell exhausted.

While the King was sitting waiting for one of his men to fetch him another horse, Merlin came by in the likeness of a child of fourteen years, and saluting the King, asked why he was so pensive. Arthur replied that he had much to make him pensive, whereupon Merlin made him very angry by saying he knew all his thoughts, who he was, and all about him. Then Merlin departed, and presently came again in the likeness of an old man of four-score years, and again asked the King why he was so sad.

"I may well be sad," said Arthur, "because of many things."

And he told the old man about his dream, and also about the strange child who had just been there, and who had told him things he never knew before about his own father and mother. Then Merlin told him that everything the child said was quite true; and he went on to say that in the years to come much evil would fall upon the land, for King Lot's wife would have a child who would destroy Arthur and all the knights of his realm.

"What are you," said Arthur, "that tell me these tidings?"

"I am Merlin, and I was he in the child's likeness."

"Ah," said King Arthur, "you are a marvellous man; but I wonder much at your words that I must die in battle."

"Wonder not," said Merlin, "for it is God's will to punish your body for wrong deeds done on earth. But I may well be sorry," added the old man, "for I shall die a shameful death— to be put into the earth alive; but you shall die an honourable death."

As they talked thus, there came one with the King's horse, and Merlin got on another horse, and they rode to Carleon.

The prophecy that Merlin foretold of his own death really came to pass. For some years later the great magician fell in love with a damsel of the Court, named Nimue, or as some call her "Vivien," who pretended to like him in return till she had learned all manner of things that she desired. He taught her all kinds of magic and enchantments, so that she could work spells herself. But Merlin got so foolish in his affection that he would never let her out of his sight, and the lady grew quite weary of his love, and longed to be free. She was afraid of Merlin because he was a magician, and she could find no way to get rid of him.

At last it happened that once Merlin showed her a wonderful rock, in which was a great stone that worked by enchantment. Then Nimue cunningly persuaded Merlin to step into the rock to let her know of the marvels there, but when he was once inside she replaced the great stone by the spells he had taught her, so that in spite of all his crafts he could never again come out. Then Nimue fled away and left Merlin in the rock.

Thus the prophecy relating to his own fate was fulfilled, and later on what he had foretold with regard to King Arthur also came to pass. For Merlin once said that the person who should destroy Arthur should be born on May-Day. So the King sent for all the children who were born on the first of May; there were a great many sons of lords and ladies, and among the rest was his nephew Mordred, the son of King Lot's wife. All the children were put into a ship, and sent away out of the country, and some were only four weeks old. But the ship drove against a rock, and was wrecked to pieces, and all the children perished, excepting one. Little Mordred was cast up by the sea, and a good man found him, and took care of him till he was fourteen years old, when he brought him to Court. Mordred, like his mother, was very sly and treacherous.

Many of the lords and barons of the realm were very angry because of this loss of their children, but many put the blame more on Merlin than on Arthur; so what for dread and for love they held their peace.

The Knight of the Fountain

When King Arthur learnt from Merlin that his mother Igraine was still alive, he sent for her in all haste; and the Queen came, and brought with her Morgan le Fay, her daughter, who was as fair a lady as any might be. Igraine had never known what became of the little babe she entrusted to Merlin, for she had never seen the child afterwards, and did not even know what name was given to it. Then Merlin took the King by the hand, saying, "This is your mother." Therewith Arthur took his mother, Queen Igraine, into his arms, and kissed her, and each wept. Then the King commanded a feast to be held that lasted eight days.

One day there came to the Court a squire on horseback, leading a knight before him, wounded to death. He told how there was a knight in the forest who had reared a pavilion by a well, and how he had slain his master, a good knight; he besought that his master might be buried, and some knight revenge his death.

There was much stir in the Court because of this knight's death, every one giving his advice, and a young squire called Griflet, who was about the same age as Arthur, came to the King and besought him to make him a knight.

"Thou art full young and tender," said Arthur, "to take so high an order on thee."

"Sir," said Griflet, "I beseech you make me knight."

"Sir, it were great pity to lose Griflet," said Merlin, "for he will be a passing good man when he is of age, abiding with you the term of his life."

So the King made him knight. "Now," he said, "since I have made you knight, you must give me a gift."

"What you will," said Griflet.

Then the King made him promise that when he had fought with the knight at the fountain he would return straight to the Court without further debate.

So Griflet took his horse in great haste, and got ready his shield, and took a spear in his hand, and rode at a gallop till he came to the fountain. There he saw a rich pavilion, and near by under a cloth stood a fair horse, well saddled and bridled, and on a tree a shield of many colours, and a great spear. Griflet smote on the shield with the butt of his spear, so that it fell down.

With that the knight came out of the pavilion, and said: "Fair knight, why smote you down my shield?"

"Because I would joust with you," said Griflet.

"It is better you do not," said the knight, "for you are but young and lately made a knight, and your might is nothing to mine."

"As for that," said Griflet, "I will joust with you."

"I am loath to do it," said the knight, "but since I needs must, I will make ready. Whence be ye?"

"Sir, I am of Arthur's Court."

The two knights ran together, so that Griflet's spear was all shivered to pieces, and therewith the other knight, whose name was Pellinore, smote Griflet through the shield and left side, and broke his own spear, while horse and knight fell down.

When Pellinore saw Griflet lie so on the ground he alighted, and was very sad, for he thought he had slain him. He unlaced his helm, and gave him air, and set him again on his horse, saying he had a mighty heart, and if he lived he would prove a passing good knight. So Sir Griflet rode back to Court, where great dole was made for him. But through good doctors he was healed.

King Arthur was very wrathful because of the hurt to Sir Griflet, and he commanded one of his men to have his horse and armour ready waiting for him outside the city before daylight on the following morning. On the morrow, before dawn, he mounted, telling the man to wait there till he came again.

He rode softly till day, and then he was aware of Merlin

being chased by three churls, who would have slain him. The King rode towards them, and bade them "Flee, churls!" They were frightened when they saw a knight, and fled.

"O, Merlin," said Arthur, "here hadst thou been slain, for all thy crafts, had I not been here!"

"Nay, not so," said Merlin, "for I could save myself if I would. And thou art nearer thy death than I am, for thou are going towards thy death, if God be not thy friend."

As they went thus talking they came to the fountain, and the rich pavilion there beside it. Then King Arthur was aware where sat a knight, armed, in a chair.

"Sir Knight," said Arthur, "for what cause abidest thou here, that no knight may ride this way unless he joust with thee? I counsel thee to leave that custom."

"This custom," said Pellinore, "I have used, and will use, despite who saith nay; and whoever is grieved with my custom, let him mend it who will."

"I will amend it," said Arthur.

"I shall prevent you," said Pellinore.

He quickly mounted his horse, adjusted his shield, and took his spear. They met so hard against each other's shields that their spears shivered. Thereupon Arthur at once pulled out his sword.

"Nay, not so," said the knight, "it is fairer that we twain run once more together with sharp spears."

"I will, readily," said Arthur, "if I had any more spears."

"I have enough," said Pellinore.

A squire came and brought two good spears, and again the knight and the King spurred together with all their might, so that both the spears were broken off short. Then Arthur set hand on his sword.

"Nay," said the knight, "ye shall do better. Ye are a passing good jouster as ever I met withal, and for the love of the high order of knighthood let us joust once again."

"I assent," said Arthur.

Then two more great spears were brought, and each knight took one, and they ran together, so that Arthur's spear was all shivered. But Pellinore hit him so hard in the middle of the shield that horse and man fell to the earth. Then Arthur eagerly pulled out his sword, saying, "I will assay thee, Sir Knight, on foot, or I have lost the honour on horseback," and he ran towards him with his sword drawn.

When Pellinore saw that, he too alighted, for he thought it no honour to have a knight at such disadvantage, for himself to be on horseback, and the other on foot. Then began a strong battle with many great strokes, both hacking and hewing, till the field was wet with blood. They fought long, and rested, and then went to battle again. At last they both smote together, so that their swords met evenly, but Pellinore's sword smote Arthur's in two pieces, wherefore the King was much grieved.

Then said the knight unto Arthur:

"Thou art in danger whether I choose to save thee or to slay thee; and unless thou yield thee as overcome and recreant thou shalt die."

"As for death," said King Arthur, "welcome be it, when it cometh; but to yield me unto thee as recreant, I had rather die than be so shamed." And with that he leapt unto Pellinore, and threw him down, and tore off his helm.

When the knight felt this he was sorely frightened, though he was a very big and mighty man; but he quickly got Arthur underneath, and raised off his helm, and would have smitten off his head.

But up came Merlin, and said:

"Knight, hold thy hand, for if thou slay that knight thou puttest this realm in the greatest damage that ever realm was in. For this knight is a man of more honour than thou art aware of."

"Why, who is he?" said Pellinore.

"It is King Arthur."

Then Pellinore would have slain himself, for dread of his wrath, and lifted up his sword. But Merlin cast an enchantment on the knight, so that he fell to the earth in a great sleep.

The Sword Excalibur

After throwing Pellinore into an enchanted sleep, Merlin took up King Arthur, and rode forth on Pellinore's horse.

"Alas!" said Arthur, "what hast thou done, Merlin? Hast thou slain this good knight by thy crafts? There lived not so worshipful a knight as he was; I would rather than a year's income that he were alive."

"Do not be troubled," said Merlin, "for he is less hurt than you. He is only asleep, and will wake within three hours. There liveth not a greater knight than he is, and he shall hereafter do you right good service. His name is Pellinore, and he shall have two sons, that shall be passing good men,—Percival of Wales, and Lamerack of Wales."

Leaving Sir Pellinore, King Arthur and Merlin went to a hermit, who was a good man, and skilled in the art of healing. He attended so carefully to the King's wounds, that in three days they were quite well, and Arthur was able to go on his way with Merlin. Then as they rode, Arthur said, "I have no sword."

"No matter," said Merlin, "near by is a sword that shall be yours if I can get it."

So they rode till they came to a lake, which was a fair water and broad; and in the midst of the lake, Arthur saw an arm, clothed in white samite, that held in its hand a beautiful sword.

"Lo," said Merlin, "yonder is the sword I spoke of."

With that they saw a damsel rowing across the lake.

"What damsel is that?" said Arthur.

"That is the Lady of the Lake," said Merlin, "and within that lake is a rock, and therein is as fair a place as any on earth, and richly adorned. This damsel will soon come to you; then speak you fair to her, so that she will give you that sword."

Presently the damsel came to Arthur, and saluted him, and he her again.

"Damsel," said Arthur, "what sword is that which yonder the arm holdeth above the water? I would it were mine, for I have no sword."

"Sir Arthur, King," said the damsel, "that sword is mine; the name of it is Excalibur, that is as much as to say Cut-Steel. If you will give me a gift when I ask you, ye shall have it."

"By my faith," said Arthur, "I will give you what gift ye shall ask."

"Well," said the damsel, "go you into yonder barge, and row yourself to the sword, and take it and the scabbard with you, and I will ask my gift when I see my time."

So King Arthur and Merlin alighted, and tied their horses to two trees, and went into the barge, and when they came to the sword that the hand held, Arthur lifted it by the handle, and took it with him. And the arm and hand went under the water; and so they came to the land, and rode away.

Then Arthur looked on the sword, and liked it passing well.

"Which like you the better, the sword or the scabbard?" asked Merlin.

"I like the sword better," replied Arthur.

"You are the more unwise," said Merlin, "for the scabbard is worth ten of the sword. While you have the scabbard upon you, ye shall never lose any blood, be ye never so sorely wounded. Therefore keep well the scabbard always with you."

So they returned to Carleon, where King Arthur's knights were passing glad to see him. When they heard of his adventures they marvelled that he would so jeopardy himself alone. But all men of honour said it was merry to be under such a chieftain who would put his person in adventures as other poor knights did.

Some time after this, Merlin again warned King Arthur to keep the scabbard of the sword Excalibur very securely, for as long as he had it upon him he would never lose any blood, however sorely he might be wounded. For greater safety, Arthur entrusted the sword and scabbard to his sister, Morgan le Fay. But Morgan le Fay was a false and treacherous woman. She loved another knight better than her husband King Uriens, or her brother King Arthur, and she made up a wicked plot, by which they would both be slain. Then she meant to marry this other knight, Sir Accolon, and place him on King Arthur's throne, when she herself would become Queen of the whole realm. Therefore she made by enchantment another scabbard exactly like Excalibur's, which she gave to Arthur when he was going to fight; but Excalibur and its scabbard she kept for Sir Accolon.

The Round Table

When Arthur had been King for some years, and had fought and overcome many of his enemies, his Barons were anxious that he should take a wife, so according to his usual custom he went and consulted Merlin.

"It is well," said Merlin, "for a man of your bounty and nobleness should not be without a wife. Now is there any that you love more than another?"

"Yes," said King Arthur, "I love Guinevere, the daughter of King Leodegrance, of the land of Cameliard. Leodegrance holdeth in his house the Round Table, which he had of my father, Uther, and this damsel is the most noble and beautiful that I know living, or yet that ever I could find."

"Sir," said Merlin, "as to her beauty, she is one of the fairest alive. But if you loved her not as well as you do, I could find you a damsel of beauty and goodness, that would like you and please you,—if your heart were not set. But where a man's heart is set, he will be loath to go back."

"That is truth," said King Arthur.

Then Merlin warned the King that it would not be wise for him to marry Guinevere; Merlin had the gift of prophecy, and knew that if this marriage took place much unhappiness would come of it. But nothing would persuade the King from his purpose. So Merlin carried a message to Leodegrance, who rejoiced greatly.

"Those are the best tidings I ever heard," he said, "that a King of prowess and nobleness will wed my daughter. And as for my lands I would give him them if I thought it would please him, but he hath lands enough, he needeth none, but I shall send him a gift which shall please him much more. For I shall give him the Round Table which Uther Pendragon gave me, and when it is full complete there are a hundred knights and fifty. As for a hundred good knights, I have them myself, but I lack fifty, for so many have been slain in my days."

So King Leodegrance delivered his daughter to Merlin, and the Round Table, with the hundred knights; and they rode briskly, with great royalty, by water and by land, till they came near to London.

When King Arthur heard of the coming of Guinevere, and of the hundred knights with the Round Table, he made great joy because of their coming, and that rich present.

"This fair lady is passing welcome unto me," he said, "for I have loved her long, and therefore there is nothing so dear to me. And these knights with the Round Table please me more than right great riches."

Then in all haste the King commanded preparations for the marriage and coronation to be made in the most honourable way that could be devised; and he bade Merlin go forth and seek fifty knights of the greatest prowess and honour, and fill the vacant places at the Round Table.

Within a short time Merlin had found such knights as would fill twenty-eight places, but no more could he find.

Then the Archbishop of Canterbury was fetched, and he blessed the seats with great splendour and devotion, and there sat the eight-and-twenty knights in their seats.

When this was done, Merlin said:

"Fair sirs, ye must all arise and come to King Arthur to do him homage," so they arose and did their homage.

And when they were gone Merlin found in every seat letters

of gold, that told the knights' names that had sat there; but two places were empty.

Soon after this came young Gawaine, son of King Lot of Orkney, and asked a gift of the King.

"Ask," said the King, "and I shall grant it you."

"Sir, I ask that ye will make me knight that same day ye wed Guinevere."

"I will do it with a good will," said King Arthur, "and do unto you all the honour I can, because you are my nephew, my sister's son."

So the King made Gawaine knight, and at the same time, at the wedding feast, he also knighted a son of King Pellinore, a noble and gallant youth, whose name was Tor.

Then King Arthur asked Merlin what was the cause why there were two places empty among the seats at the Round Table.

"Sir," said Merlin, "there shall no man sit in those places, except they shall be of the greatest honour. But in the Siege Perilous there shall no man sit therein but one, and if there be any so hardy to do it, he shall be destroyed; and he that shall sit there shall have no equal."

Therewith Merlin took King Pellinore by the hand, and leading him next the two seats and the Siege Perilous, he said in open audience:

"This is your place, and best worthy ye are to sit therein of any that is here."

At this Sir Gawaine sat in great envy, and he said to Gaheris, his brother:

"Yonder knight is put in great honour, which grieveth me sorely, for he slew our father, King Lot; therefore I will slay him with a sword that was sent me, which is passing trenchant."

"Ye shall not do so at this time," said Gaheris, "for at present I am only a squire. When I am made knight I will be avenged on him; and therefore, brother, it is best ye endure till another time, that we may have him out of the Court; for if we killed him here we should trouble this high feast."

"I will do as you wish," said Gawaine.

Then was the high feast made ready, and the King was

wedded at Camelot to Dame Guinevere, in the church of St. Stephen's with great solemnity.

Then the King established all his knights, and to those who were not rich he gave lands, and charged them never to do outrage nor murders and always to flee treason. Also by no means to be cruel, but to give mercy to him that asked mercy, upon pain of forfeiture of their honour and lordship of King Arthur for evermore; and always to do ladies, damsels, and gentlewomen succour, upon pain of death. Also that no man should take battle in a wrongful quarrel for any law, nor for world's goods.

Unto this were all the Knights of the Round Table sworn, both old and young. And every year they renewed their vows at the high Feast of Pentecost.

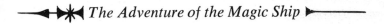 *The Adventure of the Magic Ship*

It befell one day that Arthur and many of his knights rode hunting into a great forest; the King himself, Sir Accolon of Gaul, and King Uriens, husband of Morgan le Fay, followed a fine hart, and their horses were so swift that in a little while they were ten miles ahead of their companions. Worn out with the chase, at last their horses fell exhausted, but still in front of them they saw the hart, passing weary.

"What shall we do?" said King Arthur. "We are hard bestead."

"Let us go on foot," said King Uriens, "till we meet with some lodging."

Then they saw that the hart lay on the bank of a large lake, and the dogs had got hold of him, so King Arthur blew the "prise," which is the note blown by the hunter on the death of the quarry.

After this he looked all around, and saw before him on the lake a little ship, apparelled with silk; and the ship came right up to them and grounded on the sands. King Arthur went to the bank and looked in, and saw no earthly creature therein.

"Come," said the King, "let us see what is in the ship."

So they all three went in, and found it richly hung with cloth of silk. By then it was dark night, and suddenly there were about them a hundred torches, set upon all the sides of the ship, which gave great light. Therewith came out twelve fair damsels, who saluted King Arthur on their knees, and called him by his name, and said he was right welcome, and such cheer as they had he should have of the best. The King thanked them courteously.

The damsels led the King and his two companions into a beautiful chamber, where there was a table richly spread with all manner of good things; and here they were served with all the wines and meats they could think of, which made the King marvel, for he had never fared better in his life at any one supper.

When they had supped at their leisure King Arthur was led into another chamber, more richly adorned than he had ever seen; and so also was King Uriens served; and Sir Accolon was led into a third chamber, passing richly and well adorned; and so they went gladly to bed, and fell asleep at once.

But on the morrow when he awoke, King Uriens found himself in Camelot, with his wife, Morgan le Fay, and this greatly astonished him, for on the evening before, he was two days' journey from Camelot.

And when King Arthur awoke he found himself in a dark prison, hearing about him many complaints of woeful knights.

"What are ye that so complain?" said King Arthur.

"We be here twenty knights prisoners," said they, "and some of us have lain here seven years, and some more and some less."

"For what cause?" said Arthur.

"We will tell you," said the knights.

"The lord of this Castle is named Sir Damas, and he is the falsest knight alive, and full of treason, and the veriest coward that ever lived. He has a younger brother, a good knight of prowess, named Sir Ontzlake, and this traitor Damas, the elder brother, will give him no part of his heritage, except what Sir Ontzlake can keep through his own prowess. But the younger brother holds a full fair manor and a rich, and therein he dwells in honour, and is well beloved of all people, while Sir Damas is equally ill beloved, for he is without mercy, and a coward. Great war has been betwixt them both, but Ontzlake always gets the better; and he keeps offering Damas to fight for the heritage, and if he will not do it himself, to find a knight to fight for him.

"Unto this Sir Damas agreed, but he is so hated that there is never a knight will fight for him. Seeing this, Damas hath daily lain in wait with many knights, and taken all the other knights in this country separately by force, as they rode on their adventures, and brought them to his prison. And many good knights, to the number of eighteen, have died in this prison from hunger. If any of us that have been here would have fought with his brother Ontzlake, he would have delivered us, but because this Damas is so false and so full of treason we would never fight for him. And we be so lean with hunger we can hardly stand."

"God in His mercy deliver you," said Arthur.

Just then there came a damsel to Arthur, and asked him, "What cheer?"

"I cannot say," said he.

"Sir," said she, "if you will fight for my lord you shall be delivered out of prison, otherwise you will never escape with life."

"Now," said Arthur, "that is hard, but I would rather fight with a knight than die in prison. On condition that I may be delivered, and all these prisoners, I will do the battle."

"Yes," said the damsel.

"I am ready," said Arthur, "if I had horse and armour."

"Ye shall lack nothing," was the reply.

"It seems to me, damsel, that I have seen you in the Court of Arthur?"

"Nay," said the damsel, "I never went there, I am the daughter of the Lord of this Castle."

Yet was she false, for she was one of the damsels of Morgan le Fay.

Then she went quickly to Sir Damas, and told him how Arthur would do battle for him, and so he sent for Arthur. And when he came he was so handsome that all the knights who saw him said it was a pity that such a knight should die in prison.

Then Sir Damas and he agreed that he should fight for him on this covenant—that all the other knights should be delivered. Sir Damas swore to Arthur that this should be done, and Arthur, in return, swore to do battle to the uttermost.

And with that, all the twenty knights were brought out of the dark prison into the hall, and set at liberty. And so they all waited to see the battle.

The False Craft of Morgan le Fay

Now let us turn to Sir Accolon of Gaul, who was with King Arthur and King Uriens when they went to sleep on the magic ship.

When he awoke he found himself by the side of a deep well, within half a foot of the edge, in great peril of death. Out of the fountain came a pipe of silver, and out of the pipe ran water all on high in a marble basin.

When Sir Accolon saw this, he said:

"Heaven save my lord King Arthur and King Uriens, for these damsels in the ship have betrayed us. They were demons, and no women, and if I escape this misadventure, I shall destroy wherever I find them all false damsels that use enchantments."

At that moment up came a dwarf with a great mouth and a flat nose, who saluted Sir Accolon, and said he had come from Queen Morgan le Fay.

"She greeteth you well, and biddeth you be of strong heart, for ye shall fight to-morrow with a knight at the hour of noon, and therefore she hath sent you here Excalibur, Arthur's sword, and the scabbard. She biddeth you, as ye love her, that ye do the battle to the uttermost, without any mercy, exactly as you promised her when ye spake together in private. And the damsel who brings her the head of the knight with whom ye shall fight, she will make her a queen."

"Now I understand you well," said Accolon. "I shall keep my promise now that I have the sword. Commend me unto my lady queen, and tell her all shall be done that I promised her, or else I shall die for it. Now I suppose," he added, "she has made all these crafts and enchantments for this battle?"

"Ye may well believe it," said the dwarf.

Then up came a knight with a lady and six squires, who saluted Sir Accolon, and begged him to go and rest himself at his manor. This knight was Sir Ontzlake, brother of Sir Damas, with whom King Arthur had already promised Damas to fight. So Accolon mounted a spare horse, and went with the knight to a fair manor by a priory, where he had passing good cheer.

Sir Damas, meanwhile, had sent to his brother to bid him make ready by the next day, at the hour of noon, and to be in the field to fight with a good knight, for he had found a good knight who was ready to do battle at all points. When this word came to Sir Ontzlake he was much disturbed, for he was already wounded through both thighs with a spear, but hurt as he was he would have taken the battle in hand. But when Sir Accolon heard of the battle, and how Ontzlake was wounded, he said he would fight for him, because Morgan le Fay had sent him Excalibur and the sheath.

The next morning when King Arthur was mounted and ready to ride forth, there came a damsel who brought to the King a sword like Excalibur, and the scabbard, and said:

"Morgan le Fay sendeth you here your sword for great love."

He thanked her, and thought it had been so, but she was false, for the sword and the scabbard were counterfeit, and brittle.

Then King Arthur and Sir Accolon made ready, and their horses rushed so swiftly together, that each smote the other with their spear's head in the midst of the shield, so that both horse and man were borne to the earth; and then both knights started up and pulled out their swords. The wicked Queen had cast a spell over them, so that neither knew the other. But while they were thus fighting, came the damsel of the lake, who had put Merlin under the stone, and she came for love of Arthur, for she knew how Morgan le Fay had so ordained that Arthur should be slain that day; therefore Nimue came to save his life.

Thus they went eagerly to the battle, and gave many great strokes. But King Arthur's sword never hit like Sir Accolon's sword; nearly every stroke that Accolon gave he sorely wounded Arthur, so that it was a marvel he stood, and always his blood fell from him fast. When Arthur saw the ground all covered with blood, he was dismayed, and guessed there was treason, and that his sword had been changed. For his sword bit not steel as it was wont to do, therefore he feared to be killed; it seemed to him that the sword in Accolon's hand was Excalibur, for at every stroke it drew blood, but he was so full of knighthood that he nobly endured the pain. And all the men that beheld him said they never saw knight fight so well as Arthur did, considering how sorely he was wounded. All the people were sorry for him, but the two brothers Sir Damas and Sir Ontzlake would not agree, so the knights went on fighting fiercely. Then suddenly King Arthur's sword broke at the hilt, and fell in the grass. Then he greatly feared he would be killed, but always he held up his shield, and lost no ground.

How King Arthur Got His Sword Again

When Sir Accolon saw that King Arthur's sword was broken he tried to tempt him to give in.

"Knight, thou art overcome and mayst not endure, and also thou art weaponless, and thou hast lost much blood; I am full loath to slay thee; therefore yield thee to me as recreant."

"Nay," said Arthur, "I may not so, for I have promised to do battle to the uttermost by the faith of my body, while life lasteth; and therefore I had rather die with honour than live with shame; and if it were possible to die a hundred times, I would rather die so often than yield me to thee, for though I lack weapon, I shall lack no honour, and if thou slay me weaponless, that shall be thy shame."

"Well," said Accolon, "as for the shame I will not spare; now keep thee from me, for thou art but a dead man," and therewith he gave him such a stroke that he fell nearly to the earth, and he hoped Arthur would have cried him mercy.

But the King pressed forward to Accolon, and gave him such a buffet with the pommel of the broken sword that the knight went three strides back.

When the damsel of the lake beheld Arthur, and how valorous he was, and the false treason that was wrought to have him slain, she had great pity that so good a knight and noble a man should be destroyed. And by her enchantment, at the next stroke the sword fell out of Accolon's hand to the earth. Then Arthur leaped lightly to it, and got it in his hand, and immediately he knew that it was his own sword Excalibur.

"Thou hast been from me all too long," he cried, "and much damage hast thou done me."

Then he espied the scabbard hanging by Accolon's side, and he suddenly started to him, and seized the scabbard, and threw it from him as far as he could.

"O knight!" he said, "now are ye come unto your death, for I warrant ye shall be as well rewarded with this sword before ever we depart, as thou hast rewarded me." Therewith he rushed on him with all his might, and pulled him to the ground, and dashed off his helm, and gave him such a buffet on the head that it nearly killed him.

"Now will I slay thee," said Arthur.

"Slay me ye well may, if it please you," said Accolon, "for ye are the best knight that ever I found, and I see well that God is with you. But because I promised to do this battle to the uttermost, and never to be recreant, therefore shall I never yield me with my mouth, but God do with my body what He will."

Then King Arthur thought he must have seen him.

"Now tell me," he said, "or I will slay thee, of what country art thou, and of what Court?"

"Sir Knight," said Sir Accolon, "I am of the Court of King Arthur, and my name is Accolon of Gaul."

Then was Arthur more dismayed than before, for he remembered his sister Morgan le Fay, and the enchantment of the ship.

"Sir Knight," he said, "pray tell me who gave you this sword?"

Then Sir Accolon told him how Morgan le Fay had sent it him to the intent that he might kill King Arthur her brother. For King Arthur was the man in the world whom she most hated, because of his valour and renown. And if she should succeed in killing Arthur by her crafts, she would also lightly slay her husband, and then she had devised that Accolon should be king in the land, and she would be queen.

"But that is now done," said Accolon, "for I am sure of my death. But now I have told you truth, I pray you tell me whence ye are, and of what Court?"

"O, Accolon," said Arthur, "now I let you know that I am King Arthur, to whom thou hast done great damage."

When Accolon heard that, he cried aloud:

"Fair sweet lord, have mercy on me, for I knew you not!"

"Mercy thou shalt have, Sir Accolon," said Arthur, "because I see that just now thou knewest not my person. But I understand well by thy words that thou hast agreed to my death, and therefore thou art a traitor; but I blame thee the less, for my sister Morgan le Fay by her false crafts made thee agree and consent to her wickedness."

Then King Arthur called the keepers of the field, and told them what had happened.

"Had either of us known the other, here had been no battle, nor stroke stricken," he said.

Then Sir Accolon cried aloud to all the knights and men that were there gathered together, "O lords, this noble knight that I have fought with, for which I sorely repent, is the greatest man of prowess, of manhood, and of worship in the world, for it is King Arthur himself, the liege lord of us all!"

Then all the people fell down on their knees, and cried mercy of King Arthur, which the King at once granted.

Then he went on to deliver judgment between the two brothers for whom he and Sir Accolon had fought. As Sir Damas was a haughty knight, and full of villainy, he commanded that he should give to his younger brother the manor and all that belonged to it, and that in return Sir Ontzlake should yearly give him a palfrey to ride upon, for that would become him better to ride on than a charger. And on pain of death Sir Damas was evermore forbidden to distress any knights-errant who rode on adventure. And to those twenty knights whom he had so long kept prisoner he was to restore all their armour.

"And if any of them come to my Court and complain of thee, by my head thou shalt die for it," said the King. "And to you, Sir Ontzlake, because ye are named a good knight, and full of prowess, and true and gentle in all your deeds, this shall be your charge: I bid you that in all goodly haste ye come unto me and my Court; and ye shall be a knight of mine; and if your deeds be truly thus, I will so prefer you by the grace of God, that ye shall in a short time live in as much state as Sir Damas."

Then King Arthur and Sir Accolon rode to a rich abbey near at hand, to rest themselves and have their wounds attended to, and soon the King was well recovered. But Sir Accolon died within four days, for he was sorely hurt.

When Accolon was dead, the King had him sent on a horse-bier, with six knights to Camelot, and said:

"Bear him to my sister Morgan le Fay, and say that I send him to her as a present; and tell her that I have my sword Excalibur and the scabbard."

The Mantle of Precious Stones

When tidings came to Morgan le Fay that Accolon was dead, and that Arthur had his sword again, she was so sorrowful that her heart was like to break. But because she would not have it known, she outwardly kept her countenance and made no sign of sorrow. But she knew well that if she abode where she was till her brother Arthur came, no gold would save her life, for he had sworn to be avenged.

She went, therefore, to Queen Guinevere, and asked her leave to ride into the country.

"You can wait," said Queen Guinevere, "till your brother the King comes."

"I can not," said Morgan le Fay, "for I have such hasty tidings that I may not tarry."

"Well," said Guinevere, "you may depart when you will."

So early on the morrow, before it was day, she took her horse, and rode all that day and most part of the night, and on the morrow by noon she came to the same abbey where King Arthur was. Knowing he was there, she asked how he was, and they answered that he was asleep in bed, for he had had but little rest these three nights.

"Well," she said, "I charge you that none of you awake him till I do."

Then she alighted off her horse, and thought to steal away Excalibur, his sword. So she went straight to his chamber, and no man durst disobey her command, and there she found Arthur asleep on his bed, and Excalibur in his right hand naked. When she saw that, she was greatly vexed that she could not get the sword unless she waked him, which she knew well would be her death. So she took the scabbard, and went her way on horseback.

When the King awoke and missed the scabbard he was very

angry, and he asked who had been there. They told him it was his sister, Morgan le Fay, who had put the scabbard under her mantle, and was gone.

"Alas!" said Arthur, "falsely have ye watched me!"

"Sir," said they all, "we durst not disobey your sister's command."

"Fetch the best horse that can be found," said the King, "and bid Sir Ontzlake arm in all haste, and take another good horse and ride with me."

So the King and Ontzlake were quickly well armed, and rode after Queen Morgan le Fay. Presently they met a cowherd, whom they asked if any lady had lately ridden that way.

"Sir," said the poor man, "just now came a lady riding with forty horsemen, and she rode to yonder forest."

Then they spurred their horses, and followed fast, and within a little while Arthur had a sight of Morgan le Fay; then he chased as fast as he could. When she espied him following her, she quickened her pace through the forest till she came to a plain. And when she saw she could not escape she rode to a lake thereby, and said: "Whatsoever becometh of me, my brother shall not have this scabbard," and she threw it into the deepest of the water, so that it sank, for it was heavy with gold and precious stones.

Then she rode into a valley, where many great stones were and seeing that she must be overtaken she shaped herself, by enchantment, into a great marble stone. When the King came, with Ontzlake, he did not know his sister and her men, nor one knight from another.

"Ah," said the King, "here ye may see the vengeance of God, and now I am sorry that this misadventure is befallen."

Then he looked for the scabbard, but it could not be found. So he returned to the abbey where he came from.

When Arthur had gone, Morgan le Fay turned herself and all her knights back into the likeness that they were before, and said: "Sirs, now we may go where we will."

So she departed into the country of Gore, where she was richly received; and she made her castles and towns passing strong, for always she dreaded much King Arthur.

After the King had well rested at the abbey, he rode to Camelot, where he found his Queen and his Barons right glad at his coming. When they heard of his strange adventures they all marvelled at the falsehood of Morgan le Fay; and because of her wicked enchantments many of the knights wished her burnt.

The next day there came a damsel from Morgan to King Arthur, and she brought with her the richest mantle that ever was seen in that Court, for it was set as full of precious stones as they could stand one by another, and they were the richest stones that ever the King saw.

"Your sister sendeth you this mantle," said the damsel, "and desireth that you should take this gift of her, and in what thing she hath offended you she will mend it at your own pleasure."

When the King beheld the mantle it pleased him much, but he said but little.

With that came the damsel of the lake to the King, and said: "Sir, I must speak with you in private."

"Say on," said the King, "what ye will."

"Sir," said the damsel, "do not put this mantle on you till ye have seen more, and in no wise let it come on you nor on any knight of yours till ye command the bringer thereof to put it on her."

"Well," said King Arthur, "it shall be done as you counsel me." Then he said to the damsel who came from his sister, "Damsel, this mantle that ye have brought me I will see it upon you."

"Sir," said she, "it will not beseem me to wear a King's garment."

"By my head," said Arthur, "ye shall wear it before it goes on my back, or any man's that is here."

So the mantle was put on her, and immediately she fell dead, and never spoke a word thereafter, for she was burnt to a cinder.

Then was Arthur terribly wroth, more than he was before-hand, and he said to King Uriens:

"My sister, your wife, is always about to betray me, and well I know that either you or my nephew, your son, is in council with her to have me destroyed. As for you, I do not much think you are in her council, for Accolon confessed to me with his own mouth that she would have destroyed you as well as me, therefore I hold you excused. But as for your son, Sir Uwaine, I hold him suspected, therefore I charge you put him out of my Court."

So Sir Uwaine was dismissed.

When Sir Gawaine, King Lot's son, knew this, he made ready to go with him.

"Whoso banisheth my cousin shall banish me," he said, so they two departed.

When Arthur was aware that Sir Gawaine had left the Court, there was much sorrow among all the lords.

"Now," said Gaheris, Gawaine's brother, "we have lost two good knights for the sake of one."

The Dream of the Dragon and the Boar

After long war King Arthur rested, and held a royal feast with his allies of kings, princes, and noble knights, all of the Round Table. And as he sat on his royal throne, there came into the hall twelve ancient men, bearing each of them a branch of olive, in token that they came as ambassadors and messengers from Lucius, Emperor of Rome. Having done their obeisance to the King they delivered their greeting from the Emperor Lucius, commanding Arthur to acknowledge him as lord, and pay the tribute due from England to Rome, as his father and predecessors had done before. If he refused this demand, then strong war would be made against him, his realms and his subjects, so that it would be a perpetual example to all kings and princes who dared to deny tribute to Rome, sovereign of the whole world.

When they had delivered their message, the King commanded them to withdraw, and called together all his lords and knights of the Round Table, for counsel on the matter, and to give their advice. They all said the demand for tribute was unjust, and every man agreed to make war and to aid after his power; the King of Scotland, the King of Little Britain, and the lord of West Wales, all promised men and money; and Sir Lancelot and the other knights also promised likewise. When King Arthur understood their courage and goodwill he thanked them heartily. The ambassadors, laden with presents, were sent back to Rome, with the answer that he owed no tribute to earthly prince, Christian or heathen, he claimed sovereignty of the realm of England by right of his predecessors; and he was fully determined to go with a strong and powerful army to Rome, by the Grace of God to take possession of the empire, and to subdue those that were rebellious.

When the ambassadors returned with this message to Lucius, the Emperor sent over the whole world, to all dominions that were subject to the Empire of Rome to summon warriors to fight against Arthur. So a great multitude of kings and dukes and captains, and thousands of people assembled round about Rome. Also he had with him fifty giants, who were ordained to guard his person, and to break the front of the battle.

In the meanwhile King Arthur held a Parliament at York, and appointed that, during his absence, Queen Guinevere and the realm should be in the governance of Sir Baldwin of Britain and Sir Constantine, son of Sir Cador of Cornwall, who, after his death, became king of the realm. Then King Arthur, with all his army, departed, sailing from Sandwich, with a great multitude of ships, galleys, boats, and men-of-war.

And as the King lay in his cabin in the ship he fell asleep, and dreamt a marvellous dream. It seemed to him that a dreadful dragon drowned much of his people, and he came flying out of the west; his head was enamelled with azure, and his shoulders shone as gold, his body like mail of a marvellous hue, his tail full of tatters, his feet covered with sable, and his claws like fine gold; a hideous flame of fire flew out of his mouth, as if land and water all flamed fire.

After him there came out of the east a grimly boar, all black, in a cloud; his paws were as big as a post, he was rough and rugged-looking—the vilest beast that ever man saw; he roared and growled so hideously that it was a marvel to hear.

Then the dreadful dragon advanced, and fought with the boar, who gnashed at him with his tusks, so that all the sea was red with blood; but at last the dragon smote the boar to powder, both flesh and bones, so that it was scattered in fragments all abroad on the sea.

Therewith King Arthur awoke, and was sorely abashed because of this dream, and he sent at once to a wise philosopher, commanding him to tell the meaning of it.

"Sir," said the philosopher, "the dragon that thou dreamedst of betokeneth thine own person, and the colour of his wings be the realms that thou hast won; and his tail which is all tattered signifieth the noble Knights of the Round Table. And the boar which the dragon slew, coming from the clouds, betokeneth some tyrant that tormenteth the people, or else thou art like to fight with some giant thyself, whose peer ye never yet saw. Wherefore of this dreadful dream doubt ye nothing, but as a conqueror go forth thyself."

Soon after King Arthur's dream of the dragon and the boar they arrived in France, and here a husbandman came to Arthur and told him that for seven years a fearful giant had been ravaging the land of Brittany, and had slain, murdered, and devoured many people of the country. Lately he had seized the Duchess of Brittany as she rode with her train, and had carried her to his dwelling, which was in a mountain, to keep to her life's end. Many people followed her, more than five hundred, but not all of them together could rescue her.

"She was wife to thy cousin, Duke Howell, whom we call full nigh of thy blood," ended the man; "now, as thou art a rightful King, have pity on this lady; and, as thou art a noble conqueror, revenge us all."

"Alas!" said King Arthur, "this is a great mischief! I had rather than the best realm I have that I had been a furlong before him to have rescued that lady. Now, fellow, canst thou bring me there where this giant haunteth?"

"Yea, sir," said the good man, "lo, yonder where thou seest those two great fires, there thou shalt find him, and more treasure than I suppose there is in all France."

When the King understood this piteous case, he returned into his tent. There he called to him Sir Kay and Sir Bedivere, and commanded them secretly to make ready horse and armour for himself and them twain, for after evensong he would ride on pilgrimage with those two only to St. Michael's Mount. So they three departed, and rode forth as fast as ever they could, till they came to the foot of the Mount. There they alighted, and the King commanded them to tarry there, for he would himself go up into the Mount.

He ascended the hill till he came to a great fire, and there he found a widow wringing her hands, and making great sorrow, sitting by a grave new-made. King Arthur saluted her, and asked her why she made such lamentation.

"Sir knight, speak soft," she answered, "for yonder is a devil. If he hear thee speak he will come and destroy thee. O unhappy man, what dost thou here in this mountain? If ye were fifty such as ye be, ye were not able to make resistance against this monster. Here lieth a duchess dead, who was the fairest of all the world, wife to Howell, Duke of Brittany—he hath murdered her."

"Dame," said the King, "I come from the noble conqueror King Arthur, to treat with that tyrant for his liege people."

"Fie upon such treaties!" said the widow, "for he setteth not by the King, nor by any man. Beware, approach him not too near, for he hath vanquished fifteen kings, and hath made him a coat full of precious stones, embroidered with their beards, which they sent him to save their people this last Christmas. And if thou wilt, speak with him at yonder great fire, at supper."

"Well," said Arthur, "for all your fearful words, I will accomplish my message."

Then he went forth by the crest of the hill, and saw the giant where he sat at supper, gnawing a huge bone, and baking his broad limbs by the fire, while three fair damsels turned three spits, whereon were broached twelve young children, like young birds. When King Arthur beheld this piteous sight, he had great compassion for them, so that his heart bled for sorrow, and he hailed the giant, saying:

"He that wieldeth all the world give thee short life and shameful death! Why hast thou murdered these young innocent children, and slain this duchess? Arise and make ready, thou glutton, for this day thou shalt die at my hand."

Then the giant started up at once, and took a great club in his hand, and smote at the King, so that his helmet was crushed, and the King hit him again, and wounded him sorely. Then the giant threw away his club, and caught the King in his arms, so that he crushed his ribs. Then the three maidens knelt down and called to Christ for help and comfort to Arthur. The King wrestled and strove, so that sometimes he was under, and sometimes above, and thus wrestling and striving, they rolled down the hill, till they came to the sea-mark; and ever as they wrestled, Arthur smote the giant with his dagger; and thus it happened they come to the place where the two knights were with Arthur's horse.

When they saw the King in the giant's arms they came and set him free, and by that time the giant was dead. King Arthur commanded them to smite off his head, and to set it on a spear, and bear it to Duke Howell, and tell him that his enemy was slain; and afterwards to put the head on a tower that all people might behold it.

"And go ye two up the mountain, and fetch me my shield, my sword, and the club of iron," said King Arthur, "And as for the treasure, take ye it, for ye shall find there goods out of number. So that I have the kirtle and the club, I desire no more."

Then the knights fetched the club and the kirtle, and some of the treasure they took to themselves, and returned again to the army. And this was immediately known all through the country, wherefore the people came and thanked the King. But he answered:

"Give the thanks to God, and part the goods among you."

And after that, King Arthur commanded his cousin Duke Howell that he should ordain a church to be built on that same mountain, in honour of St. Michael.

The next day the King set out again on his expedition against the Emperor Lucius. After many fierce battles he defeated the Romans, killed Lucius, and was crowned Emperor of all the lands from Rome to France. Then he returned home in triumph with all his knights, crossing the sea, and landing at Sandwich, where Queen Guinevere, his wife, came to meet him. All the people in every city and burgh received him nobly, and great gifts were presented to welcome him at his homecoming.

SIR LANCELOT OF THE LAKE

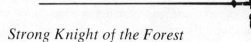

Strong Knight of the Forest

At the Court of King Arthur were many valiant knights, and some among them increased so in arms and worship that they surpassed all their fellows in prowess and noble deeds. But chief among them all was Sir Lancelot of the Lake, for in all tournaments and jousts and deeds of arms, both for life and death, he excelled all other knights, and never was he overcome, unless it were by treason or enchantment. Because of this, Queen Guinevere held him in higher favour than all other knights, and Sir Lancelot for his part loved the Queen above all other ladies and damsels all his life; and for her he did many deeds of arms, and more than once saved her from death by his noble chivalry.

When King Arthur returned to England from Rome all the Knights of the Round Table resorted to him, and many jousts and tournaments were held. Sir Lancelot rested himself for some time with sport and play, but at last he longed again to make trial of himself in strange adventures. Therefore, bidding his nephew Sir Lionel make ready, they mounted their horses, armed at all points, and rode into a deep forest, and so on to a wide plain.

About noon the weather was very hot, and Sir Lancelot felt sleepy. Then Sir Lionel espied a great apple tree that stood by a hedge, and he said: "Brother, yonder is a fair shadow; there we may rest ourselves and our horses."

"It is well said," answered Sir Lancelot; "for this seven years I have not been so sleepy as I am now."

So they alighted there, and tied their horses to a tree, and Lancelot lay down, and put his helm under his head, and fell very fast asleep. But Lionel kept awake.

In the meanwhile came three knights riding, fleeing as fast as ever they could ride, and these three were followed by one knight. When Sir Lionel saw him he thought he had never seen so great a knight, nor so well faring a man, nor one so well apparelled. In a little while this strong knight overtook one of the three, and smote him a spear's length behind his horse's tail. Then he bound all three knights fast with the reins of their own bridles.

When Sir Lionel saw him do thus he thought he would assay him, so making ready he took his horse very quietly in order not to awake Sir Lancelot. He soon overtook the strong knight, and bade him turn, but the latter smote Sir Lionel so hard that he bore horse and man to the earth. Then he alighted and bound him fast, and threw him and the three other knights each across his own horse, and rode with them away unto his own castle. There he took away from the four captured knights their armour, and beat them with thorns, and put them into a deep dungeon, where there were many more knights who made much lamentation.

Sir Ector de Maris in the meanwhile, finding that Sir Lancelot had left the Court to seek adventures, was angry with himself, and made ready to go in search of him. Riding through a great forest he met a man who looked like a forester, and he asked this man if he knew of any adventures near at hand. The forester replied that within a mile was a strong manor, with a moat all round it; and near the manor on the left hand was a ford for horses to drink from. At the ford grew a beautiful tree on which hung many fair shields that had once belonged to gallant knights. On the tree hung also a basin of brass and copper, and the forester bade Sir Ector strike thrice on the basin with the butt of his spear, and he would soon hear new tidings, unless he had the greatest luck of any knight who had passed through that forest.

Thanking the man Sir Ector departed, and soon came to the tree, where he found many fair shields; among them he saw his brother's shield, Sir Lionel, and many more that he knew were his fellows of the Round Table, which grieved his heart, and he promised to revenge his brother.

He beat at once on the basin, as if he were mad, and then he gave his horse drink at the ford. There came a knight behind him, and bade him come out of the water and make him ready. Sir Ector turned sharply, and cast his spear, and smote the other knight a great buffet, so that his horse reeled twice round.

"That was well done," said the strong knight, "and knightly hast thou stricken me"; and therewith he rushed his horse on Sir Ector, and catching him under his right arm, he bore him clean out of the saddle, and rode with him away into his own hall, where he threw him down in the middle of the floor.

The name of this knight was Sir Turquine.

"Because thou hast done this day more unto me than any knight did these twelve years," said he to Sir Ector, "now will I grant thee thy life, if thou wilt swear to be my prisoner all the days of thy life."

"Nay," said Sir Ector, "that I will never promise thee."

"I am sorry for that," said Sir Turquine.

Then he took Sir Ector's armour away, and beat him with thorns, and put him down in a deep dungeon, where he found many companions whom he knew. But when he saw Sir Lionel there he made great sorrow. "Alas," he said, "where is my brother Sir Lancelot?"

"I left him asleep, under an apple tree, when I went from him," said Lionel, "and what is become of him I cannot tell you."

"Alas," said the knights, "unless Sir Lancelot help us we shall never be delivered, for we know now no knight that is able to match our master Turquine."

The Four Queens

In the meanwhile Sir Lancelot of the Lake still lay asleep under the apple tree. Then about noon there came by four Queens of great estate; and in order that the heat of the sun should not annoy them there rode four knights beside them, bearing a cloth of green silk on four spears betwixt them and the sun; and the Queens rode on four white mules.

Thus as they rode they heard near them a great horse grimly neigh, and they were aware of a sleeping knight that lay all armed under an apple tree; and directly these Queens looked on his face they knew it was Sir Lancelot. Then they began to quarrel as to which should win his love.

"Do not let us quarrel," said Morgan le Fay, King Arthur's sister. "I will put an enchantment on him that he shall not wake in six hours, and I will carry him away into my Castle. And when he is safely within my hold, I will take the enchantment from him, and then let him choose which of us he shall have."

So they threw a spell over Sir Lancelot, and then they laid him on his shield and bore him so on horseback between two knights to the Castle Chariot. There he was placed in a cold chamber, and at night they sent to him a fair damsel with his supper. By that time the enchantment was past, and when she came she saluted him, and asked, "What cheer?"

"I cannot say, fair damsel," said Sir Lancelot, "for I know not how I came into this Castle, unless it were by enchantment."

"Sir," said she, "ye must make good cheer, and if ye be such a knight as ye are said to be, I will tell you more to-morrow."

So she departed, and there Lancelot lay all night without comfort of anybody.

On the morrow early came these four Queens, richly bedecked, and they bade him good-morrow, and he them again. Then they told him they knew well who he was—Sir Lancelot of the Lake, King Ban's son, the noblest knight alive.

"We know well that no lady has thy love, but one, and that is Queen Guinevere; now thou shalt lose her for ever, and she thee, therefore thou must choose one of us four. I am the Queen Morgan le Fay, Queen of the land of Gore; and here is the Queen of North Wales; and the Queen of Eastland; and the Queen of the Outer Isles. Now choose ye one of us which thou wilt have, or else die in this prison."

"That is a hard case," said Sir Lancelot, "that either I must die or choose one of you. Yet I would rather die in this prison with honour than have one of you to be my lady against my will. And therefore ye are answered; I will have none of you, for ye are false enchantresses."

"Well," said the Queens, "is this your answer?"

"Yea, on my life," said Sir Lancelot, "ye are refused by me."

So they departed, and left him there alone in great sorrow.

At noon came the damsel to him with his dinner, and asked him, "What cheer?"

"Truly, fair damsel," said Lancelot, "in all the days of my life never so ill."

"Sir," said she, "I am sorry for that, but I will help you out of this distress, if you will make me a promise."

"That I will grant you; and I am sore afraid of these Queen sorceresses, for they have destroyed many a good knight."

Then the damsel went on to say that on the next Tuesday her father had made a tournament between himself and the King of North Wales, and if Sir Lancelot would be there to help her father she would deliver him early the next morning.

"Fair maiden," said Lancelot, "tell me what is your father's name, and then I will give you an answer."

"My father is King Bagdemagus, who was defeated at the last tournament by three knights of King Arthur's Court."

"I know your father well for a noble king, and a good knight," said Lancelot, "and by my faith ye shall have my body ready to do your father and you service at that day."

So the maiden thanked him and bade him be ready very early the next morning, and she would come and deliver him. He was to take his armour, and his horse, shield, and spear, and to ride to an abbey of white monks not ten miles away, where he was to stay, and there she would bring her father to him.

"All this shall be done," said Lancelot, "as I am true knight."

The next morning the maiden came early, and found him ready. Then she took him through twelve locked doors, and brought him to his armour; and when he was well armed she led him to his own horse, and he saddled him, and rode forth.

"Fair damsel," he said, "I shall not fail you, by the grace of God."

So he rode into a great forest all that day, and could never find any highway, and at last the night fell on him.

The next day he came to the abbey, where the daughter of King Bagdemagus was waiting to receive him, and she gave him a glad welcome. In all haste she sent for her father, who was within twelve miles of the abbey, and before evening he arrived with a gallant company of knights. Sir Lancelot told the king how he had been betrayed, and how his nephew Sir Lionel had departed from him he knew not where; and how the king's daughter had delivered him out of prison,—"therefore while I live I shall do her service, and all her kindred," he ended.

"Then am I sure of your help on this coming Tuesday."

"Yea, sir," said Lancelot, "I shall not fail you, for so I have promised my lady, your daughter. But, sir, what knights are they of my lord Arthur's that were with the King of North Wales?"

The king replied that they were Sir Mador de la Porte, and Sir Mordred, and Sir Gahalatine, and against these three neither he nor his knights had any strength.

"Sir," said Lancelot, "as I hear say that the tournament shall be within three miles of this abbey, ye shall send unto me three knights of yours such as you trust, and look that the three knights have all white shields, and I also, and no painting on the shields. We four will come out of a little wood in the midst of both parties, and we will fall on the foremost of our enemies, and grieve them all we can; and thus it shall not be known what knight I am."

That night, which was the Sunday, they took their rest, and the next day King Bagdemagus departed; and he sent to Sir Lancelot the three knights with the four white shields.

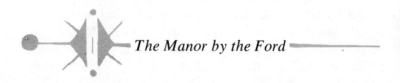

The Manor by the Ford

On the Tuesday Sir Lancelot and the three knights from King Bagdemagus, with the white shields, lodged in a little leafy wood beside where the tournament would be held. There were stands erected, so that lords and ladies could see, and give the prize.

Then came into the field the King of North Wales with eight-score of helms, and the three knights of Arthur stood by themselves.

Then came into the field King Bagdemagus with fourscore helms. They put their spears in rest, and dashed at each other, and at the first encounter twelve knights of King Bagdemagus were slain, and six of the King of North Wales, and King Bagdemagus' party was driven far back.

With that came Sir Lancelot of the Lake, and he thrust with his spear in the thickest of the press, and knight after knight went down before him, and among the throng he smote down the King of North Wales. King Arthur's three knights saw this deed of Lancelot's, and each in turn attacked him, and each was vanquished.

After this he fought with twenty-eight knights, and overthrew every one of them, and then the knights of the King of North Wales would joust no more, and the prize was given to King Bagdemagus.

So each party departed to his own place, and Sir Lancelot rode forth with King Bagdemagus to his Castle, where he had passing good cheer both with the king and his daughter, and they offered him great gifts.

On the morrow he took his leave, and told King Bagdemagus that he would go and seek his brother Sir Lionel, who went from him when he was asleep. So he took his horse, and commended them all to God. And to the king's daughter he said:

"If ye have need any time of my service, I pray you let me know, and I shall not fail you as I am a true knight."

So Sir Lancelot departed, and by chance he came into the same forest where he was taken sleeping. And in the midst of a highway he met a damsel riding a white palfrey, and they each saluted the other.

"Fair damsel," said Sir Lancelot, "know ye in this country any adventures?"

"Sir Knight," said the damsel, "here are adventures near at hand, if thou darest prove them."

"Why should I not prove adventures?" said Sir Lancelot, "for that cause came I into the country."

"Well," said she, "thou seemest indeed to be a good knight, and if thou dare meet with a good knight I will bring thee where is the best and the mightiest that ever thou found, so thou wilt tell me what is thy name, and what knight thou art."

"To tell thee my name I am ready; it is Sir Lancelot of the Lake."

"Sir, thou art a well-seeming knight; here are adventures to suit thee. For hereby dwelleth a knight that will not be overmatched by any one I know, unless ye over-match him; his name is Sir Turquine. And, as I understand, he hath in his prison threescore and four good knights of Arthur's Court, whom he hath won with his own hands. But when ye have done this day's work ye shall promise me as ye are a true knight to go with me and help me and other damsels that are distressed daily with a false knight."

"I will fulfil all your desire, damsel, so that you bring me to this knight."

So she brought him to the ford and to the tree where hung the basin.

Sir Lancelot let his horse drink, and then he beat with all

his might on the basin with the butt of his spear, till at last the bottom fell out, but he saw nothing. He rode up and down in front of the gates of that manor for nearly half an hour; then he was aware of a great knight coming who drove a horse before him, and across the horse lay an armed knight, bound. As they came nearer and nearer Sir Lancelot thought he should know him, and then he saw it was Sir Gaheris, Gawaine's brother, a Knight of the Round Table.

By that time Sir Turquine had seen Lancelot, and they both gripped their spears.

"Now, fair knight," said Lancelot, "put that wounded knight off the horse, and let him rest awhile, and let us two prove our strength. For, as I am told, thou dost, and hast done, great despite and shame unto Knights of the Round Table; therefore, now defend thee!"

"If thou be of the Round Table I defy thee and all thy fellowship," said Sir Turquine.

"That is saying overmuch," said Lancelot.

Then they put their spears in rest, and came together with their horses as fast as they could run, and each smote the other in the midst of their shields, so that the two horses' backs were broken. Both knights were astonished, and as soon as they could get clear of the horses they flung their shields in front of them, and drew their swords, and rushed together eagerly, so that neither shields nor armour could withstand their strokes. Within a little while they had both grim wounds, and thus it fared for two hours or more. Then at the last they were both breathless, and stood leaning on their swords.

"Now, fellow," said Sir Turquine, "hold thy hand awhile and tell me what I shall ask thee."

"Say on," said Lancelot.

"Thou art the biggest man that ever I met withal, and the most skilled, and like one knight that I hate above all other knights. If so be that thou art not he then I will willingly agree with thee, and for thy love I will deliver all the prisoners I have, who are threescore and four, so thou wilt tell me thy name. And thou and I will be friends together and never fail, as long as I live."

"Well said," answered Sir Lancelot, "but since I may have thy friendship, what knight is he whom thou so hatest above all others?"

"Faithfully he is Sir Lancelot of the Lake, for he slew my brother at the Dolorous Tower, who was one of the best knights living. Therefore him I except, for may I once meet with him, the one of us shall make an end of the other, I swear a vow. And for Sir Lancelot's sake I have slain a hundred good knights, and as many have I maimed, and many have died in prison, and still I have threescore and four. But all shall be delivered if thou wilt tell me thy name, so it be that thou art not Sir Lancelot."

"Now see I well," said Sir Lancelot, "that I might be such a man that I might have peace, and I might be such a man that there should be deadly war betwixt us. And now, Sir Knight, at thy request I desire that thou learn and know that I am Lancelot of the Lake, King Ban's son, of Benwick, and true Knight of the Table Round. And now I defy thee, do thy best!"

"Ah, Lancelot," said Turquine, "thou art most welcome to me that ever was knight, for we shall never part till the one of us be dead."

Then they hustled together like two wild bulls, rashing and lashing with their shields and swords. Thus they fought still two hours and more, and never would have rest. And Sir Turquine gave Sir Lancelot many wounds, so that all the ground there where they fought was bespeckled with blood. Then at the last Sir Turquine waxed faint, and gave somewhat aback, and bore his shield low for weariness. Sir Lancelot espied this, and leaped upon him fiercely, and got him by the beaver of his helmet, and plucked him down on his knees. Then he quickly raised off his helm and smote his neck in sunder.

And when Sir Lancelot had done this, he went to the damsel, and said:

"Damsel, I am ready to go with you where you will have me, but I have no horse."

"Fair sir," said she, "take this wounded knight's horse, and send him to the Manor, and command him to deliver all the prisoners."

So Lancelot went to Gaheris, and prayed him not to be aggrieved at lending him his horse.

"Nay, fair lord," said Gaheris, "I will that ye take my horse at your own commandment, for ye have saved both me and my horse; and this day I say you are the best knight in the world, for you have slain here in my sight the mightiest man and the best knight, except you, that ever I saw. I pray you, sir, tell me your name."

"Sir, my name is Lancelot of the Lake, that ought to help you of right for King Arthur's sake, and in especial for my Lord Gawaine's sake, your own dear brother. And when you come within yonder Manor, I am sure you will find there many Knights of the Round Table, for I have seen many of their shields that I know on yonder tree. And among them are my two kinsmen's shields, Sir Ector de Maris, and Sir Lionel. Wherefore I pray you, greet them all from me, and say that I bid them take such treasure as they find in the Manor, and that in any case let my kinsmen go to the Court and wait till I come, for by the Feast of Pentecost I purpose to be there; for at this time I must ride with this damsel to keep my promise."

So Sir Lancelot departed, and Sir Gaheris went into the Manor, and there he found a yeoman porter, keeping many keys. Sir Gaheris quickly threw the porter to the ground, and took the keys from him, and hastily he opened the prison door, and let out all the prisoners; and every man loosed each other's bonds.

When they saw Gaheris they all thanked him, for they saw he was wounded.

"Not so," said Gaheris, "it was Lancelot that slew your captor. I saw it with my own eyes. And he greeteth you all well, and prayeth you to hasten to Court; and as for Sir Lionel and Sir Ector de Maris, he prayeth you to wait for him at Court."

"That shall we not do," said the brothers, "we will find him, if we live."

"I shall find him before I go to Court, as I am a true knight," said Sir Kay.

Then all the knights sought the house where the armour was, and armed themselves, and every knight found his own horse, and all that belonged to him. And when this was done there came a forester with four horses laden with fat venison.

"Here is good meat for us for one meal," said Sir Kay, "for we have had no good repast for many a day."

So the venison was roasted, baked, and boiled, and after supper some of the knights abode there in the Manor all that night, but Sir Lionel and Ector de Maris and Sir Kay rode after Sir Lancelot to find him if they could.

How Lancelot Slew Two Giants

Sir Lancelot rode away with the damsel, as he had promised, to aid her against the wicked knight who robbed and distressed all ladies and gentlewomen.

"He doeth shame unto the order of knighthood and contrary unto his oath," he said; "it is pity that he liveth. But, fair damsel, you shall ride on in front, and I will keep myself in covert, and if he trouble or distress you, I will rescue you, and teach him to be ruled as a knight."

So the maid rode gently along the highway.

Soon out of the wood came the wicked knight on horseback, and his page with him, and he took the damsel from her horse, and she cried out.

With that came Sir Lancelot as fast as he could.

"O thou false knight, and traitor unto knighthood!" he said. "Who taught thee to distress ladies and gentlewomen?"

When the knight heard this rebuke he made no answer, but drew his sword and rode at Sir Lancelot. Then Lancelot threw his spear from him, and drew out his sword, and struck him such a buffet on the helmet that he clave his head and neck to the throat.

"Now thou hast thy payment which thou hast long deserved, and that is truth," said the damsel. "For as Sir Turquine watched to destroy knights, so did this knight wait to destroy and distress ladies, damsels, and gentlewomen; and his name was Sir Peris of Forest Savage."

"Damsel," said Sir Lancelot, "will ye any more service of me?"

"Nay, sir, not at this time," she said, "but Christ preserve you wheresoever you ride or go! For the courtliest knight thou art, and meekest unto all ladies and gentlewomen that now liveth."

And so Sir Lancelot and she parted.

Then Sir Lancelot rode in a deep forest two days and more, and had hard lodging. On the third day he rode over a long bridge, and there suddenly started out on him a horrible churl, who smote his horse on the nose so that it turned away, and asked him why he rode over that bridge without his permission.

"Why should I not ride this way?" said Sir Lancelot.

"Thou shalt not choose," said the churl, and lashed at him with a great club shod with iron.

Then Sir Lancelot drew his sword and thrust the stroke aside, and cleft the villain's head.

At the end of the bridge was a fair village, and all the people, men and women, cried to Sir Lancelot:

"A worse deed for thyself didst thou never, for thou hast slain the chief porter of our Castle."

Sir Lancelot let them say what they would, and went straight into the Castle; and when he came there he alighted, and tied his horse to a ring on the wall. There he saw a fair green court, and to this he went, for he thought it was a good place to fight in. And looking about he saw many people at the doors and windows, who said:

"Fair knight, thou art in evil luck!"

Soon there came upon him two great giants, well armed, all except the heads, and with two horrible clubs in their hands. Flinging his shield before him, Sir Lancelot turned away the stroke of the one giant, and with his sword clave his head asunder. When his companion saw that, he ran away as if he were mad, for fear of the horrible strokes; but Lancelot ran after him with all his might, and smote him on the shoulder, and killed him.

Then Sir Lancelot went into the hall, and there came sixty ladies and damsels, who all knelt to him and thanked God and him for their deliverance.

"For, sir," said they, "most of us have been prisoners here seven years, and we have worked all manner of silk works for our meat, and we are all highborn gentlewomen. Blessed be the time, knight, that ever thou wert born, for thou hast done the noblest deed that ever knight did, and that we will bear record. We all pray thee to tell us thy name, that we may tell our friends who delivered us out of prison."

"Fair damsels," he said, "my name is Sir Lancelot of the Lake."

"Ah, sir," said they, "well mayst thou be he, for save thyself, as we deemed, there might never knight have the better of these two giants. Many good knights have assayed it, and here have ended, and many times have we wished for thee, for these two giants dreaded no knight but thee."

"Now you can say to your friends how and by whom you have been delivered," said Lancelot, "and greet them all from me. What treasure there is in this Castle I give it all to you, as a reward for your grievance; and the lord that is owner of this Castle, I would that he receive it, as is right."

"The name of this Castle is Tintagel," said the ladies, "and for some time a duke had it, who was wedded to the fair Igraine. And after his death she married King Uther Pendragon, and Arthur was their son."

"Well," said Sir Lancelot, "I understand now to whom this Castle belongs."

And so he commended them to God, and departed.

Then he mounted his horse, and rode into many wild and strange countries, and through many waters and valleys, and evil was he lodged. At last one night he happened by chance to come to a fair courtyard, and there he found an old gentleman who lodged him with a good will, and he had good cheer for himself and his horse. And when it was time, his host took him to a fair room over the gate, to go to bed. There Sir

Lancelot unarmed him, and set his armour beside him, and went to bed, and quickly fell asleep.

Soon after, came one on horseback, and knocked at the gate in great haste. When Sir Lancelot heard this he arose, and looking out at the window, he saw by the moonlight three knights come riding after that one knight, and all three lashed on him at once with swords, and that one knight turned on them valiantly again, and defended himself.

"Truly," said Sir Lancelot, "yonder one knight shall I help, for it were shame to me to see three knights on one, and if he be slain, I am partner in his death."

Therewith he took his armour, and went out of the window, letting himself down by a sheet, to the four knights.

"Turn, you knights, unto me!" he cried aloud, "and leave your fighting with that knight."

Then they all left the other, who was Sir Kay, and turned to Sir Lancelot, and there began a great battle, for they all three alighted, and struck great strokes at Lancelot, and assailed him on every side. But when Sir Kay would have gone to Lancelot's help, the latter bade him let them fight him alone, so to please him, Sir Kay stood aside. And quickly then, in six strokes, Sir Lancelot had stricken them to the earth.

Then they all cried, "Sir Knight, we yield us unto you as a man of matchless might."

"As to that," said Sir Lancelot, "I will not take your yielding unto me, but if ye yield you unto Sir Kay the Seneschal, on that covenant I will save your lives, and not else."

"That were we loath to do, fair knight," they said, "for as for Sir Kay we chased him hither, and had overcome him, if you had not been here; therefore there is no reason why we should yield to him."

"As to that, be well advised," said Lancelot, "for you can choose whether you shall die or live; but if you yield, it shall be to Sir Kay."

"Well," they answered, "as you have saved our lives, we will do as you command."

Then Lancelot bade them go to the Court of King Arthur on the coming Whitsunday, and there yield them to Queen

Guinevere, and put themselves in her grace and mercy, saying that Sir Kay had sent them to be her prisoners. And every knight swore faithfully upon his sword that he would do this. So Sir Lancelot suffered them to depart.

Then he knocked on the gate with the pommel of his sword, and therewith came his host, and in they entered.

His host had heard nothing of the disturbance, and was surprised to see them. "Sir," he said, "I thought you were in bed."

"So I was, said Sir Lancelot, "but I arose and leaped out of my window to help an old comrade of mine."

And so when they came near the light Sir Kay knew well that it was Sir Lancelot, and he knelt down and thanked him for all his kindness, because he had this second time helped him from death.

"Sir," said Lancelot, "I have done nothing but what I ought to do, so you are welcome; and here shall you repose, and take your rest."

When Sir Kay was unarmed he asked for some food, which was brought him, and he ate hungrily. After he had supped, he and Sir Lancelot went to their beds, and lodged together.

In the morning Sir Lancelot rose early, and left Sir Kay sleeping; and Sir Lancelot took Sir Kay's armour and shield, and armed himself; then he went to the stable and fetched his horse, and took leave of his host, and so he departed.

Then soon after Sir Kay arose and missed Sir Lancelot; and then he espied that he had taken his armour and his horse.

"Now by my faith I know well that he will grieve some of the Court of King Arthur; for knights will be bold to him, believing him to be me, and thus they will be deceived. And because of his armour and shield I am sure I shall ride in peace."

Then Sir Kay thanked his host, and soon departed.

Chapel Perilous and the Sorceress

Sir Lancelot, dressed in Sir Kay's armour, rode long in a great forest, and at last he came to a flat country, full of fair rivers and meadows. Before him he saw a long bridge, and on it three pavilions of silk and sandal, of different colours. Outside the pavilions hung three white shields on truncheons of spears, and great long spears stood upright by the pavilions, and at every pavilion door stood a squire. Sir Lancelot passed by these and spoke no word.

"There goes the proud Sir Kay," said the knights to whom the pavilions belonged. "He thinks no knight so good as himself, but the contrary has often been proved."

"By my faith I will assay him, for all his pride," said one of the knights, "and you shall see how I speed." And arming himself he rode quickly after Lancelot, and challenged him to fight.

But Sir Lancelot smote him down, horse and man, and after that, when the other two knights came to their brother's assistance, he overthrew them too. One of them started up with his head bleeding and came straight to Sir Lancelot.

"Now let be," said Lancelot, "I was not far from thee when thou wert made knight, Sir Raynold, and also I know thou art a good knight, and loath I should be to slay thee."

"Gramercy, as for your goodness," said Sir Raynold, "and I dare say as for me and my brethren we will not be loath to yield to you, if we knew your name; for well we know you are not Sir Kay."

"As for that, be it as it may," answered Lancelot, "for ye shall yield you unto Queen Guinevere. Look that ye be with her on Whitsunday, and yield you unto her as prisoners, and say that Sir Kay sent you unto her."

Then they swore it should be done, and Lancelot went on his way.

Riding on through the deep forest he saw there in a glade four knights standing under an oak. They were all of King Arthur's Court, and Sir Lancelot knew them well,—they were Sagramour le Desirous, Sir Ector de Maris, Sir Gawaine, and Sir Uwaine. When they saw Lancelot they thought by his armour it was Sir Kay, so they agreed to fight him, to test his power. But Sir Lancelot rode at them all in turn, and overthrew them all, and went on his way smiling.

"What say ye of this deed," said Gawaine, "that one spear hath felled us four?"

"We commend him to the devil," said they all, "for he is a man of great might."

"Ye may well say that he is a man of might," said Gawaine, "for I dare lay my head it is Sir Lancelot, I know it by his riding. Let him go, for when we get to the Court then we shall know."

Sir Lancelot rode on for a great while in the deep forest, and at last he saw a black dog seeking about as if it were in the track of a hurt deer, and then he saw on the ground a trail of blood. So he rode after the dog, which kept looking back at him. It went through a great marsh, and Lancelot followed, and then he saw an old manor, and thither the dog ran across a bridge. Riding over the bridge, which was old and feeble, Sir Lancelot came to a great hall, and in the midst he saw lying a dead knight, a noble-looking man, and the dog licked his wounds.

Then there came out a lady weeping and wringing her hands.

"O, knight," she said, "much sorrow hast thou brought me!"

"Why say you so?" said Sir Lancelot. "I never did this knight any harm, for hither by track of blood this dog brought me. Therefore, fair lady, be not displeased with me, for I am full sorely grieved for your grievance."

"Truly, sir," she said, "I know it is not you who have slain my husband, for he who did the deed is sorely wounded, and never likely to recover,—I shall make sure of that."

"What was your husband's name?" asked Sir Lancelot.

"Sir," said she, "he was Sir Gilbert, one of the best knights of the world, and I know not the name of him that hath slain him."

"Now God send you better comfort," said Sir Lancelot, and so he departed.

Then he went again into the forest, and there he met with a damsel who knew him well.

"Well found, my lord!" she said. "Now I require thee on thy knighthood help my brother, who is sore wounded. For this day he fought with Sir Gilbert, and slew him in plain battle, and there my brother was sorely wounded. And there is a lady, a sorceress, who dwells in a castle close by, and this day she told me my brother's wounds would never be whole till I could find a knight who would go into the Chapel Perilous, and there he would find a sword and a blood-stained cloth that Sir Gilbert was lapped in; and the sword and a piece of that cloth should heal my brother's wounds."

"This is a marvellous thing," said Lancelot, "but what is your brother's name?"

"Sir," said she, "his name is Sir Meliot de Logres."

"I am sorry for that," said Lancelot, "for he is a fellow of the Round Table, and to help him I will do all in my power."

"Then, sir," said the damsel, "follow this highway, and it will bring you to the Chapel Perilous. And here I shall bide till God send you here again; and unless you succeed I know no knight living who may achieve that adventure."

So Sir Lancelot departed, and when he came to the Chapel Perilous he alighted, and tied his horse to a little gate.

As soon as he was within the churchyard he saw many rich shields, turned upside down, and many of the shields Sir Lancelot had seen knights bear formerly.

Then he saw standing there by him thirty great knights, each taller by a yard than any he had ever seen, and all these grinned and gnashed at Sir Lancelot. When he saw their countenance he was in sore dread, so he put his shield before him, and took his sword in his hand, ready for battle; and all the knights were armed in black harness, ready with their shields and their swords drawn. But when Sir Lancelot would have passed through them, they scattered on every side, and gave him way, whereupon he waxed quite bold, and entered the chapel.

There he saw no light but a dim lamp burning, and then he was aware of a dead body covered with a cloth of silk.

Sir Lancelot stooped down and cut away a piece of the cloth, whereupon it seemed as if the earth quaked a little, at which he feared. Then he saw a fair sword lying by the dead knight, and he took the sword in his hand and went out of the chapel.

As soon as ever he was in the chapel-yard all the knights spoke to him with a grim voice.

"Knight, Sir Lancelot, lay that sword from thee, or else thou shalt die."

"Whether I live or die," said Lancelot, "no big words will get it again, therefore fight for it, if you choose," and right so he passed through them.

Beyond the chapel-yard there met him a fair damsel, who said: "Sir Lancelot, leave that sword behind thee, or thou wilt die for it."

"I shall not leave it, for any entreaties," said Lancelot.

"No," said she, "if thou didst leave that sword thou wouldst never again see Queen Guinevere."

"Then I were a fool if I left it," said Lancelot.

"Now, gentle knight," said the damsel, "I require thee to kiss me but once."

"Nay," said Lancelot, "God forbid!"

"Well, sir," said she, "if thou hadst kissed me, all the days of thy life would have been done. But now, alas!" she said, "I have lost all my labour, for I ordained the chapel for thy sake. And now, Sir Lancelot, I tell thee I have loved thee these seven years, but no woman may have thy love but Queen Guinevere; since I might not rejoice to have thee alive, I had no greater joy in this world than to have thy body dead. Then would I have had it embalmed, and so have kept it all the days of my life, and daily I would have kissed thee, in spite of Queen Quinevere."

"Ye say well," said Sir Lancelot. "God preserve me from thy subtle crafts!"

And therewith he took his horse, and departed from her.

And when Sir Lancelot departed she took such sorrow that she died within a fortnight; and her name was Hellawes, the sorceress, lady of the Castle Nigramous.

Sir Lancelot soon met with the damsel, Sir Meliot's sister, and when she saw him, she clapped her hands, and wept for joy, and then they rode to a castle near by where Sir Meliot lay.

Directly Sir Lancelot saw him he recognized him as one of Arthur's knights, but Sir Meliot was as pale as death from bleeding; then Lancelot sprang to him, and touched his wounds with Sir Gilbert's sword, and wiped them with a piece of the cloth in which Sir Gilbert had been wrapped, and immediately Sir Meliot was more well and strong than he had ever been in his life.

Then there was great joy between them, and they made Sir Lancelot all the cheer they could. When Sir Lancelot took his leave in the morning, he bade Sir Meliot hie to the Court of King Arthur, for it drew nigh to the Feast of Pentecost, and there by the grace by God he would find him.

The Deceit of the Falcon

In this way Sir Lancelot rode through many strange countries, over marshes and valleys, till by fortune he came to a fair castle, and as he passed beyond the castle he thought he heard two bells ring. Then he was aware of a falcon that came flying over his head to a high elm; long lines were about her feet, and as she flew into the elm to take her perch the lines caught in a bough. When she would have taken her flight, she hung by the legs fast, and Sir Lancelot saw how she hung, and was sorry for the beautiful peregrine falcon.

Meanwhile a lady came out of the castle, and cried:

"O, Lancelot, Lancelot, as thou are flower of all knights, help me to get my hawk, for if my hawk be lost, my lord will destroy me. For I kept the hawk, and she slipped from me, and if my husband know it, he is so hasty he will slay me."

"What is your husband's name?" said Lancelot.

"Sir," she said, "his name is Sir Phelot, a knight of the King of North Wales."

"Well, fair lady, since you know my name and require me of knighthood to help you, I will do what I can to get your hawk; and yet truly I am an ill climber, and the tree is passing high, and there are few boughs to help me."

Therewith Sir Lancelot alighted, and tied his horse to the same tree, and begged the lady to help him off with his armour. And when he was unarmed he put off all his clothes to his shirt and breeches, and with might and skill he climbed up to the falcon, and tied the lines to a great, rotten branch, and threw it and the falcon down.

The lady at once took hold of the falcon. Then suddenly out of the grove came Sir Phelot, her husband, all armed, and with his naked sword in his hand.

"O knight, Lancelot, now have I found thee as I would," he said, and stood at the bole of the tree to slay him.

"Ah, lady," said Sir Lancelot, "why have you betrayed me?"

"She has only done as I commanded her," said Sir Phelot, "and there is no help for it but thine hour is come that thou must die."

"That were shame unto thee," said Sir Lancelot, "thou an armed knight to slay an unarmed man by treason."

"Thou gettest no other grace," said Sir Phelot, "Therefore help thyself if thou canst."

"Truly," said Lancelot, "that shall be thy shame; but since thou wilt do no other, take my armour with thee, and hang my sword upon a bough, and then do thy best to slay me."

"Nay," said Sir Phelot, "for I know thee better than thou thinkest. Therefore, thou gettest no weapon, if I can keep thee from it."

"Alas!" said Lancelot, "that a knight should die weaponless!"

Then he looked above him, and under him, and over his head he saw a branch, leafless, with other branches growing out of it, and this he broke off from the great trunk. Then he came lower, and marked how his own horse stood, and suddenly he leaped on the farther side of the horse from the knight. Sir Phelot lashed at him eagerly, thinking to have slain him; but Sir Lancelot thrust away the stroke with the branch, and smote him on the side of the head, so that he fell in a swoon to the ground. Then Lancelot took Sir Phelot's sword and struck off his head.

"Alas, why hast thou slain my husband?" cried the lady.

"I am not to blame," said Sir Lancelot, "for with falsehood ye would have slain me, and now it has fallen on you both."

Then the lady swooned as though she would die.

Sir Lancelot got all his armour as well as he could, and put it on him, for he dreaded further attack, because the knight's castle was so near. As quickly as possible he took his horse and departed, thanking God that he had escaped that adventure.

Two days before the Feast of Pentecost he went home, and the King and all the Court rejoiced greatly at his coming. When the four knights with whom he had fought in the wood saw Sir Lancelot in Kay's armour they knew well it was he who had smote them all down with one spear, and there was much laughing and smiling among them. And now all the knights whom Sir Turquine had kept as prisoners came trooping home, and worshipped Sir Lancelot. When Sir Gaheris heard them speak, he said, "I saw all the battle, from beginning to end," and there he told King Arthur how it was, and how Sir Turquine was the strongest knight that ever he saw, except Sir Lancelot; and there were nearly threescore knights who bore him record.

Then Sir Kay told the King how Sir Lancelot had rescued him when he would have been slain in the night, outside the manor where Lancelot was lodging; and how he made the knights yield to Sir Kay, and not to himself. And there the knights were, all three, and bore record.

"And by my faith," said Sir Kay, "because Sir Lancelot took my harness and left me his, I rode in good peace, and no man would touch me."

Then also came the three knights who fought with Lancelot

at the long bridge, and they would have yielded them at the Court to Sir Kay; but Sir Kay refused them, and said he never fought with them.

"But I will ease your hearts," he said; "yonder is Sir Lancelot."

When they knew that, they were glad.

Then Sir Meliot de Logres came home, and told King Arthur how Sir Lancelot had saved him from death by facing the unknown dangers, and the evil spells in the Chapel Perilous.

And all his deeds were known,—how four Queens, sorceresses, had him in prison, and how he was delivered by King Bagdemagus' daughter. Also there were told all the great deeds of arms that Sir Lancelot did in the tournament betwixt the two kings, that is to say, the King of North Wales and King Bagdemagus.

So at that time Sir Lancelot had the greatest name of any knight of the world, and he was the most honoured, both by high and low.

THE BOY OF THE KITCHEN

The Three Gifts

Once when King Arthur held his Round Table in its full glory, it happened that he commanded that the high Feast of Pentecost should be held at a castle in a city which in those days was called King-Kenadon, upon the sands that marched next to Wales. The King had always a special custom at the Feast of Pentecost,—namely, that he would not sit down to meat until he had heard of, or seen, a great marvel. And because of this custom all manner of strange adventures came before Arthur at that feast more than at any other festival.

On this day of Pentecost, a little before noon, Sir Gawaine espied from a window three men on horseback and a dwarf on foot. The three men alighted, and the dwarf kept their horses, and one of the three men was taller than the other two by a foot and a half.

Then Sir Gawaine went to the King, and said: "Sir, go to your meat, for here at hand come strange adventures."

So Arthur went to meat with many other Kings, and all the Knights of the Round Table were there, save those who were prisoners or who had been slain in battle. For at the high feast the whole number of one hundred and fifty should always be present, for then was the Round Table fully complete.

Then came into the hall two men, richly clad, with the goodliest young man and the fairest that they had ever seen, leaning on their shoulders, as if he could not go by himself. He was large and tall, and broad in the shoulders, handsome of face, and had the largest and most beautiful hands that ever a man saw.

As soon as King Arthur saw him, place and room were made, and the two strange men went with him right up to the high dais without saying a word.

Then this great young man pulled himself back, and easily stretched up straight, saying:

"King Arthur, God bless you and all your fair fellowship, and in especial the fellowship of the Round Table. And for this cause I am come hither, to pray you and require you to give me three gifts, and they shall not be unreasonably asked, but such as ye may worshipfully and honourably grant to me, at no great hurt or loss. The first gift I will ask now, and the other two gifts I will ask this day twelvemonth, wheresoever you hold your high feast."

"Now ask," said Arthur, "and ye shall have your asking."

"Sir, this is my petition for this feast—that you will give me meat and drink sufficient for this twelvemonth, and at that day I will ask my other two gifts."

"My fair son," said Arthur, "ask better, I counsel thee, for this is but a simple asking; my heart assures me greatly that thou art come of men of worship, and much my judgment fails me unless thou prove a man of right good worship."

"Sir," said the young man, "let that be as it may, I have asked that which I will ask."

"Well," said the King, "you shall have meat and drink enough. I never forbade that to any one, either my friend or my foe. But what is your name?"

"I cannot tell you."

"That is a marvel, that thou knowest not thy name," said the King. "Thou art the goodliest young man that ever I saw." And he went to Sir Kay, the steward, and charged him that he should give the stranger lad all manner of meat and drinks of the best, and that he should be provided for in every way as if he were a lord's son.

"There is little need to spend so much on him," said Sir Kay, "for I dare undertake he is of mean birth, and will never make a man; if he had come of gentle folk he would have asked of you horse and armour, but he asks according to his own nature. And since he hath no name I will give him one—*Beaumains*, that is, 'Fairhands'—and I will bring him into the kitchen, and there he shall have rich broth every day, so that by the twelve months' end he shall be as fat as a pork hog."

So the two strange men departed, leaving the tall lad to Sir Kay, who scorned and mocked him.

Sir Gawaine and Sir Lancelot were very angry at the way in which Sir Kay treated the lad, but the steward persisted he would never make a man of worship, because he only desired meat and drink. He bade him get a place and sit down to meat, so Beaumains went to the hall door, and sat down among the serving boys and lads, and there he ate sadly.

After the meal Sir Lancelot bade him come to his chamber, and there he should have meat and drink enough, and Sir Gawaine offered the same. But he refused them both. He would do nothing but what Sir Kay commanded him.

As for Sir Gawaine, it was natural he should offer Beaumains lodging, with meat and drink, for the boy was nearer kin to him than he guessed. But what Sir Lancelot did was of his great gentleness and courtesy.

So Beaumains was put into the kitchen, and lay nightly as the boys of the kitchen did. And he endured it all a twelvemonth, and never displeased man or child, but was always meek and mild. But if ever there were any jousting of knights, he would see it, if he could. Sir Lancelot and Sir Gawaine often gave him gold to spend, and clothes. Wherever there were any feats of skill and strength, there Beaumains would be, and no one could cast bar or stone as he did, by two yards. Then Sir Kay would say:

"How like you my boy of the kitchen?"

So time passed till the feast of Whitsuntide came round again. And that year the King held it at Carleon in most royal fashion. But on Whitsunday, according to his custom, he would eat no meat until he heard some adventure. Then there came a squire to the King, and said, "Sir, you may go to meat, for here cometh a damsel with some strange adventures," whereupon the King was glad, and sat down.

At that moment a damsel came into the hall, and saluted the King, and prayed succour of him.

"For whom?" said the King. "What is the adventure?"

"Sir," said she, "I have a lady of great worship and renown, and she is besieged by a tyrant, so that she cannot get out of her castle. And because in this your Court are the noblest knights of the world, I come to pray succour of you."

"What is your lady called, and where dwelleth she? And who is he, and what is his name, who hath besieged her?"

"Sir King," said the damsel, "as for my lady's name, that ye shall not know from me at present, but on my word she is a lady of great worship, and of many lands. As for the tyrant who besieges her and destroys her lands, he is called the Red Knight of the Red Lawns."

"I know him not," said the King.

"Sir," said Gawaine, "I know him well, for he is one of the most dangerous knights in the world. Men say that he hath seven men's strength, and from him I escaped once full hardly with my life."

"Fair damsel," said the King, "there be knights here who would do their utmost to rescue your lady, but because you will not tell her name, nor where she dwells, therefore by my will none of my knights that are now here shall go with you."

"Then I must seek further," said the damsel.

As she said these words Beaumains came before the King and spoke:

"Sir King, God thank you, I have been these twelve months in your kitchen, and have had my full sustenance, and now I will ask my two gifts that are left."

"Ask," said the King.

"Sir, these shall be my two gifts. First, that you will grant me to have this adventure of the damsel, for it belongs to me."

"Thou shalt have it," said the King, "I grant it thee."

"Then, sir, this is the other gift, that thou shalt bid Lancelot of the Lake make me knight, for of him I will be made knight, or else of none. Therefore when I am gone I pray you let him ride after me, and make me knight when I require him."

"All this shall be done," said the King.

"Fie on thee!" said the damsel. "Shall I have none but one that is your kitchen page?"

Then she took her horse, in great wrath, and departed.

The Scornful Damsel

Then came a messenger to Beaumains and told him that his horse and armour had come, and that the dwarf was there with everything he needed, in the richest style. All the Court marvelled greatly where such beautiful array came from. When he was armed there were few indeed who looked so goodly as he.

Thus he came into the hall, and took his leave of King Arthur, and Sir Gawaine, and Sir Lancelot; and begging the latter to follow after him, he departed thence, and rode after the damsel.

Many followed him to behold how well he was horsed, and trapped in cloth of gold, but he had neither shield nor spear. Then Sir Kay said all openly in the hall:

"I will ride after my boy of the kitchen, to find out whether he will know me for his better."

Sir Lancelot and Sir Gawaine said, "Ye had best abide at home." But Sir Kay made ready and took horse and spear, and rode after Beaumains.

Just as Beaumains overtook the damsel, up came Sir Kay. "Beaumains! What, sir, do you not know me?" he cried.

Beaumains turned his horse, and knew it was Sir Kay, who had always treated him with scorn.

"Yes," he said, "I know you for an ungentle knight of the Court, and therefore, beware of me."

Therewith Sir Kay put spear in rest and ran straight at him, and Beaumains, sword in hand, came equally fast against Sir Kay. With his sword he dashed away Sir Kay's spear, and thrust him in the side, so that he fell down as if he had been dead. Then Beaumains alighted and took Sir Kay's shield and spear, and bidding his dwarf mount Sir Kay's horse, he sprang upon his own horse and rode away.

Sir Lancelot saw all that had happened, and so did the damsel, and Sir Lancelot having by this time come up to them, Beaumains offered to joust with him.

They came together so fiercely that each bore down the other to the earth, and sorely were they bruised. Then Lancelot arose, and helped Beaumains to get free from his horse. Throwing his shield from him, Beaumains offered to fight with Sir Lancelot on foot. They rushed together like boars, tracing, racing, and foining, for the whole of an hour, and Sir Lancelot marvelled at the strength of Beaumains, for he fought more like a giant than a knight, and his fighting was steady, measured and very dangerous.

Sir Lancelot had such ado to hold his own that he dreaded being disgraced.

"Beaumains," he said, "fight not so sore, your quarrel and mine is not so great but we may leave off."

"Truly that is truth," said Beaumains, "but it doth me good

to feel your might; and yet, my lord, I did not show my utmost strength."

"Well," said Sir Lancelot, "I swear to you that I had as much as I could do to save myself from you unshamed, therefore have no doubt of any earthly knight."

"Do you hope that I may ever at any time stand a proved knight?" said Beaumains.

"Yes," said Lancelot, "do as you have done, and I will be your warrant."

"Then I pray you give me the order of knighthood."

"Well, you must tell me your name and of what kin you are."

"Sir, if you will not reveal it, I will."

"Nay," said Sir Lancelot, "and that I promise you by the faith of my body, until it be openly known."

"Then, sir, my name is Gareth," said Beaumains, "and I am the brother of Sir Gawaine, by the same father and mother."

"Now I am more than ever rejoiced," said Lancelot, "for I always thought you must be of noble race, and that you came not to the Court either for meat or drink."

And then Sir Lancelot gave him the order of knighthood.

After this, Lancelot left Beaumains, and went to Sir Kay, and had him carried home on his shield. Sir Kay barely escaped with his life, and all men scorned him, and in especial Sir Gawaine; and Sir Lancelot said it was not his part to rebuke any young man, when he knew little of what birth he came, and for what cause he came to Court.

In the meanwhile Beaumains had overtaken the damsel, but as soon as he came near she cried rudely:

"What are you doing here? You smell of the kitchen! Your clothes reek of the grease and tallow that you gained in King Arthur's kitchen. Do you suppose I will accept you because of yonder knight you killed? Nay, truly, for you slew him by ill chance, and cowardly. Therefore turn back, vile kitchen page! I know you well, for Sir Kay named you Beaumains. What are you but a clumsy fellow, and a turner of spits, and a ladle-washer?"

"Damsel," replied Beaumains, "say to me what you will; I will not go from you, whatsoever you say, for I have undertaken to King Arthur to achieve your adventure. I shall finish it to the end, or I shall die for it."

"Fie on thee, kitchen knave! Will you finish my adventure? You will meet one whom, for all the broth that ever you supped, you would not once look in the face."

"I'll try," said Beaumains.

As they rode thus in the forest there came a man flying as fast as he could.

"O, lord," he said, "help me, for hard by in a glade are six robbers, who have taken my lord and bound him; I am afraid lest they slay him."

"Take me there," said Beaumains.

So they went together till they came to where the knight was bound, and then Sir Beaumains rode at the robbers, and struck one unto death, and then another, and at the third stroke he slew the third robber; and then the other three fled. Beaumains rode after them and overtook them, whereupon they all assailed him hard, but at last he slew them, and returned and unbound the knight.

The knight thanked him, and prayed him to ride with him to his Castle a little way off, and he would reward him honourably for his good deeds.

"Sir," said Beaumains, "I will have no reward. This day I was made knight of noble Sir Lancelot, and therefore I will have no reward, except God reward me. Also I must follow this damsel."

But when he came near she bade him ride at a distance.

"You smell of the kitchen!" she said scornfully. "Do you think I am glad to have you? For this deed you have done is nothing but chance. You shall soon see a sight that will make you turn again, and that briskly!"

Then the same knight who had been rescued from the robbers rode after the damsel, and begged her to lodge with him that evening. And because it was near night the damsel rode with him to his Castle, and there they were made very welcome.

At supper the knight placed Beaumains above the scornful damsel.

"Fie, fie, Sir Knight!" she said. "You are uncourteous to set a kitchen page above me! He is better fitting to kill a pig than to sit above a lady of high parentage."

The knight was ashamed at her rude words, and taking Beaumains he placed him at a side-table, and sat down beside him.

They had good cheer, and rested well.

The Black Knight of the Black Lawns

On the morrow the damsel and Beaumains, thanking the knight, took their leave, and rode on their way until they came to a great forest. Here there was a great river, and but one passage, and two knights on the further side to stop their crossing.

"What sayest thou?" said the damsel. "Wilt thou match yonder knights, or turn again?"

"Nay," said Sir Beaumains, "I will not turn again if there were six more."

Thereupon he rushed into the water, and one of the knights did the same. They fought in the midst of the river, and Beaumains smote the knight on the helm, so that he fell down into the water and was drowned. Then Beaumains spurred his horse to the further side of the river, where the other knight fell upon him and brake his spear, and so they drew their swords and fought long together. But at last Beaumains clave his head and and his helm down to the shoulders.

Then he went back to the damsel and bade her ride forth on her way.

"Alas," she said, "that ever a kitchen page should have the fortune to destroy two such doughty knights! Thou imaginest thou hast done valiantly! That is not so; as for the first knight, his horse stumbled, and there he was drowned in the water,—it was never by thy strength nor thy might. And the last knight by mishap thou camest behind him, and by evil luck slewest him."

"Damsel," said Beaumains, "you may say what you will, but with whomsoever I have to do I trust to God to vanquish him before he departs, and therefore I reck not what you say, if only I may reach your lady."

"Fie, fie, kitchen knave! Thou shalt see knights who shall abate thy boast!"

"Fair damsel, give me goodly language, and then I mind nothing; for what knights soever they be I care not, neither do I fear them."

"I say it for thine own sake," she said, "that thou mayest yet turn back with triumph; for if thou follow me thou art but slain, for I see that all thou ever dost is but by misadventure, and not by prowess of thy hands."

"Well, damsel, you may say what you will, but wheresoever you go, I will follow you."

So Beaumains rode with the lady until evensong time, and ever she chid him and would not rest. Then they came to a black lawn, where there was a black hawthorn; thereon hung a black banner, and on the other side hung a black shield; by the tree stood a black spear, great and long, and a great black horse covered with silk, and a black stone fast by.

There sat a knight all armed in black harness, and his name was the Knight of the Black Lawns.

When the damsel saw the knight, she bade Beaumains flee down the valley, for the black horse was not saddled.

"Thanks," said Beaumains, "for always ye would have me a coward!"

With that, the Black Knight, when she came near him, spoke and said: "Damsel, have ye brought this knight of King Arthur to be your champion?"

"Nay, fair knight," said she, "this is but a kitchen knave, who was fed in King Arthur's kitchen for alms."

"Why cometh he in such array?" said the knight. "It is shame that he beareth you company."

"Sir, I cannot be delivered from him," she said, "for with me he rideth, in spite of all I can do. Would that you would put him from me, or else slay him if you can, for he is an unhappy knave, and unhappily hath done this day. Through mishap I saw him slay two knights at the passage of the water; and other deeds he did before, right marvellous, and through ill fortune."

"It astonishes me that any man who is of worship will have to do with him," said the knight.

"They know him not," replied the damsel, "and because he rideth with me they think he is some man of high birth."

"That may be," said the Black Knight. "Howbeit as ye say he is no man of worship, he is a right goodly person, and full like to be a strong man. But this much I will grant you," he continued; "I shall put him down on foot, and his horse and his harness he shall leave with me, for it were shame to me to do him any more harm."

When Sir Beaumains heard him say this, he said:

"Sir Knight, thou art full liberal of my horse and my harness. I let thee know it cost thee nothing, and whether it liketh thee or not, this lawn will I pass, in spite of thee. And horse or harness gettest thou none of me unless thou win them with thy hands; and therefore let see what thou canst do!"

"Sayst thou that?" said the Black Knight. "Now yield thy lady from thee, for it beseemeth never a kitchen page to ride with such a lady."

"Thou liest," said Beaumains; "I am a gentleman born, and of more high lineage than thou, and that I will prove on thy body."

Then in great wrath they drew apart their horses, and came together as if it had been thunder; and the Black Knight's spear broke, and Beaumains thrust him through both his sides, and therewith his spear broke, and the truncheon was left still in his side. Nevertheless the Black Knight drew his sword, and smote many eager strokes and of great might, and hurt Beaumains full sore. But at the last, within an hour and a half, the Black Knight fell down off his horse in a swoon, and died.

Beaumains seeing him so well horsed and armed, alighted, and armed himself in his armour, and taking his horse he rode after the damsel. When she saw him come near she cried:

"Away, kitchen knave, out of the wind, for the smell of thy greasy clothes grieveth me! Alas," she said, "that ever such a knave as thou art should by mishap slay so good a knight as thou hast done, but all this is thy evil luck! But hereby is one who shall pay thee, and therefore still I counsel thee—flee!"

"It may happen me to be beaten or slain," said Beaumains, "but I warn you, fair damsel, I will not flee away nor leave your company for all that ye can say; ye are for ever declaring they will kill me or beat me, but howsoever it happeneth, I escape, and they lie on the ground. And therefore it were good for you to hold you still, thus all day rebuking me, for I will not go away till I see the very end of this journey, unless I am slain, or truly beaten. Therefore ride on your way, for follow you I will, whatsoever happen."

The Green Knight

As Beaumains and the damsel rode together they saw a knight come driving by them all in green, both his horse and his harness; and when he came near the damsel he asked her, "Is that my brother the Black Knight that ye have brought with you?"

"Nay, nay," said she, "this unhappy kitchen knave hath slain your brother through evil chance."

"Alas," said the Green Knight, "it is great pity that so noble a knight as he was should so unhappily be slain, and above all by a knave's hand, as ye say he is. Ah, traitor, ye shall die for slaying of my brother; he was a full noble knight, and his name was Sir Percard."

"I defy thee," said Beaumains, "for I let thee know I slew him knightly, and not shamefully."

Therewith the Green Knight rode to a horn, which was green, and which hung on a thorn tree; and he blew three deadly notes, and there came two damsels, who quickly armed him. Then he took a great horse, and a green shield and a green spear. Beaumains and the Green Knight charged with all their might, and their spears broke up to their hands. Then they drew their swords, and gave many sad strokes, and each of them sorely wounded the other. And at the last Beaumains' horse struck the Green Knight's upon the side, and it fell to the earth.

The Green Knight lightly leaped clear of his horse, and prepared to fight on foot, and Beaumains seeing this, also alighted, and they rushed together like two mighty champions, and long was the battle. Then the scornful damsel came near and began to taunt the Black Knight's brother.

"My lord the Green Knight, why for shame stand ye so long fighting with the kitchen knave? Alas, it is shame that ever ye were made knight, to see such a lad match such a knight, as if the weed overgrew the corn."

At this the Green Knight was ashamed and therewithal he gave a mighty stroke, and clave Beaumains' shield through. When Beaumains saw his shield cloven asunder he was vexed at that stroke, and at the damsel's language, and he gave the Green Knight such a buffet on the helm that he fell on his knees; and thus suddenly Beaumains pulled him upon the ground.

Then the Green Knight cried him mercy, and yielded him to Sir Beaumains, and prayed him to slay him not.

"All is in vain," said Beaumains, "for thou shalt die, unless this damsel that came with me pray me to save thy life."

Therewith he unlaced his helm as if he would slay him.

"Fie upon thee, false kitchen page!" cried the damsel. "I will never pray thee to save his life, for I never will be so much in thy power."

"Then shall he die," said Beaumains.

"Thou wilt never be so bold as to kill him, thou knave!" said the damsel.

"Alas," said the Green Knight, "suffer me not to die, for a fair word may save me. Gentle knight, save my life, and I will forgive thee the death of my brother, and for ever become thy man; and thirty knights that follow me shall for ever do you service."

"Now in the fiend's name that such a low kitchen knave should have thee and thirty knights' service!" said the damsel.

"Sir Knight," said Beaumains, "all this availeth thee not unless my damsel speak with me for thy life." And therewithal he made a semblance of slaying him.

"Let be, thou knave," said the damsel, "slay him not, for if thou do, thou shalt repent it."

"Damsel," said Beaumains, "your charge is to me a pleasure and at your commandment his life shall be saved, and not else." Then he said, "Sir Knight with the green arms, I release thee at this damsel's request, for I will not make her wroth."

Then the Green Knight knelt down and did him homage with his sword.

Then said the damsel: "I am sorry, Green Knight, for your damage, and for your brother's death, the Black Knight, for of your help I have great need, for I dread to pass this forest."

"Nay, dread not," said the Green Knight, "for ye shall lodge with me this night, and to-morrow I will help you through."

So they took their horses and rode to his Manor.

The damsel never ceased from rebuking Beaumains, and when they reached the Manor she would not suffer him to sit at her table, so the Green Knight took him and set him at a side-table.

"I marvel," he said to the damsel, "why ye rebuke this noble knight as ye do, for I warn you, damsel, he is a full noble knight, and I know no knight able to match him; therefore ye do great wrong to rebuke him, for he shall do you right good service. Whatsoever he maketh himself out, ye shall prove at the end that he is come of noble blood, and of king's lineage."

"Fie, fie," said the damsel, "it is shame of you to say such honour of him."

"Truly," said the Green Knight, "it were shame of me to say of him any dishonour, for he hath proved himself a better knight than I am, yet have I met with many knights in my day, and never before this time have I found any knight his match."

So they went to rest, and all that night the Green Knight commanded thirty knights privily to watch Beaumains, to shield him from treason.

On the morrow they all arose, and having said their prayers, and broken their fast, they took their horses and rode on their way. The Green Knight conveyed them through the forest, and there he said:

"My lord Beaumains, I and these thirty knights shall be always at your summons, both early and late, at your calling, and wherever ye send us."

"It is well said," answered Beaumains. "When I call upon you, ye must yield you unto King Arthur, and all your knights."

"If ye so command us we shall be ready at all times," said the Green Knight.

"Fie, fie upon thee," cried the damsel, "that any good knights should be obedient to a kitchen knave!"

So the Green Knight departed.

"Why followest thou me, thou kitchen boy?" said the damsel rudely to Beaumains. "Cast away thy shield and thy spear, and flee away, I still counsel thee betimes, or thou shalt say right soon, '*Alas!*' For wert thou brave as ever was Wade, or Lancelot, Tristram, or the good knight Sir Lamorak, thou shalt not cross a pass here that is called the Pass Perilous."

"Damsel," said Beaumains, "he that is afeard, let him flee; it were shame to turn back since I have ridden so long with you."

"Well," said the damsel, "you will soon, whether you wish it or not."

 *The Scornful Damsel Grows Kind*

Within a little while they saw a tower as white as snow, having a double moat, and the parapets of the walls well provided with holes for hurling stones or pouring molten lead on the heads of any foes who might besiege it. Over the tower gate hung fifty shields of divers colours, and under the tower was a fair meadow. In the meadow were many knights and squires looking after scaffolds, for on the morrow was to be a tournament there.

The lord of the Castle was called the Red Knight, and he was the brother of the Black Knight and the Green Knight.

When he saw Beaumains, he came forth to fight with him but after a furious struggle Beaumains vanquished him. He declared he would spare his life at the request of the scornful damsel, so unwillingly, she had to beg mercy for him. Then the Red Knight did homage to Sir Beaumains, and offered him his fealty at all times, he and his threescore knights, to do him service and bidding whensoever and wheresoever he commanded.

That night Beaumains and the damsel lodged in the Castle of the Red Knight, and the next morning they went on their way.

But all this time the scornful damsel kept scolding and rebuking Beaumains in the rudest manner.

"Damsel," said Beaumains, "you are uncourteous to rebuke me as you do, for it seems to me I have done you good service; you keep on threatening me I shall be beaten by knights whom we meet, but ever, for all your boast, they lie in the dust or in the mire; therefore, I pray you, rebuke me no more. When you see me beaten or yielding as recreant, then you may bid me go from you in disgrace; but first I let you know I will not depart from you, for I were worse than fool if I went when all the time I am winning honour."

"Well," said she, "right soon thou shalt meet a knight who will pay thee all thy wages, for he is the man of greatest renown in the world, except King Arthur."

"I wish nothing better," said Beaumains. "The more renowned he is, the more it shall be to my renown to have to do with him."

Then they were soon aware of a rich and beautiful city before them, and between them and the city for the space of a mile and a half stretched a fair meadow, that seemed newly mown, and therein were many pavilions, splendid to see.

"Lo," said the damsel, "yonder is a lord who owneth yonder city, and it is his custom when the weather is fair to live in this meadow to joust and tourney; and he has always about him five hundred knights and gentlemen of arms, and there are all manner of games that any gentleman can devise."

"I would fain see that goodly lord," said Beaumains.

"Thou shalt see him in time enough," said the damsel; and just then, as they rode near, she espied the pavilion where he was. "Lo," said she, "seest thou yonder pavilion that is of the colour of Inde—dark blue? And everything that is about, men and women, and horses with trappings, shields and spears, all the colour of Inde? His name is Sir Persant of Inde, the lordliest knight that ever thou lookedst on."

"It may well be he," said Beaumains, "but be he never so stout a knight, in this field I shall abide till I see him under his shield."

"Ah, fool, thou hadst better flee betimes."

"Why?" said Beaumains. "If he be such a knight as ye make him, he will not set upon me with all his men, or with his five hundred knights. For if there come no more but one at a time, I shall not fail him, while my life lasteth."

"Fie, fie," said the damsel, "that ever a kitchen knave should utter such a boast!"

"Damsel," he said, "ye are to blame thus to rebuke me, for I would rather fight five battles than thus to be rebuked. Let him come, and then let him do his worst."

"Sir," she said, "I marvel of what kin thou art come; boldly thou speakest, and boldly hast thou done, that have I seen. Therefore I pray thee save thyself if thou canst, for thy horse and thou have had great travail, and I dread we stay over long from the siege, for it is but seven miles hence. And we are past all perilous passages, save only this passage; and here I sorely dread lest ye shall catch some hurt. Therefore I would you were hence, that you may not be bruised by this strong knight. But I tell you, this Sir Persant of Inde is nothing of might nor strength to the knight who laid the siege against my lady."

"As for that," said Beaumains, "be it as it may, for since I have come so nigh this knight I will prove his might before I depart from him, else I shall be shamed if I now withdraw. Therefore, damsel, doubt not that by the grace of God I shall so deal with this knight that within two hours after noon I shall be free from him, and then we shall come to the siege by daylight."

"Oh, indeed I marvel what manner of man you be," said the damsel, "for it cannot be otherwise than that ye come of noble blood, for so rude and shamefully did never woman rule a knight as I have done you, and ever courteously ye have suffered me, and that never came but of gentle blood."

"Damsel," said Beaumains, "a knight can do little that cannot suffer a woman. Whatsoever ye said to me I took no heed to your words, for the more you said, the more you angered me, and my wrath I wreaked upon those with whom I had to do withal. Therefore all the unseemly words you spoke furthered me in my battle, and caused me to resolve to show and prove myself what in the end I was; for peradventure, though I had meat in King Arthur's kitchen, yet I might have had meat enough in other places. But all this I did to prove and assay my friends, and that shall be known another day. Whether I be a gentleman born or none, fair damsel, I have done you gentleman's service, and peradventure better service will I yet do before I depart."

"Alas," she said, "fair Beaumains, forgive me all I have missaid or done against thee."

"With all my heart I forgive it you," he said, "for you did nothing but as you should do, for all your evil words pleased me. And, damsel, since you speak thus fairly to me, know well it gladdens my heart greatly, and now it seems to me there is no knight living but I am able enough for him."

By this time Sir Persant of Inde had espied them as they hovered in the field, and knightly sent to ask whether they came in war or peace. To this Beaumains replied that was exactly as Sir Persant pleased, whereupon Sir Persant said he would fight with him to the uttermost. So he armed himself and rode against him. Long and fierce was the encounter, but in the end Beaumains was the victor; Sir Persant surrendered and asked for mercy. The damsel, too, came and prayed for his life, which Beaumains granted right willingly, "For it were pity this noble knight should die," he said.

Then Sir Persant knew it was Beaumains who slew his brother the Black Knight, at the black thorn, and who had also overcome his brother the Green Knight, Sir Pertolepe; and his brother the Red Knight, Sir Perimones. And he said Beaumains should have homage and fealty of him and a hundred knights, to be at his command, to ride wherever he should command them. So they went to Sir Persant's pavilion and drank wine and ate spices.

The next morning when the damsel and Beaumains were taking their leave Sir Persant asked whither they were going.

"Sir," said the damsel, "this knight is going to the siege that besiegeth my sister in the Castle Perilous."

"Ah, ah," said Persant, "that is the Knight of the Red Lawns, who is the most dangerous knight that I know now living, and a man that is without mercy; and men say that he hath seven men's strength. God save you from that knight," he said to Beaumains; "for he doth great wrong to that lady; she is one of the fairest ladies of the world, and your damsel, I think, is her sister. Is not your name Linet?"

"Yes, sir, and my lady sister's name is Dame Liones."

"Now I will tell you," said Sir Persant, "this Red Knight of the Red Lawns hath lain well-nigh two years at siege; and many times he might have captured the lady, but he prolonged the time, hoping to have Sir Lancelot of the Lake to do battle with him or Sir Tristram, or Sir Lamorak of Wales, or Sir Gawaine; and this is his reason for tarrying so long at the siege."

"Now, my lord Sir Persant of Inde," said Linet, "I require that you will make this gentleman knight before ever he fight with the Red Knight."

"I will, with all my heart," said Sir Persant, "if it please him to take the order of knighthood from so simple a man as I am."

"Sir," said Beaumains, "I thank you for your good will. I am well sped, for the noble knight Sir Lancelot made me knight."

"Ah," said Persant, "of a more renowned knight might ye not be made knight. For of all knights he may be called the chief of knighthood. All the world saith that knighthood is evenly divided between three knights,—that is, Lancelot of the Lake,

Sir Tristram of Lyonesse, and Sir Lamorak of Wales. There are many other noble knights, but there are none that pass these three. Therefore God speed you well, for if you match the Red Knight, ye shall be called the fourth knight of the world."

"Sir," said Beaumains, "I would fain be of good fame and knighthood. I would have you know I come of good men, for my father was a noble man. And if you will keep it secret, and this damsel, I will tell you of what kin I am."

Then they both promised faithfully not to reveal who Beaumains was until he gave them leave.

"Truly, then," said he, "my name is Gareth of Orkney, and King Lot was my father, and my mother is King Arthur's sister; and Sir Gawaine is my brother, and Sir Agrivaine, and Sir Gaheris, and I am the youngest of them all. And neither King Arthur nor Sir Gawaine know yet who I am."

The Red Knight of the Red Lawns

Now the lady who was besieged in Castle Perilous heard that her sister Linet was approaching with a noble knight to rescue her. So she bade the dwarf who brought the tidings go to a hermitage near, and to take with him wine in two silver flagons, loaves of bread, fat venison, and dainty fowls.

"And a cup of gold I deliver thee that is rich and precious," she said; "and bear all this to my hermitage, and put it in the hermit's hands. Then go to my sister and greet her well, and commend me unto that gentle knight, and pray him to eat and to drink, and make him strong; and say to him I thank him for his courtesy and goodness for taking on him such labour for me that never did him bounty or courtesy. Also pray him that he be of good heart and good courage, for he shall meet with a noble knight, but he has no bounty, courtesy, nor gentleness, for he thinks of nothing but murder, and that is the cause I cannot praise him nor love him."

So Beaumains and the damsel went to the hermitage, and there they drank the wine and ate the venison and the baked fowls. And when they had made a good repast the dwarf returned with his vessels to Castle Perilous. On his way there he met the Red Knight of the Red Lawns, who asked him whence he came and where he had been. Then the dwarf told him his lady's sister had come, and that she had brought with her a knight of King Arthur's Court.

"Then I account her trouble but lost," said the Red Knight, "for if she had brought with her Sir Lancelot, Sir Tristram, Sir Lamorak, or Sir Gawaine, I should think myself good enough for them all."

"It may well be," said the dwarf, "but this knight hath passed all the perilous passages, and hath slain the Black Knight and two others, and vanquished the Green Knight, and the Red Knight, and the Blue Knight, Sir Persant of Inde."

"Then he is one of the four I have just said."

"He is none of those, but he is a king's son."

"What is his name?" said the Red Knight of the Red Lawns.

"That I will not tell you, but Sir Kay out of scorn called him 'Beaumains.'"

"I care not whatsoever knight he be, for I shall soon be quit of him. And if ever I am a match for him he shall have a shameful death, as many others have had."

"That were pity," said the dwarf, "and it is marvel that you should make such shameful war on noble knights."

That night Beaumains and the damsel stayed in the hermitage. On the morrow they took their horses and rode through a fair forest till they came to a plain, where they saw many pavilions and tents, and a splendid Castle, and there was much smoke and great noise. And when they came near the besiegers' camp, Beaumains as he rode espied upon great trees how there hung by the neck full goodly armed knights, their shields with their swords tied round their necks, and gilt spurs upon their heels; and thus hung there shamefully nearly forty knights richly armed.

Then Sir Beaumains' face darkened, and he said:

"What meaneth this?"

"Do not lose cheer because of this sight, fair sir," said the damsel, "for you must encourage yourself, or else you will be quite disgraced. For all these knights came hither to this siege to rescue my sister, Dame Liones; and when the Red Knight of the Red Lawns had overcome them he put them to this shameful death without mercy or pity. And in the same way he will serve you unless you quit you better."

"Now Christ defend me from such a villainous death and disgrace of arms," said Beaumains, "for rather than fare thus I would be slain like a man in plain battle."

"So it were better for you," said Linet. "Trust not there is any courtesy in the Red Knight; all his foes go to death or shameful murder. And that is pity, for he is a full likely man, well made of body, and a lord of great lands and worthy possessions."

"Truly he may well be a good knight," said Beaumains, "but he useth shameful customs, and it is a marvel he endureth so long, and that the noble knights of my lord Arthur have not dealt with him."

Then they rode to the dikes, and saw they were double-diked, with full warlike walls, and there were lodged many great knights near the walls, and there was a great noise of minstrelsy. And the sea beat against one of the walls, where there were many ships, and the shouting of mariners, "Hale and how! Pull ho!"

Fast by was a sycamore tree, and there hung a horn, the greatest that ever they had seen, made out of an elephant's tusk. The Knight of the Red Lawns had hung it there, so that if any errant knight came he must blow that horn, and then the Red Knight would arm himself and come to do battle.

"I pray you, sir, blow not the horn till it be high noon," said the damsel Linet; "for now it is about six o'clock, and at this time his might increases, so that, as men say, he hath seven men's strength."

"Ah, fie for shame, fair damsel, never more speak so to me," said Beaumains, "for if he were as good a knight as ever was,

I shall never fail him in his greatest might, for either I will win honour honourably, or die knightly in the field."

Therewith Beaumains spurred his horse straight to the sycamore tree, and blew the horn so eagerly that all the camp and the Castle rang with it. Then there leaped knights out of their tents and pavilions, and those within the Castle looked over the walls, and out of the windows.

Then the Red Knight of the Red Lawns armed himself hastily, and two barons set his spurs upon his heels, and all was blood red, his armour, spear, and shield. And an earl buckled his helm upon his head, and then they brought him a red spear and a red steed, and so he rode into a little vale under the Castle, that all who were in the Castle and in the besieging camp might behold the battle.

The Lady of Castle Perilous

"Sir," said the damsel Linet to Sir Beaumains, "look you, be glad and gay, for here is your deadly enemy, and there at yonder window is my lady, my sister, Dame Liones."

"Where?" said Beaumains.

"Yonder," and the damsel pointed with her finger.

"She is the fairest lady that ever I looked on," said Beaumains, "and I ask no better for which to do battle. Truly she shall be my lady, and for her will I fight."

And he kept looking up to the window with a glad countenance.

And the Lady Liones made a deep curtsy to him and they both waved their hands.

With that the Red Knight of the Red Lawns called to Beaumains:

"Leave thy looking, Sir Knight, and behold me, I counsel

thee, for I warn thee well she is my lady, and for her I have done many strong battles."

"If thou hast so done," said Beaumains, "it seems to me it was but waste labour, for she loveth none of thy fellowship, and thou to love one who loveth not thee is great folly. For if I understood she was not glad of my coming, I should think again before I did battle for her. But I know by the besieging of this Castle that she will have nothing to do with thee. Therefore, know well, thou Red Knight of the Red Lawns, I love her, and will rescue her, or else die."

"Sayest thou that?" said the Red Knight. "It seems to me thou oughtest to beware, by reason of yonder knights whom thou sawest hanging on those trees."

"Fie for shame," said Beaumains, "that ever thou shouldst do or say such evil, for in that thou shamest thyself and knighthood, and thou mayst be sure that no lady who knoweth thy wicked customs will love thee. And now thou thinkest that the sight of those hanged knights should frighten me? Nay, truly, not so. That shameful sight causes me to have courage and boldness against thee more than I would have had if thou wert a well-ruled knight."

"Make thee ready," said the Red Knight of the Red Lawns, "and talk no longer with me."

Then Beaumains bade Linet go to a safe distance, and both knights put spears in rest, and rushed together with all their might, so that they hurled each other to the ground, where both lay for a while sorely stunned. All those who were in the Castle and the camp thought their necks must be broken, and many said that the strange knight was a big man and a noble jouster, for before then they had never seen any warrior ever match the Red Knight of the Red Lawns; and this they said both within the Castle and without.

Then Beaumains and the Red Knight left their horses, and put their shields before them, and ran together like two fierce lions, and each gave the other such buffets on the helms that they both reeled back two strides. Then they recovered, and dealt such strokes that they hewed great pieces out of their armour and their shields.

Thus they fought till it was past noon, and after resting awhile, the battle went on again till evening, and none who beheld them could tell which was likely to win.

The Red Knight was a wily warrior, and his crafty fighting taught Beaumains to be wise, although he bought his experience dearly. For the Red Knight smote him on the hand, so that his sword fell out of it; and then he gave him yet another buffet on the helm, so that Beaumains fell grovelling to the earth, and the Red Knight fell over him, to hold him down.

Then cried the maiden Linet aloud:

"O, Sir Beaumains, where is thy courage? Alas, my lady sister beholdeth thee, and she sobbeth and weepeth, and maketh my heart heavy!"

When Sir Beaumains heard Linet speak thus, he started up with great might, and leaped to his sword, and gripping it in his hand, he rushed again on the Red Knight, and they fought a new battle together.

But Sir Beaumains doubled his strokes, and smiting the knight's sword out of his hand, felled him to the earth. And he unlaced his helm to slay him, but the Red Knight cried aloud:

"O, noble knight, I yield me to thy mercy!"

But Beaumains bethought him of the knights whom he had made to be hanged so shamefully.

"I may not with honour save thy life," he said, "because of the shameful deaths thou hast caused full many good knights to die."

"Sir," said the Red Knight of the Red Lawns, "hold your hand, and ye shall know why I put them to so shameful a death."

"Say on," said Beaumains.

"Sir, I once loved a lady, a fair damsel, and her brother was slain, and she said it was Sir Lancelot of the Lake, or else Sir Gawaine; and she prayed me that as I loved her heartily I would make her a promise by the faith of my knighthood, to labour daily in arms until I met with one of them, and all whom I overcame I should put to a villainous death. This is the cause why I have put all these knights to death, and thus ensured her vengeance against all King Arthur's knights. And now I will tell thee that every day my strength increaseth till noon, and all this time I have seven men's strength."

Then came many earls and barons and noble knights, beseeching Beaumains to save the Red Knight's life, and to make him a prisoner; they all fell upon their knees and prayed him to have mercy.

"Fair lords," said Beaumains, "be sure I am full loath to slay this knight, nevertheless he hath done passing ill and shamefully. But insomuch as all that he did was at a lady's request, I blame him the less, and so for your sake I will release him. He shall have his life upon this covenant—that he go within the Castle Perilous, and yield him there to the Lady Liones, and if she will forgive and acquit him, I will willingly, provided that he make her amends for all the trespass he hath done against her and her lands. Also," he continued to the knight, "when that is done, that ye go unto the Court of King Arthur, and there ask Sir Lancelot mercy, and Sir Gawaine, for the evil intention ye have had against them."

"All this will I do as ye command," said the Red Knight of the Red Lawns, "and certain assurance and sureties ye shall have."

So when the assurance was made, he paid his homage and fealty, and all those earls and barons with him.

Then the damsel Linet dressed his wounds, and those of Sir Beaumains. Ten days they sojourned in their tents, and the Red Knight made his lords and servants do all the pleasure they could to Sir Beaumains. And after praying pardon of the Lady Liones for all the wrongs he had done her, the Red Knight departed to the Court of King Arthur, and there openly put himself in the mercy of Sir Lancelot and Sir Gawaine.

Then Beaumains told Linet he desired to see her sister.

"I would fain ye saw her," she replied.

So Beaumains armed himself, and took his horse and his spear, and rode straight to Castle Perilous.

When he came to the gate he found many men armed, and the drawbridge pulled up, and the port closed. He marvelled why they would not suffer him to enter. Then he looked up to the window, and there he saw the fair Liones.

"Go thy way, Sir Beaumains," she cried, "for as yet thou shalt not have wholly my love, until the time that thou art called one of the number of the worthy knights. Therefore go labour honourably for twelve months, and then thou shalt hear new tidings."

"Alas, fair lady," said Beaumains, "I have not deserved that thou shouldst show me this strangeness. I thought I should have had right good cheer with you—I am well sure that I have bought your love with part of the best blood within my body."

"Fair courteous knight, be not displeased nor over hasty," said the Lady Liones. "Know well your great travail and good love shall not be lost, for I consider your great toil and labour, your bounty and your goodness, as I ought to do. Therefore go on your way, and look that you be of good comfort, for all shall be for your glory and for the best. By my faith, a twelve-month will soon be done, and trust me, fair knight, I shall be true to you, and never forsake you, but to my death I shall love you, and none other."

Thus the noble knight, Sir Gareth, a king's son,—whom Kay had mocked at as his "Boy of the Kitchen,"—won for himself deathless honour, and his peerless bride. And he and Dame Liones, the Lady of the Castle Perilous, plighted troth to love each other, and never to fail while their life lasted.

THE QUEST OF THE HOLY GRAIL

Siege Perilous

Now we will speak of Sir Lancelot of the Lake, and Sir Galahad, Sir Lancelot's son.

Before the time when Galahad was born there came a hermit to King Arthur, on Whitsunday, as the knights sat at the Round Table. Now there was one seat at the Round Table which always stood empty, and it was called "the Siege (or seat) Perilous." When the hermit saw this seat he asked the King and all the knights why it was empty.

"There is never any one who shall sit in that seat without being destroyed, except one person," was the answer.

"Do you know who that is?" asked the hermit.

"Nay," said Arthur, and all the knights, "we know not who he is that shall sit therein."

"Then I know," said the hermit. "He that shall sit there is not yet born; and this year, he that is to sit there, in the Siege Perilous, shall be born. And he shall win the Holy Grail."

Then the hermit departed from the Court of King Arthur.

After this feast Sir Lancelot rode on his adventures, till one day by chance he passed over the bridge of Corbin, and there he saw the fairest tower he had ever seen, and under it was a beautiful town full of people; and all the people cried:

"Welcome, Sir Lancelot of the Lake, flower of all knighthood, for by thee, and by thee alone, we shall be helped out of danger."

Sir Lancelot asked why they thus called upon him, whereupon the people replied that a fair lady was cruelly shut up in a hot room in the tower, and no one but himself could deliver her. Sir Lancelot, therefore, went to the tower, and when he came to the chamber where the lady was, the iron doors unlocked and unbolted themselves. He went into the room, which was as hot as any furnace, and there he found a beautiful lady, and he took her by the hand. By enchantment Queen Morgan le Fay and the Queen of North Wales had put her into this hot room, because she was called the fairest lady of that country. There she had been five years, and never might be delivered until the best knight of the world had taken her by the hand.

When she found herself rescued from the wicked spell, the lady asked Sir Lancelot to go with her into a church, to give God thanks for her deliverance. This having been done, and all the people, learned and unlearned, having given thanks, they said to Lancelot, "Sir Knight, since ye have delivered this lady, ye shall deliver us from a serpent that is here in a tomb."

Sir Lancelot took his shield, and said, "Bring me thither, and what I can do to please God and yourselves, that will I do."

The people led him to the place, and there he saw written on the tomb letters of gold, which said thus:

> Here shall come a leopard of King's blood,
>   and he shall slay this serpent, and this
> leopard shall have a son, a lion, in this foreign country;
>   the which lion shall pass all other knights.

Sir Lancelot lifted up the tomb, and out sprang a horrible and fiendish dragon, spitting fire from his mouth. The dragon flew at Sir Lancelot, but the knight fell upon him with his sword, and at last, after a long fight, with great pain he slew him.

Therewith came King Pelles, the good and noble knight, and saluted Sir Lancelot, and he him again.

"Fair knight," said the king, "what is your name?"

"Sir, wit you well, my name is Lancelot of the Lake."

"And my name," said the king, "is Pelles, king of this country; and I am of the family of Joseph of Arimathea."

Then each made much of the other, and so they went into the Castle to take their repast. And straightway there came in a dove at a window, and in her mouth there seemed a little censer of gold; immediately there was such a savour as if all the spicery of the world had been there, and forthwith on the table were all manner of meats and drinks that they could think of.

Then in came a damsel, passing young and fair, and she bore a vessel of gold betwixt her hands. The king knelt down devoutly and said his prayers, and so did all who were there.

"What may this mean?" said Sir Lancelot.

"That is the most precious thing that ever living man hath," said King Pelles. "And when the fame of this thing goeth about, the Round Table shall be broken. Wit thou well, this is the Holy Grail that ye have seen."

Now King Pelles had a daughter, as fair a lady, and young and as wise as any at that time living; her name was Elaine. When Sir Lancelot slew the dragon, King Pelles knew that the words written in letters of gold on the tomb would come true. For "the leopard of King's blood" who came into the foreign country meant Sir Lancelot himself; and "the lion" who was to surpass all other knights was Sir Galahad, who was no other than the son of Sir Lancelot of the Lake and the Lady Elaine, daughter of King Pelles.

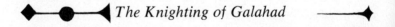

The Knighting of Galahad

Fifteen years had gone by since that Whitsunday when King Arthur and his knights held festival at Camelot, and the hermit had foretold who it was that was to sit in the Siege Perilous. And for all those years the Siege Perilous had still stood empty.

Once again it was the vigil of Pentecost, when all the fellowship of the Round Table had come to Camelot, to renew their vows and take part in the holy service. The tables were set ready for the feast when right into the hall entered a fair gentlewoman who had ridden full fast, for her horse was covered with sweat.

She alighted, and came before King Arthur, and saluted him; and he said, "Damsel, God bless thee!"

"Sir," she said, "I pray you tell me where Sir Lancelot is."

"Yonder you may see him," said the King.

Then she went to Lancelot, and said, "Sir Lancelot, I salute you on King Pelles' behalf, and I require you to come with me to a forest hereby."

Sir Lancelot asked her with whom she dwelt.

"I dwell with King Pelles," she answered.

"What will you with me?" asked Sir Lancelot.

"You shall know when you come thither."

"Well," said he, "I will gladly go with you."

So Sir Lancelot bade his squire saddle his horse, and bring his arms, and in all haste the man did his command.

Then came Queen Guinevere to Lancelot, and said, "Will you leave us at this high feast?"

"Madam," said the gentlewoman, "wit you well, he shall be with you again to-morrow by dinner-time."

"If I knew he would not be with us here to-morrow," said the Queen, "he should not go with you by my good-will."

Right so departed Sir Lancelot with the gentlewoman. They rode until they came to a forest, and into a great valley, where they saw an abbey of nuns. A squire was ready who opened the gates, so they entered, and descended off their horses, and a fair company came about Sir Lancelot, and welcomed him, and were passing glad of his coming.

They led him into the abbess' chamber, and unarmed him, and there he found two of his cousins, Sir Bors and Sir Lionel, who were greatly rejoiced and astonished to see him.

"Sir," said Sir Bors, "what adventure hath brought thee hither, for we thought to-morrow to have found thee at Camelot?"

"Truly," said Sir Lancelot, "a gentlewoman brought me hither, but I know not the cause."

In the meanwhile, as they thus stood talking together, there came twelve nuns, who brought with them a boy of about fifteen years old, so beautiful and well made, that scarcely in the world could man find his match. And all those ladies were weeping.

"Sir," they said, "we bring you here this child, Galahad, whom we have nourished, and we pray you to make him a knight; for of no worthier man's hand could he receive the order of knighthood."

Sir Lancelot beheld that young squire, and saw him seemly and demure as a dove, with all manner of good features, so that he thought he had never seen a man of his age so fair of face and form.

Then said Sir Lancelot, "Cometh this desire of himself?"

And the boy and all the nuns said, "Yea!"

"Then shall he receive the high order of knighthood to-morrow at the reverence of the high feast," said Lancelot.

That night Sir Lancelot had passing good cheer, and on the morrow, at the hour of dawn, at Galahad's desire he made him knight.

"God make you a good man," said Sir Lancelot, "for beauty faileth you not, as any that liveth. Now, fair sir, will you come with me to the Court of King Arthur?"

"Nay," said the boy, "I will not go with you at this time."

So Sir Lancelot departed from the Abbey, and took his two cousins with him, and they came to Camelot by nine o'clock in the morning on Whitsunday. By that time the King and the Queen had gone to the minster to hear the service. When the King and all the knights came back, the Barons saw that the seats of the Round Table were all written about with gold letters—here one ought to sit, and here ought another to sit.

Thus they went along until they came to the Siege Perilous, where they found letters of gold, newly written, which said:

> Four hundred winters and fifty-four
> after the passion of our
> Lord Jesus Christ,
> ought this Siege to be filled.

Then they all said, "This is a marvellous thing, and an adventurous."

"By heaven it is," said Sir Lancelot; and then he counted the period of the writing from the time of Our Lord to that day. "It seems to me," he said, "this siege ought to be filled this same day, for this is the Feast of Pentecost after the four hundredth and fifty-fourth year. And if it would please all parties, I counsel that none of these letters be seen this day, until he cometh who ought to achieve this adventure."

Then they ordered a cloth of silk to be brought to cover these letters in the Siege Perilous, after which King Arthur bade them haste to dinner.

"Sir," said Sir Kay, the steward, "if you go now to your meat, you will break the old custom of your Court. For you are not used on this day to sit down to table before you have seen some adventure."

"You speak truth," said the King, "but I had so great joy of Sir Lancelot, and of his cousins, who are come to the Court whole and sound, that I bethought me not of my old custom."

As they stood speaking, in came a squire.

"Sir," he said to the King, "I bring to you marvellous tidings."

"What are they?" said the King.

"Sir, there is here beneath, at the river, a great stone, which I saw float above the water, and therein I saw sticking a sword."

"I will see that marvel," said the King.

So all the knights went with him, and when they came to the river, they found there a stone floating, as it were of red marble, and therein stuck a fair and rich sword, in the pommel of which were precious stones, wrought with subtle letters of gold.

Then the Barons read the letters, which said in this wise:

Never shall man take me hence
but he by whose side I ought to hang,
and he shall be the
best knight of the world.

When King Arthur saw these letters he said to Sir Lancelot:

"Fair sir, this sword ought to be yours, for I am sure you are the best knight in the world."

But Sir Lancelot answered full soberly:

"Certes, sir, it is not my sword; also, wit you well, I have no hardihood to set my hand to it, for it belongeth not to hang by my side. Also, whoever assayeth to take that sword, and faileth of it, he shall receive from it a wound, of which long afterwards he shall not be whole. And I will that ye take note that this same day the adventure of the Holy Grail will begin."

Marvels, and Greater Marvels

Then King Arthur asked his nephew Sir Gawaine to try to draw the sword from the stone in the river. But Sir Gawaine said he could not do it. Then the King commanded him to make the attempt.

"Sir," said Gawaine, "since you command me, I will obey." Therewith he took the sword by the handle, but he could not stir it.

"I thank you," said the King.

"My lord Sir Gawaine," said Sir Lancelot, "now wit you well, this sword shall touch you so sore that you shall wish you had never set your hand to it, for the best castle of this realm."

"I could not withstay my uncle's will and command," said Gawaine.

King Arthur hearing this, repented greatly what he had done, nevertheless he asked Sir Percival to assay it, for his love.

"Gladly, to bear Sir Gawaine fellowship," replied Sir Percival, and therewith he set his hand on the sword, and drew it strongly, but he could not move it. Then there were others who dared to be so bold as to set their hands to it.

"Now you may go to your dinner," said Sir Kay to the King, "for a marvellous adventure have you seen."

So the King and all went back to the Palace, and every knight knew his own place, and sat therein, and young men who were knights served them.

When they were served, and the seats filled, save only the Siege Perilous, there suddenly befell a marvellous adventure— all the doors and windows shut of themselves. Yet the hall was not greatly darkened because of this, and they were one and all amazed.

King Arthur was the first to speak.

"Fair fellows and lords," he said, "we have seen this day marvels, but before night I expect we shall see greater marvels."

In the meanwhile came in a good old man, very ancient, clothed in white, and no knight knew from whence he came. He brought with him a young knight, also on foot, in red armour, without sword or shield, but with only a scabbard hanging by his side.

"Peace be with you lords!" said the old man. Then, to Arthur, "Sir, I bring here a young knight, who is of king's lineage, and of the kindred of Joseph of Arimathea, whereby the marvels of this Court and of strange realms shall be fully accomplished."

The King was very pleased at his words, and said to the old man, "Sir, you are right welcome, and the young knight with you."

The old man made the young knight take off his armour, and under it he was clad in a coat of red silk, and the old man put on him a mantle furred with ermine. Then saying to the young knight, "Sir, follow me," he led him straight to the Siege Perilous, beside which sat Sir Lancelot. The good man lifted up the silken cloth, and underneath it he found letters which said thus:

This is the seat of Galahad, the high prince.

"Sir, wit you well that place is yours," said the old man, and he made him sit down surely in that seat.

Then the young knight said to the old man, "Good sir, you may now go your way, for you have done well what you were commanded to do. Commend me to my grandsire, King Pelles, and say to him on my behalf that I will come and see him as soon as ever I can."

So the good man departed, and there were waiting for him twenty squires, and they took their horses and went their way.

All the Knights of the Round Table marvelled greatly at Galahad, because he had dared to sit there in that Siege Perilous, and he was so tender of age. They knew not from whence he came, but only that God had sent him, and they said:

"This is he by whom the Holy Grail shall be achieved, for never any one but he sat in that place without mischief befalling him."

But Sir Lancelot beheld his son, and had great joy of him.

"By my life, this young knight shall come to great honour," said Sir Bors to his companions.

There was great excitement in all the Palace, so that the news came to Queen Guinevere. She marvelled what knight it could be who ventured to sit in the Siege Perilous. Then many told her that he much resembled Sir Lancelot.

"I can well imagine," said the Queen, "that he is son of Sir Lancelot and King Pelles' daughter, and his name is Galahad. I would fain see him, for he must needs be a noble man, for so is his father."

When the meal was over, so that King Arthur and all were risen, the King went to the Siege Perilous, and lifted up the cloth, and found there the name of Galahad. He showed it to Sir Gawaine, saying:

"Fair nephew, now we have among us Sir Galahad, who shall bring honour to us all; and on pain of my life he shall achieve the Holy Grail, right so as Sir Lancelot hath given us to understand."

Then King Arthur went to Galahad, and said, "Sir, you are welcome, for you shall move many good knights to the quest of the Holy Grail, and you shall achieve that which never knight could do." Then the King took him by the hand, and went down to show Galahad the adventure of the stone in the river.

Queen Guinevere, hearing this, came after with many ladies, and showed them the stone where it moved on the water.

"Here is as great a marvel as ever I saw," said King Arthur

to Galahad, "and right good knights have assayed and failed."

"Sir, that is no marvel," said Galahad, "for this adventure is not theirs, but mine and with the certainty of this sword, I brought none with me; for here by my side hangeth the scabbard." He laid his hand on the sword and lightly drew it out of the stone, and put it in the sheath. "Now it goeth better than it did before."

"God will send you a shield," said the King.

"Now have I that sword which was sometime that good knight's, Balin the Savage," said Galahad, "and he was a passing good man of his hands. With this sword he slew his unknown brother Balan, and that was a great pity, for he was a good knight; and each slew the other, not knowing they were brothers, because of a dolorous stroke that Balan gave my grandfather, King Pelles, which is not yet whole, nor shall be till I heal him."

At that moment the King and all espied a lady on a white palfrey, who came riding down the river towards them. She saluted the King and the Queen, and asked if Sir Lancelot were there. He answered himself, "I am here, fair lady."

Then she said, all weeping: "How your great doing is changed since this day in the morning!"

"Damsel, why say you so?" said Lancelot.

"I say the truth," said the damsel, "for this morning you were the best knight in the world; but who should say so now would be a liar, for now there is one better than you. And this is well proved by the adventure of the sword, whereto you dared not set your hand; and hence comes the change and leaving of your name. Wherefore I bid you remember that you shall not ween from henceforth that you are the best knight of the world."

"As touching that," said Sir Lancelot, "I know well I was never the best."

"Yes," said the damsel; "that you were; and are so yet, of any sinful man of the world. And, Sir King, Nacien the hermit sendeth thee word that there shall befall thee the greatest honour that ever befell a King in Britain. And I will tell you wherefore. This day the Holy Grail shall appear in thy house, and feed thee, and all thy fellowship of the Round Table."

So the damsel departed, and went back the same way.

The Last Tournament

"Now," said King Arthur, "I am sure that all ye of the Round Table will depart on this quest of the Holy Grail, and never shall I see the whole of you again all together. Therefore will I see you all together in the meadow of Camelot, to joust and to tourney, that after your death men may speak of it, that such knights were wholly together on such a day."

To that counsel and the King's request they all agreed, and put on their armour that belonged to jousting. But the King did this with the intent of seeing Galahad proved, for the King deemed he would not lightly come to the Court again after his departing.

So they all assembled in the meadow, and the Queen was in a tower with all her ladies to behold that tournament. Then Galahad, at the King's entreaty, put on a noble cuirass, and also his helm, but shield he would take none, not for any entreaty of the King.

Sir Gawaine and the other knights prayed him to take a spear, and this he did. Then taking his place in the midst of the meadow he began to break spears marvellously, so that all men wondered at him. For he there surpassed all other knights, and in a little while had thrown down many good Knights of the Round Table. But Sir Lancelot and Sir Percival he did not overthrow.

King Arthur, at Queen Guinevere's request, made him alight and unlace his helm, so that the Queen might see his face. And when she beheld him she said, "Truly I dare well say that Sir Lancelot is his father, for never two men were more alike; therefore it is no marvel if he be of great prowess."

A lady that stood by the Queen said:

"Madam, ought he of right to be so good a knight?"

"Yes, in truth," said the Queen, "for both from his father's and his mother's side he is come of the best knights of the world, and of the highest lineage. I dare affirm that Sir Lancelot and Sir Galahad are the greatest gentlemen of the world."

Then the King and all the nobles went home to Camelot, and after they had been to evensong in the great minster, they went to supper; and every knight sat in his own place.

Suddenly they heard cracking and rolling of thunder, as if the place would have been riven. In the midst of this blast entered a sunbeam, clearer by seven times than ever they saw by day, and all their faces shone with a divine light. Then began every knight to look at each other, and each seemed fairer than any one had seemed before. Not a knight could speak a single word for a great while, so they looked every man at each other, as if they had been dumb.

Then there entered into the hall the Holy Grail, covered with white samite, but none could see it, nor who bore it. And all the hall was filled with good odours, and every knight had such meats and drinks as he liked best; and when the Holy Grail had been borne through the hall, then the holy vessel departed suddenly, so that they knew not what became of it.

After it had gone they all had breath to speak, and King Arthur gave thanks to God for the great favour He had sent them.

"Now," said Sir Gawaine, "we have been served this day with what meats and drinks we thought of, but one thing hath failed us,—we could not see the Holy Grail, it was covered with such care. Therefore I will here make a vow, that to-morrow without longer abiding I shall undertake the Quest of the Holy Grail. I shall hold out a twelvemonth and a day, or more, if need be, and never shall I return again to the Court till I have seen it more openly than it hath been seen here. And if I do not succeed, I shall return as one that cannot act against the will of heaven."

When the Knights of the Round Table heard what Sir Gawaine said, most of them rose up, and made the same sort of vow as Sir Gawaine had made.

King Arthur was greatly displeased at this, for he knew well they might not gainsay their vows.

"Alas," he said to Sir Gawaine, "you have almost slain me with the vow and promise you have made. For through you, ye have reft me of the fairest fellowship, and the truest of knighthood that ever were seen together in any realm of the world. For when my knights depart hence I am sure that never more will they all meet together in this world, for many of them shall die in the Quest. And so I repent it, for I have loved them as well as my life, wherefore it shall grieve me right sore, the breaking up of this fellowship. For this is an old custom that I have had kept."

And therewith his eyes filled with tears.

"Oh, Gawaine, Gawaine," he said, "you have set me in great sorrow. For I doubt much that my true fellowship shall ever more meet here again."

"Comfort yourself," said Lancelot, "for if we die in the Quest of the Holy Grail, it shall be to us a great honour, much more than if we had died in any other place; for, early or late, of death we are sure."

"Ah, Lancelot," said the King, "the great love I have had for you all the days of my life maketh me to say such doleful words. For never Christian King had so many worthy men at his table, as I have had this day at the Round Table, and that is my great sorrow."

When the Queen, ladies, and gentlewomen knew these tidings they had such sorrow and heaviness that no tongue could tell it, for those knights had holden them in honour and love. But among all the others Queen Guinevere made most sorrow.

"I marvel," said she, "that my lord, the King, would suffer them to depart from him."

Thus all the Court were troubled, because of the departing of those knights. Some of the ladies who loved knights, wanted to go with their husbands and lovers, and would have done so, had not an aged knight in religious clothing come among them.

"Fair lords, who have sworn to the Quest of the Holy Grail," he said, "Nacien, the hermit thus sendeth you word, that none in this Quest lead lady or gentlewoman, for it is a hard and high service. And, moreover, I warn you plainly that he who is not clean of his sins shall not see these mysteries."

After this, Queen Guinevere came to Galahad, and asked him whence he was, and of what country. He told her.

"And son unto Lancelot?" she asked; but to this he said neither yea nor nay.

"Truly," said the Queen, "of your father you need not be ashamed, for he is the goodliest knight, and come of the best men of the world, on both sides of a race of kings. Wherefore you ought of right to be of your deeds a passing good man— and certainly you resemble him much."

Galahad was a little abashed at this, and said:

"Madam, since you know it for certain, why did you ask me? For he that is my father shall be known openly, in good time."

Then they all went to rest. And in honour of Galahad's greatness and high race he was led into King Arthur's chamber, and rested on the King's own bed.

As soon as it was day the King arose, for he had no rest all that night for sorrow. Then he went to Gawaine and Sir Lancelot, who had risen to go to church.

"Ah, Gawaine, Gawaine," said the King, "you have betrayed me. For never shall my Court be amended by you; but you will never be as sorry for me as I am for you." And therewith the tears began to run down his face. "Ah, knight, Sir Lancelot," he said, "I pray thee counsel me, for I would this Quest were undone if it could be."

"Sir," said Lancelot, "ye saw yesterday so many worthy knights who were then sworn so that they cannot leave it."

"That I know well," said the King. "But I grieve so at their departing that I know well no manner of joy shall ever cure me."

Then the King and the Queen went to the minster.

Lancelot and Gawaine commanded their men to bring their arms, and when they were all armed save their shields and their helms they were ready in the same wise to go to the minster to hear the service.

After the service the King wished to know how many had undertaken the Quest of the Holy Grail; and they found by counting, it was a hundred and fifty, and all were Knights of the Round Table.

Then they put on their helms ready to depart, and commended them all wholly to the Queen, and there was weeping, and great sorrow. And Queen Guinevere went into her chamber, so that no one should see her great grief.

Sir Lancelot missing the Queen, went to look for her, and when she saw him, she cried aloud: "O, Sir Lancelot, you have forsaken us! You put me to death thus to leave my lord!"

"Ah, madam," said Sir Lancelot, "I pray you be not displeased, for I shall come again as soon as I can in accordance with my honour."

"Alas," said she, "that ever I saw you! But He that suffered death upon the Cross for all mankind be your good conduct and safety, and that of all the whole fellowship!"

Right so departed Sir Lancelot, and found his companions who awaited his coming. They mounted their horses, and rode through the streets of Camelot, and there was weeping of the rich and poor, and the King turned away, and could not speak for weeping.

So the Knights of the Round Table rode forth on the Quest of the Holy Grail.

That night they rested in a Castle called Vagon, where the lord was a good old man, and made them the best cheer he could. On the morrow they all agreed they should each separate from the other. So the next day, with weeping and mourning, they departed, and every knight took the way that seemed to him best.

Sir Galahad's White Shield

Now Galahad was yet without a shield, and he rode four days without adventure.

On the fourth day after evensong he came to an abbey of white friars, and there he was received with great reverence, and led to a chamber, and unarmed. Then he was aware of two Knights of the Round Table, one was King Bagdemagus, the other was Sir Uwaine; and they were very pleased to see him.

"Sirs," said Galahad, "what adventures brought you hither?"

"It is told us," they replied, "that in this place is a shield that no man may bear about his neck, without being hurt or dead within three days, or else maimed for ever."

"I shall bear it to-morrow to assay this strange adventure," added King Bagdemagus to Galahad; "and if I cannot achieve this adventure of the shield, ye shall take it upon you."

"I agree right well," said Galahad, "for I have no shield." On the morrow they arose early and after hearing service, King Bagdemagus asked where the adventurous shield was. A monk at once led him behind an altar, where the shield hung. It was white as any snow, but in the midst was a red cross.

"Sir," said the monk, "this shield ought not to hang around the neck of any knight, unless he be the worthiest knight of the world; therefore I counsel you knights to be well advised."

"Well," said King Bagdemagus, "I know well I am not the best knight of the world, but yet I shall assay to bear it."

So he bore it out of the monastery, saying to Galahad, "If it please you, I pray you abide here still, till you know how I shall speed."

"I will await you here," said Galahad.

King Bagdemagus took with him a squire, to carry back tidings to Galahad how he sped. When they had ridden about two miles they came to a fair valley before a hermitage, and there they saw coming from that direction a goodly knight, in white armour, horse and all. He came as fast as his horse could run, with his spear in the rest, and King Bagdemagus dressed his spear against him, and broke it upon the white knight. But the other struck him so hard that he shattered the mail, and thrust him through the right shoulder, and so bore him from his horse.

Then the knight alighted, and took the white shield from Bagdemagus, saying:

"Knight, thou hast done thyself great folly, for this shield ought not to be borne but by him that shall have no peer."

Then he came to King Bagdemagus' squire and said, "Bear this shield to the good knight Sir Galahad, whom thou left in the abbey, and greet him well from me."

"Sir," said the squire, "what is your name?"

"Take thou no heed of my name," said the knight, "for it is not for thee to know, nor any earthly man."

"Now, fair sir," said the squire, "for the love of heaven, tell me for what cause this shield may not be borne, without the bearer thereof coming to mischief."

"This shield belongeth to no man but Galahad," said the knight.

The squire went to King Bagdemagus and asked if he were sore wounded or not.

"Yea, forsooth," he said, "I shall hardly escape death."

The squire fetched his horse, and took him with great pain to an abbey. There he was gently unarmed, and laid in a bed, and his wounds were looked to. And there he lay for a long while.

The squire carried the shield to Galahad, with the knight's message.

"Now blessed be God and fortune," said Galahad. Then he asked for his armour, and mounted his horse, and hung the white shield about his neck, and bade them good-bye. Sir Uwaine said he would bear him fellowship, but Galahad replied that he could not do so, for he must go alone except for his squire.

Within a little while Sir Galahad came near the hermitage, and there was the white knight awaiting him. Each saluted the other courteously, and then the strange knight told him the legend of the white shield.

It had been made over four hundred years ago by Joseph of Arimathea for a King called Evelake, who was at war with the Saracens. On the eve of a great battle Joseph of Arimathea went to King Evelake, and showed him the right belief of the Christian faith, to which he agreed with all his heart. Then this shield was made for King Evelake, and through it he got the better of his enemies. For when he went into battle there was a cloth placed over the shield, and when he found himself in the greatest peril, he drew aside the cloth, and then his enemies saw the cross, and were all discomfited.

Afterwards befell a strange marvel, for the cross on the shield vanished away, so that no man knew what became of it.

At the end of the war King Evelake was baptized, and so were most of the people in his city. And when Joseph of Arimathea departed, King Evelake insisted on going with him. So it chanced they came to this land, which was called Great Britain.

Not long after, Joseph of Arimathea fell ill, and was like to die. King Evelake was deeply grieved, and prayed him to leave some token of remembrance. "That will I do full gladly," said the holy man, and he bade him bring the shield, which was not quite white. Then with his own blood Joseph of Arimathea traced on it a red cross.

"Now you may see a remembrance that I love you," he said, "for you shall never see this shield but you shall think of me. And it shall be always as fresh as it is now. And never shall any man bear this shield round his neck but he shall repent it, until the time that Galahad, the last of my lineage shall have it about his neck, and shall do many marvellous deeds."

"Now," said King Evelake, "where shall I put this shield, that this worthy knight may have it?"

"You shall leave it where Nacien the hermit shall be put

after his death. For thither shall that good knight come the fifth day after he receive the order of knighthood."

"So that day which they appointed is this time that you have received the shield," said the knight to Galahad. "And in the same abbey lieth Nacien the hermit. And you are grandson of King Pelles, who is of the race of Joseph of Arimathea."

And with that, the White Knight vanished away.

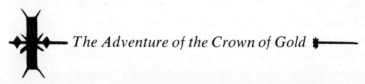

The Adventure of the Crown of Gold

As soon as the squire heard what the White Knight said to Sir Galahad he alighted off his hackney, and kneeling down at Galahad's feet, prayed that he might go with him till he had made him knight. "And that order, by the grace of God, shall be well held by me," he added. So Sir Galahad granted his petition. Then they returned to the abbey where they had come from and great joy was made of Sir Galahad, and there he rested.

On the morrow he knighted the squire, and asked him his name, and of what kindred he was come.

"Sir," said he, "men call me Melias of the Isle, and I am the son of the King of Denmark."

"Now, fair sir," said Galahad, "since ye be come of kings and queens, look you that knighthood be well set in you, for you ought to be a mirror to all chivalry."

"Sir, you say truth," said Melias. "But since you have made me a knight you must by rights grant me my first desire, if it is reasonable."

"That is true," said Galahad.

"Then will you suffer me to ride with you in this Quest of the Holy Grail?" asked Melias.

And Galahad granted it.

His armour, his spear, and his horse were then brought to Sir Melias, but Sir Galahad and he rode forth all that week before they found any adventure.

On a Monday, in the morning, after leaving an abbey, they came to a cross which parted two ways, and on that cross were letters written, which said thus:

Now ye knights errant, who go to seek knights adventurous, see here two ways: one way it is forbidden thee to go, for none shall come out of that way again, unless he be a good man and a worthy knight; if thou go this way on the left hand, thou shalt not there lightly win prowess, for thou shalt in this way be soon assayed.

"Sir," said Melias to Galahad, "if it please you to suffer me to take this way on the left hand, tell me, for there I shall well test my strength."

"It were better ye rode not that way," said Galahad, "for I deem I should escape better in that way than you."

"Nay, my lord, I pray you let me have that adventure."

"Take it, in heaven's name," said Galahad.

Then Melias rode into an old forest, through which he travelled two days and more, till he came to a green meadow, where there was a fair lodge of boughs. And he espied in the lodge a chair, wherein was a crown of gold, subtly wrought. Also, there were cloths spread upon the ground, on which were set many delicious meats.

Sir Melias beheld this adventure, and thought it marvellous. He had no hunger, but he had great desire of the crown of gold, so he stooped down, took it up, and rode his way with it. Soon he saw a knight come riding after him, who said:

"Knights, set down that crown of gold, which is not yours, and therefore defend yourself!"

"Fair Lord of Heaven, help and save Thy new-made knight!" prayed Sir Melias.

Then they urged on their horses as fast as they could, and the other knight smote Sir Melias through hauberk, and through the left side, so that he fell to the earth nearly dead. The knight took the crown of gold and went his way, and Sir Melias lay still.

In the meanwhile, by good fortune, came Sir Galahad.

"Ah, Melias, who hath wounded you?" he said. "It would have been better to have ridden the other way."

"Sir, for God's love let me not die in this forest," said Melias, "but bear me to the abbey here beside, that I may be confessed and have heavenly comfort."

"It shall be done," said Galahad; "but where is he that hath wounded you?"

At that moment Sir Galahad heard through the trees a loud cry—"Knight, keep thee from me!"

"Ah, sir, beware!" said Melias, "that is he who hath slain me."

"Sir Knight, come at your peril!" answered Sir Galahad.

Then each turned towards the other, and they came together as fast as their horses could run, and Galahad smote the stranger so that his spear went through his shoulder, and bore him down off his horse, and in the falling Galahad's spear broke. With that, out came another knight from among the trees, and broke a spear upon Galahad, before ever he could turn. Then Galahad drew out his sword, and smote off his left arm, whereupon he fled. After chasing him for some distance Sir Galahad returned to Melias, and placing him gently on his horse, sprang up behind, and held him in his arms, and so brought him to the abbey. There his wound was carefully tended, and an old monk told Sir Galahad he hoped it would be healed within seven weeks. Sir Galahad said he would stay at the abbey for three days.

At the end of that time he said, "Now I will depart, for I have much on hand; many good knights are full busy about it, and this knight and I were in the same Quest of the Holy Grail."

"For his sin was he thus wounded," said a good man. "And I marvel," he added to Melias, "how you dare take upon you so rich a thing as the high order of knighthood without clean confession, and that was the cause you were bitterly wounded. For the road on the right hand betokeneth the highway of our Lord Jesus Christ, and the way of a true, good liver. And the other road betokeneth the way of sinners and misbelievers. And when the devil saw your pride and presumption tempt you into the Quest of the Holy Grail, that made you to be overthrown.

"Also, the writing on the cross was a signification of heavenly deeds, and of knightly deeds in God's works, and no knightly deeds in worldly works; and pride is head of all deadly sins, which caused thee, Melias, to depart from Sir Galahad. And when thou tookest the crown of gold, thou sinnedst in covetousness and theft. All these were no knightly deeds. And this Galahad, the holy knight, who fought with the two knights,— the two knights signify the two deadly sins pride and covetousness, which were wholly in Sir Melias, and they could not stand against Sir Galahad, for he is without deadly sin."

Now departed Galahad, and bade them all good-bye.

"My lord Galahad," said Melias, "as soon as I can ride, I shall seek you."

"God send you health," said Galahad.

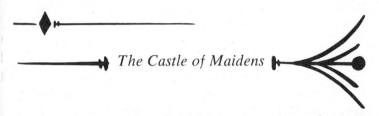

The Castle of Maidens

Sir Galahad rode many journeys, backward and forward, as adventure led him, and at last one day he came to a mountain, where he found an old chapel, and nobody there, for all was desolate. Then he knelt before the altar, and prayed for good counsel, and as he prayed he heard a voice that said, "Go thou now, thou adventurous knight, to the Castle of Maidens, and there do away with the wicked customs."

When Sir Galahad heard this, he thanked God and took his horse. He had ridden only half a mile when he saw in a valley before him a strong Castle, with deep ditches; beside it ran a fair river, called the Severn, and there he met with a very old man. Each saluted, and Galahad asked him the Castle's name.

"Fair sir," he said, "it is the Castle of Maidens."

"That is a cursed Castle," said Galahad, "and all who are connected with it, for pity is outside, and mischief within."

"For that reason I counsel you, Sir Knight, to turn again."

"Sir, wit you well I shall not turn again," said Sir Galahad. Then he looked to his arms that nothing failed him, and put his shield before him, and there met him seven fair maidens.

"Sir Knight," they said, "you ride here in great folly, for you have the river to pass over."

"Why should I not pass over the river?" said Galahad. So he rode away from them.

Next there met him a squire, who said: "Those knights in the Castle forbid you to go further till they know what you want."

"Fair sir, I come to destroy the wicked custom of this Castle."

"Sir, if you keep to that, you will have enough to do."

"Go you now," said Galahad, "and hasten my needs."

Then the squire entered into the Castle. And immediately after, there came out of the Castle seven knights, who were all brethren. When they saw Galahad, they cried, "Knight, keep thee, for we assure thee nothing but death!"

"Why, will you all fight with me at once?" said Galahad.

"Yea," said they, "you may trust to that."

Galahad thrust forth his spear, and struck the foremost to the earth, so that he nearly broke his neck, whereupon all the other brothers smote him on his shield great strokes, so that their spears broke. Then Galahad drew out his sword and set upon them so hard that it was a marvel to see, and thus through great might he made them forsake the field. As they fled, he chased them till they entered into the Castle, and passing right through the Castle, escaped out at another gate.

Now there met Sir Galahad an old man, clad in religious clothing, who said, "Sir, have here the keys of the Castle." Then Galahad opened the gates, and so many people came thronging round him that he could not number them.

"Sir," they all said, "you are welcome, for long have we waited here our deliverance."

Then came to him a gentlewoman. "These knights are fled," said she, "but they will come again this night, and begin again their evil customs."

"What will you that I shall do?" asked Galahad.

"That you send after all the knights to come hither who hold their lands of this Castle, and make them swear to use the customs that were formerly used here in the old times."

"I will gladly," said Galahad.

She brought him a horn of ivory, richly bound with gold, and said, "Blow this; it will be heard two miles round the Castle."

When Galahad had blown the horn he went to rest, and presently there came a priest, who told him the story of the Castle.

"It is just seven years ago," he said, "that these seven brethren came to this Castle, and lodged with the lord of it, who was called the Duke Lianor, and who was lord of all this country. When they espied the duke's daughter, who was a very beautiful woman, they began to weave false plots as to which should marry her, till they took to quarreling among themselves. The duke in his goodness would have parted them, but in their anger they slew him and his oldest son. Then they seized the maiden, and the treasure of the Castle. Afterwards, by great strength they held all the knights of this Castle in great bondage and extortion, besides robbing and plundering the poor country people of all that they had. So it happened on a day the duke's daughter said, 'You have done me great wrong, to slay my own father and my brother, and thus to hold our lands. But you shall not hold this Castle for many years, for by one knight you shall be overcome.' Thus she prophesied seven years ago. 'Well,' said the seven knights, 'since you say so, never lady nor knight shall pass this Castle, but they shall abide here, in spite of their will, or die for it, until that knight come by whom we shall lose this Castle.' Therefore it is called the Castle of Maidens, for many fair ladies have here been destroyed."

"Now," said Galahad, "is she here for whom this Castle was lost?"

"Nay," said the priest, "she was dead within three nights after speaking the prophecy. And since then they have kept prisoner her younger sister, who with many other ladies endureth great pain and hardship."

By this time the knights of the country were come. Then Galahad made them do homage and fealty to the duke's younger daughter, who was still alive, and set them in great ease of heart.

And the next morning a man brought tidings that Gawaine, Gareth, and Uwaine had slain the seven brethren.

"Well done!" said Galahad, and took his armour and his horse, and bade good-bye to the Castle of Maidens.

The Vision at the Forest Chapel

After leaving the Castle of Maidens, Sir Galahad rode till he came to the forest, and there he met with Sir Lancelot and Sir Percival, but they did not know him, for he was newly disguised. Sir Lancelot rode straight at him, and broke his spear on him, and Sir Galahad smote him so again that he bore down horse and man. Then he drew his sword, and turned to Sir Percival, and smote him on the helm so that it rove to the coif of steel; if the sword had not swerved, Sir Percival would have been slain; with the stroke he fell out of the saddle.

This joust took place before a hermitage where dwelt a recluse, who was really aunt to Sir Percival, although he did not know it at that moment. When she saw Sir Galahad she said, "God be with thee, best knight of the world! Ah, certes," she said quite loud, so that Lancelot and Percival could hear it, "if yonder two knights had known thee as well as I do, they would not have encountered with thee."

Galahad, hearing her say this, was sorely afraid of being known, and therefore rode swiftly away. Then both knights perceived he was Galahad, and up they got on their horses, and rode fast after him, but he was soon out of sight. So they returned.

"Let us ask some tidings of yonder recluse," said Percival.

"Do so, if you please," said Lancelot, but when Percival went to the hermitage he rode on alone. This way and that he rode across a wild forest, and held no path except as adventure led him. At last he came to a strong cross, which pointed two ways in waste land; by the cross was a stone that was of marble, but it was so dark that Sir Lancelot could not tell what it was.

Sir Lancelot looked about him, and near at hand he saw an old chapel, where he expected to find people. He tied his horse to a tree, and taking off his shield, hung it upon the tree. Then he went to the chapel door, but found it waste and broken. And looking within, he saw a fair altar, fully richly arrayed with cloth of clean silk, where stood a shining candlestick, which bore six great candles, and the candlestick was of silver.

When Sir Lancelot saw this light he desired greatly to enter into the chapel, but could find no place where he could enter, which greatly grieved and perplexed him. He returned to his horse and took off the saddle and bridle, and let him pasture; and unlacing his helm, and ungirding his sword, he laid himself down to sleep on his shield before the marble cross.

So he fell asleep, and, half-waking and half-sleeping, he saw a vision.

He saw come past him two palfreys all beautiful and white, which bore a litter, and in the litter lay a sick knight. When they were near the cross the litter stood still, and Sir Lancelot heard the knight say:

"O, sweet Lord, when shall this sorrow leave me? And when shall the holy vessel come by, through which I shall be blessed? For I have endured thus long through little trespass."

Thus for some time lamented the knight.

Then Sir Lancelot saw the candlestick with the six tapers come before the marble cross, and he saw nobody that brought it. Also there came a table of silver, and the sacred vessel of the Holy Grail, which Sir Lancelot had seen in King Pelles' house.

Therewith the sick knight sat up, and held up both his hands, and prayed to God, and kneeling down, he kissed the holy vessel, and immediately he was whole.

"Lord God, I thank thee, for I am healed of this sickness."

So when the Holy Grail had been there a long time, it went into the chapel, with the candlestick and the lights, so that Lancelot did not know what became of it. He was overmastered by a feeling of his sinfulness, and had no power to rise.

Then the sick knight rose, and kissed the cross, and the squire at once brought him his armour, and asked his lord how he did.

"Truly, I thank God, right well," he answered; "through the holy vessel I am healed. But I greatly marvel at this sleeping knight, who had no power to awake when this holy vessel was brought hither."

"I dare right well say," said the squire, "that he dwelleth in some deadly sin, whereof he has never repented."

"By my faith," said the knight, "whatsoever he be, he is unhappy, for, as I deem, he is of the fellowship of the Round Table, which has entered into the Quest of the Holy Grail."

"Sir," said the squire, "here have I brought you all your arms, save your helm and your sword, and therefore, by my advice ye may now take this knight's helm and his sword."

So the knight did this; and when he was fully armed he took also Sir Lancelot's horse. And so he and his attendants departed.

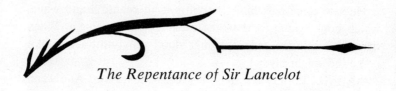

The Repentance of Sir Lancelot

Straightway Sir Lancelot awoke, and sat up, and bethought him what he had seen there, and whether it were a dream or not. Right so he heard a voice that said:

"Sir Lancelot, more hard than is the stone, and more bitter than is the wood, and more naked and bare than is the leaf of the fig-tree! Therefore withdraw thee from this holy place."

When Sir Lancelot heard this, he was passing heavy, and knew not what to do; so he rose, sore weeping, and cursed the time that he was born, because he thought he would never more have honour. For those words went to his heart till he knew why he was called so.

He went to fetch his helm, his sword, and his horse, but

found they had all been taken away. Then he called himself a wretch, and most unhappy of all knights. "My sin and my wickedness have brought me to great dishonour," he said. "For when I sought worldly adventures for worldly desires, I ever achieved them, and had the better in every place, and never was I discomfited in any quarrel, were it right or wrong. And now I take upon me the adventures of holy things, but I see and understand that my old sin hindereth me, and shameth me, so that I had no power to stir nor speak when the holy vessel appeared."

Thus he sorrowed till it was day, and he heard the little birds sing; then he was somewhat comforted.

But when he missed his horse and his arms Sir Lancelot knew well God was displeased with him. He departed from the cross on foot into the forest, and by dawn came to a high hill, where a hermit dwelt, whom he found just about to begin his morning devotions. Then Lancelot knelt down, and cried to the Lord for mercy for his wicked works. When their prayers were over, Lancelot begged the hermit for charity to hear his life.

"Right willingly," said the good man. "Are you not of King Arthur's Court, and of the fellowship of the Round Table?"

"Yea, truly, and my name is Sir Lancelot of the Lake, who hath been right well spoken of, and now my good fortune is changed, for I am the most wretched man in the world."

The hermit marvelled why he was so abashed.

"Sir," said the hermit, "you ought to thank God more than any knight living, for He hath caused you to have more worldly worship than any knight that now liveth. Because of your presumption to take upon yourself, while you were still in deadly sin, to behold His holy chalice, that was the cause you might not see it with worldly eyes. For He will not appear where such sinners be, except it be to their great hurt and their great shame. And there is no knight living now who ought to give God such thanks as you. For He hath given you beauty, seemliness, and great strength, above all other knights, and therefore you are the more beholden unto God than any other man, to love Him and dread Him; for your strength and manhood will little avail you, if God be against you."

Then Sir Lancelot wept for grief, and said: "Now I know well you speak truth to me."

"Sir," said the good man, "hide from me no old sin."

"Truly, I am full loath to reveal it," said Sir Lancelot. "For these fourteen years I have never revealed one thing, and for that I now blame my shame and misadventure."

And then he told that good man all his life, and how he loved a Queen beyond all measure, and longer than he could reckon.

"And all my great deeds of arms that I have done, I did the most part for the Queen's sake, and for her sake would I do battle, were it right or wrong; and never did I battle only for God's sake, but to win worship, and to cause me to be the better beloved. I pray you counsel me."

"I will counsel you," said the hermit, "if you will assure me that you will never come into the presence of that Queen, if you can help it."

Then Sir Lancelot promised him faithfully he would not.

"Look that your heart and your mouth agree," said the good man, "and you shall have more worship than ever you had."

"I marvel at the voice which said to me those strange words I told you of," said Lancelot.

"Have no marvel," said the good man, "for it seemeth well God loveth thee. Men can understand a stone is hard by nature, and one kind harder than another,—by which is meant *thee*, Sir Lancelot. For thou wilt not leave thy sin, for any goodness that God hath sent thee, therefore art thou harder than any stone; and thou wouldst never be made soft, neither by water nor by fire,—and that is, the Holy Spirit could not enter into thee. Now take heed; in all the world men shall not find one knight to whom our Lord hath given so much of grace as He hath given thee. For He hath given thee beauty, with seemliness: He hath given thee wit, discretion to know good from evil; He hath given thee prowess and hardihood; and hath given thee to work so greatly that thou hast had at all times the better where-soever thou camest. And now our Lord will suffer thee no longer, but that thou shalt know Him, whether thou wilt, or wilt not.

"And why that voice called thee bitterer than wood;—where

overmuch sin dwelleth, there can be but little sweetness, wherefore thou art likened to an old rotten tree. Now have I shown thee why thou art harder than the stone, and bitterer than wood.

"Now shall I show thee why thou art more naked and barer than the fig-tree. It befell that our Lord on Palm Sunday preached in Jerusalem, and there He found in the people all hardness, and there He found in all the town not one that would harbour Him. Then He went outside the town, and found in the midst of the way a fig-tree, which was right fair, and wellgarnished with leaves, but fruit had it none. Then our Lord cursed the tree that bore no fruit,—and by the fig-tree was betokened Jerusalem, which had leaves and no fruit. So thou, Sir Lancelot, when the Holy Grail was brought before thee, He found in thee no fruit, nor good thought, nor good will; but thou wert stained with sin."

"Verily," said Sir Lancelot, "all that you have said is true; and from henceforth I purpose by the grace of God never to be so wicked as I have been, but to follow knighthood, and do feats of arms."

Then the good man enjoined Sir Lancelot such penance as he could do, and to follow knighthood; and so he gave him his blessing, and prayed Sir Lancelot to abide with him all that day.

"I will gladly," said Sir Lancelot, "for I have neither helm, nor horse, nor sword."

"As for that," said the good man, "I will help you before to-morrow evening with a horse, and all that belongs to you."

And so Sir Lancelot repented him greatly of all his past misdoings.

The Chamber with the Shut Door

Among the Knights of the Round Table who started on the Quest of the Holy Grail, besides Sir Galahad and Sir Lancelot, the chief were these—the good Sir Percival; Sir Ector de Maris, brother of Sir Lancelot; Sir Bors de Ganis, and Sir Gawaine. Many and strange were the adventures that befell them, and marvellous were the visions they saw, but at no time did they come within sight of the Holy Grail. For except Sir Galahad and Sir Percival, no knight was accounted worthy to behold that divine vision.

But after the penitence of Sir Lancelot, and many long months of wandering, it at last happened to him nearly to achieve the great Quest. For one night being near the sea, a vision came to him in his sleep, and bade him enter into the first ship he could find. When he heard these words he started up, and saw a great clearness all round him, so he took his armour and made ready; and when he came to the shore he found a ship without sail or oar. As soon as he was within the ship he felt the greatest sweetness that ever he felt, and a joy that passed all earthly joy that he had ever known. And on this ship he stayed a month or more sustained by the grace of heaven.

One day there came riding by a knight on horseback, who dismounted when he reached the ship. Then Sir Lancelot found it was his own son, Galahad, and no tongue can tell the joy they made of each other.

They told each other all the adventures and marvels that had befallen them both in many journeys since they departed from King Arthur's Court.

Lancelot and Galahad dwelt within that ship half a year,

and served God daily and nightly with all their power. And often they arrived in islands far from folk, where nothing but wild beasts were to be found, and they achieved many adventures strange and perilous.

One day it befell that their ship arrived at the edge of a forest, and there they saw a knight armed all in white, richly horsed, and in his right hand he led a white horse. He came to the ship and saluted the two knights, and said:

"Galahad, sir, ye have been long enough with your father; come out of the ship, and start upon this horse, and go where adventures shall lead thee in the Quest of the Holy Grail."

Then Galahad went to his father, and kissed him tenderly, and said:

"Fair sweet father, I know not when I shall see you more, until I have seen the Holy Grail."

"I pray you," said Lancelot, "pray you to the high Father that He hold me in His service."

So Galahad took his horse, and there they heard a voice that said:

"Think to do well, for the one shall never again see the other till the dreadful day of doom."

"Now, son Galahad," said Lancelot, "since we shall part, and never see each other more, I pray the high Father to preserve both me and you."

"Sir," said Galahad, "no prayer prevaileth so much as yours," and therewith he rode away into the forest.

Then the wind arose, and for more than a month drove Lancelot through the sea, where he slept but little, but prayed to God that he might see some tidings of the Holy Grail.

It befell on a night, at midnight, that he arrived before a Castle, which on the back side was rich and fair. A postern opened towards the sea, and it was open without any warders, save that two lions kept the entry, and the moon shone clear.

Then Sir Lancelot heard a voice that said, "Lancelot, go out of this ship, and enter into this Castle, where thou shalt see a great part of thy desire."

So he ran and armed himself, and came to the gate, and saw the lions; and then he set hand to his sword, and drew it. But there came a dwarf suddenly, and smote him on the arm so sore that the sword fell out of his hand.

"Oh, man of evil faith and poor belief!" he heard a voice say, "wherefore dost thou trust more in thy weapons than in thy Maker? For He in whose service thou art, might more avail thee than thine armour."

Then said Lancelot, "I thank Thee, Lord Christ, for Thy great mercy, that Thou reprovest me of my misdeed. Now see I well that Thou holdest me for Thy servant."

Then he took his sword again, and put it up in his sheath, and signed his forehead with the cross, and came to the lions, and they made semblance to do him harm. Nevertheless he passed by them without hurt, and entered into the Castle to the chief fortress, where all the inmates seemed at rest. Then Lancelot, armed as he was, entered in, for he found no gate nor door but it was open. And at the last he found a chamber the door of which was shut; he set his hand to it, to open it, but he could not. He lay the whole strength of his body against it but could not so much as make it in the least yield.

Then he listened and heard a voice which sang so sweetly that it seemed no earthly thing; and he thought the voice said, "Joy and honour be to the Father of Heaven!"

Then Lancelot knelt down before the chamber door, for he well knew that the Holy Grail was within that chamber, and he prayed to God that if ever he had done anything pleasing in His sight, that He would have pity on him, and show him something of what he sought.

With that, he saw the chamber door open, and there came out a great clearness, so that the house was as bright as if all the torches of the world had been there. Lancelot went to the door and would have entered, but immediately a voice said:

"Flee, Lancelot, and enter not, for thou oughtest not to do so; and if thou enter, thou shalt repent it."

So Lancelot withdrew himself back, right heavy.

Then he looked up into the midst of the chamber, and he saw a table of silver, and the holy vessel covered with red samite, and many angels about it, one of whom held a candle of wax burning. Before the holy vessel he saw a good man clothed as a priest, and it was as if a solemn service were being held. Three men stood near, and it seemed to Lancelot that the priest lifted up the youngest of them, as if to show him to the people. Lancelot marvelled not a little, for he thought that the priest be so burdened with the figure that he would fall to the ground. When he saw no one near would help the priest, Lancelot ran quickly to the door.

"Lord Christ," he said, "take it for no sin, though I help the good man, for he hath great need of help."

Right so he entered into the chamber, and went towards the table of silver; and when he came nigh, he felt a breath of air as if it were mixed with fire, and it smote him so sore in the face that it seemed to burn him, and therewith he fell to the earth, and had no power to rise. Then he felt about him many hands, which took him up, and bore him out of the chamber, and left him seemingly dead. And on the morrow he was found by the people of the Castle outside the chamber door.

Four-and-twenty days Sir Lancelot lay as if dead, but on the twenty-fifth day he opened his eyes. Then they told him that the Castle belonged to King Pelles, where long ago he had seen the vision of the Holy Grail for the first time. All the people marvelled when they found that this stranger was Lancelot, the good knight, and they sent word to King Pelles, who was right glad to hear the news, and went to see him, and made great joy of him. And there the king told Lancelot that his fair daughter Elaine, the mother of Galahad, was dead; and Lancelot was passing grieved to hear the tidings.

Four days Sir Lancelot stayed at the Castle, and then he took leave of King Pelles. He knew now that his Quest was ended, for that he would never see more of the Holy Grail than he had seen. So he said he would go back to the realm of Logris, which he had not seen for over a twelvemonth.

When he came to Camelot he found that some of the Knights of the Round Table had returned home, but that many of them —more than half—had been slain and destroyed.

King Arthur, Queen Guinevere, and all the Court, were passing glad to see Sir Lancelot again, and the King asked him many tidings of his son Galahad. Lancelot told the King all the adventures that had befallen him since he departed, and he also told him whatever he knew of the adventures of Galahad, Percival, and Bors.

"Now would to God," said the King, "that they were all here!"

"That shall never be," said Lancelot, "for two of them shall ye never more see. But one of them shall come again."

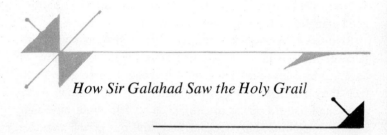

How Sir Galahad Saw the Holy Grail

After leaving Sir Lancelot, Galahad rode many journeys in vain. Wherever he went, strange signs and marvels followed, but not yet did he behold the vision of the Holy Grail.

It befell on a day that as he rode out of a great forest he was overtaken by Sir Percival, who had followed him for five days, and just afterwards at a cross-road they met Sir Bors. They told each other their adventures, and all rode on together.

Thus they travelled a great while, till they came to the same Castle of King Pelles where Sir Lancelot had already been, and directly they entered within the Castle King Pelles knew them. Then there was great joy, for all the people knew well by their coming that they had fulfilled the Quest of the Holy Grail.

A little before evening when they were gathered in the hall, a voice was heard among them, and it said, "They that ought not to sit at the table of Jesus Christ arise, for now shall true knights be fed." So every one went away save King Pelles and Eliazar his son, who were holy men, and a maid who was his niece; these three and the three knights were left, no more.

Soon they saw nine knights, all armed, come in at the hall door, and take off their helms and their armour.

"Sir," they said to Galahad, "we have hied right much to be with you at this table, where the holy meat shall be parted."

Then said he, "Ye be welcome, but from whence come ye?"

Three said they were from Gaul, and three said they were from Ireland, and the other three said they were from Denmark.

Then a voice said, "There are two among you who are not in the Quest of the Holy Grail; therefore let them depart." So King Pelles and his son departed.

The knights who remained now saw the table of silver, whereon was the Holy Grail, and it seemed to them that angels stood about it, and that a solemn service was being held. They set themselves at the table in great dread, and began to pray. Then came One, as it seemed to them, in the likeness of the Lord Christ, and He said:

"My knights, and my servants, and my true children, which are come out of deadly life into spiritual life, I will no longer hide Me from you, but ye shall see now a part of My secrets, and My hid things; now hold and receive the high meat which ye have so much desired." Then He Himself took the holy vessel, and came to Galahad, who knelt down and received the sacred food, and after him, in like manner, all his companions received it; and they thought it so sweet it was marvellous to tell.

Then said He to Galahad, "Son, knowest thou what I hold between My hands?"

"Nay," said he, "unless Thou wilt tell me."

"This is," said He, "the holy dish wherein I ate the lamb at the Last Supper. And now hast thou seen that which thou most desired to see, but yet hast not seen it so openly as thou shalt see it in the city of Sarras, in the spiritual place. Therefore thou must go hence and bear with thee this holy vessel, for this night it shall depart from the realm of Logris, and shall never more be seen here. And wouldst thou know wherefore? Because these of this land are turned to evil living, therefore, I shall disinherit them of the honour which I have done them. Therefore, go ye three to-morrow to the sea, where ye shall find your ship ready —you and Sir Percival, and Sir Bors, and no more with you. And two of you shall die in My service, but one of you shall go back again to Camelot, and bear the tidings."

Then He blessed them and vanished from their sight.

So Galahad, Percival, and Bors let the Castle of King Pelles. After riding three days they came to the sea-shore where they found the same ship in which Galahad had stayed with Lancelot; and when they went on board they saw in the midst the table of silver, and the Holy Grail, which was covered with red samite. Then were they glad to have such things in their fellowship.

So they sailed away, till they came to the city of Sarras, where they landed, taking with them the table of silver. As they went in at the gate of the city, they saw sitting there a crooked old man, and Galahad called to him, and bade him help them carry the heavy table.

"Truly," said the old man, "for ten years I have not walked, except with crutches."

"Never mind," said Galahad, "rise up, and show thy good will."

The old man tried to rise, and immediately found himself as whole as ever he had been. Then he ran to the table, and took the side opposite Galahad.

The fame of this cure went through the city, and when the king of the city saw the three knights, he asked them whence they came, and what thing it was they had brought upon the table of silver. They told him the truth of the Holy Grail, and the power God had placed in it to cure sick people.

The king, however, was a tyrant, and came of a line of pagans, and he took the three knights, and put them into prison, in a deep dungeon. But all the time they were in prison they were supported by the holy grace of heaven.

At a year's end it came to pass that the king lay sick, and felt that he should die. Then he sent for the three knights, and when they came before him he begged mercy of them for all that he had done to them, and they willingly forgave him, and so he died.

When the king was dead all the city was dismayed, and knew not who could be their king. Right so, as they were in council, came a voice among them, and bade them choose the youngest knight of the three to be their king. So they made Galahad king, with the assent of the whole city.

When he had surveyed the country, Galahad caused to be built round the table of silver a chest of gold and of precious stones, which covered the holy vessel, and every morning early the three knights would come before it and say their prayers.

Now at the year's end, on the very day that Galahad was given the crown of gold, he arose up early, he and his companions, and came to the palace, to the holy vessel. There they saw before them a man kneeling in the likeness of a bishop; and round about him was a great fellowship of angels.

"Come forth, Galahad, servant of Jesus Christ," he said, "and thou shalt see that which thou hast long desired to see."

Then Galahad began to tremble, for a vision of spiritual things rose before his earthly eyes; and holding up his hands to heaven, he said:

"Lord, I thank Thee, for now I see that which hath been my desire many a day. Now, blessed Lord, I would not longer live, if it might please Thee, Lord."

Then the good man took the holy food, and proffered it to Galahad, and he received it right gladly and meekly.

When this was done, Galahad went to Sir Percival and Sir Bors, and kissed them, and commended them to God. And to Sir Bors he said, "Fair lord, salute me to my lord, Sir Lancelot, my father, and as soon as ye see him, bid him be mindful of this unstable world."

Afterwards he knelt down before the table, and said his prayers, and suddenly his soul departed to Jesus Christ.

Then it seemed to the two knights that there came a hand from heaven, and bore away the holy vessel. And since that time there was never any man so bold as to say he had seen the Holy Grail.

When Percival and Bors saw Galahad dead they made as much sorrow as ever did two men, and if they had not been good men they might easily have fallen into despair. And the people of the city and the country were right heavy. As soon as Galahad was buried Sir Percival retired to a hermitage, and here for a year and two months he lived a full holy life, and then he passed away.

Sir Bors stayed always with Sir Percival as long as he lived, but when he was dead Sir Bors took ship and went back to the realm of Logris, and so came to Camelot, where King Arthur was. Great joy was made of him in the Court, for they all thought he must be dead, because he had been so long out of the country. Sir Bors told them all the adventures of the Holy Grail, and to Sir Lancelot he gave Galahad's message.

"Sir Lancelot," he said, "Galahad prayeth you to be mindful of this uncertain world, as ye promised him when ye were together more than half a year."

"That is true," said Lancelot. "Now I trust to God his prayer shall avail me."

THE DEATH OF ARTHUR

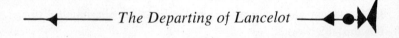

The Departing of Lancelot

After the Quest of the Holy Grail had been fulfilled, and all the knights that were left living were come again to the Round Table, then there was great joy at Court, and in especial King Arthur and Queen Guinevere rejoiced, and were passing glad because of Sir Lancelot and Sir Bors. And for a time all went well, and there was much feasting and gaiety.

But Sir Lancelot forgot his promise to the good hermit to see as little as possible of Queen Guinevere, and because he was held in such high favour by the King and Queen and all the people, some of the other knights were jealous of him, and tried to do him all the mischief they could.

Among the knights at King Arthur's Court, the most spiteful

and malicious was Sir Mordred. He was the youngest son of King Arthur's sister, the wife of King Lot of Orkney, and it was to him that Merlin referred when he prophesied that a child born on May-Day should bring destruction to King Arthur. He was half-brother to the noble knights Gawaine, Gaheris, and Gareth, but nothing at all like them in disposition. The only brother who in the least resembled him was Sir Agrivaine, and it was owing to the evil-speaking of these two malicious knights that the storm of anger and misfortune arose, which never ceased till the flower of chivalry of all the world was destroyed and slain.

In the pleasant month of May, when every noble heart glows with life—when earth is looking her sweetest and brightest, and all men and women rejoice and are glad because summer is coming with freshest flowers—in the beautiful month of May, these two knights, Agrivaine and Mordred, set their mischief on foot. In open assembly before many knights they told slanderous tales of Sir Lancelot and Queen Guinevere, and suggested that these should be repeated to the King. Then spoke Sir Gawaine:

"Brother Sir Agrivaine," he said, "I pray you and charge you, speak no more of such things before me, for wit ye well, I will not be of your counsel."

"Truly," said Sir Gaheris and Sir Gareth, "we will have nothing to do with your deeds."

"Then I will," said Mordred.

"I well believe that," said Sir Gawaine, "for always, if there is any mischief you will be sharer in it, brother Sir Mordred: I wish you would leave this, and not make yourself such a busy-body, for I know what will come of it."

"Come of it what come may," said Sir Agrivaine, "I shall speak to the King."

"Not by my counsel," said Sir Gawaine, "for if there arise war and wreck between Sir Lancelot and us, wit you well, brother, many kings and great lords will hold with Sir Lancelot. And for my part I will never be against Sir Lancelot, when he rescued me from King Carados of the Dolorous Tower, and slew him, and saved my life. Also, brothers Agrivaine and Mordred, in like wise Sir Lancelot rescued you both, and threescore knights, from Sir Turquine. Such good deeds and kindness should be remembered."

"Do as you like," said Sir Agrivaine, "I will hide it no longer."

At that moment King Arthur came near.

"Now, brother, stay your noise," said Gawaine.

"We will not," said Agrivaine and Mordred.

"Will you not?" said Gawaine; "then God speed you, for I will not hear your tales, nor be of your counsel."

"No more will we," said Sir Gareth and Sir Gaheris, "for we will never speak evil of that man."

And accordingly these three knights left the assembly.

"Alas," said Gawaine and Gareth, "now is this realm wholly put in mischief, and the noble fellowship of the Round Table is dispersed."

So, very sorrowfully, they went their way.

King Arthur coming up at that moment asked what the noise was about, whereupon Agrivaine and Mordred were only too ready to repeat their spiteful slander. As the King would scarcely believe what they said, they laid a plot to entrap Sir Lancelot. In escaping from this ambush, Sir Lancelot slew Sir Agrivaine and twelve of his companions. Sir Mordred managed to escape, and riding all wounded and bleeding to the King, told him his own version of the story.

"Alas!" said King Arthur, "I sorely repent that ever Sir Lancelot should be against me. Now I am sure the noble fellowship of the Round Table is broken for ever, for with him will hold many a noble knight."

It all fell out as the King and Sir Gawaine had foreseen. From that day there was constant fighting in England, some knights taking part with Sir Lancelot and some with the King, and on both sides many gallant lives were lost. Through sad mischance, the noble knights Sir Gaheris and Sir Gareth, who were unarmed at the time, were accidentally slain by Lancelot's party, after which Sir Gawaine, who had hitherto refused to fight against him, became his most bitter enemy. Many a time the King and Sir Lancelot would have made peace, but it was always Sir Gawaine who urged the King on to fresh fighting, and persuaded him not to listen to any attempts at conciliation, although Sir Lancelot made the most noble offers of penitence, and expressed the deepest sorrow for the unintentional slaying of Gaheris and Gareth.

At last the Pope sent a command that the fighting should cease, and a stately meeting between the King and Sir Lancelot took place at Carlisle. Here Sir Lancelot spoke such noble words that all the knights and ladies who were present wept to hear him and the tears fell down King Arthur's cheeks. But the King, to gratify Gawaine's revenge for the loss of his brothers, had already promised that Lancelot should be banished, and now instead of accepting his offer of penitence and good will, he allowed Sir Gawaine to declare to Sir Lancelot his doom of exile, that he was forbidden to abide in England more than fifteen days.

Then Sir Lancelot sighed, and the tears fell down his cheeks.

"Alas, most noble Christian realm," he said, "whom I have loved above all other realms, in thee have I gotten a great part of my honour, and now I shall depart in this wise! Truly I repent that ever I came into this realm, that am thus shamefully banished, undeserved and without cause! But fortune is so variant, and the wheel so movable, there is no constant abiding, and that may be proved by many old chronicles, of noble Hector, and Troilus, and Alexander the mighty conqueror, and many others more. When they were highest in their royalty they alighted lowest, and so it fareth with me," said Sir Lancelot, "for in this realm I had honour, and by me and the knights of my blood the whole Round Table increased more in renown than by any other."

Then Sir Lancelot bade good-bye to Queen Guinevere in hearing of the King and them all.

"Madam," he said, "now I must depart from you and this noble fellowship for ever, and since it is so, I beseech you to pray for me, and say me well. And if you be hard bested by any false tongues, my lady, have word sent to me, and if any knight's hands can deliver you by battle, I shall deliver you."

And therewith Sir Lancelot kissed the Queen, and then he said: "Now let us see any one in this place that dare say the

Queen is not true to my lord Arthur! Let us see who will dare speak!"

With that he brought the Queen to the King, and then Sir Lancelot took his leave and departed. And there was neither king, duke nor earl, baron or knight, lady or gentlewoman, but all of them wept, as people out of their minds, except Sir Gawaine. And when the noble Sir Lancelot took his horse to ride out of Carlisle, there was sobbing and weeping for pure sorrow at his departing. So he took his way to his Castle of Joyous Gard, and ever after that he called it Dolorous Gard.

And thus departed Sir Lancelot from the Court of King Arthur for ever.

When Sir Lancelot came to Joyous Gard he called his company of knights together, and asked them what they would do. They answered with one voice that they would do as he did.

"My fair fellows," said Sir Lancelot, "I must depart out of this most noble realm, and now I shall depart it grieveth me sore, for I shall depart with no honour. For a banished man never departed out of any realm with any honour, and that is my cause of grief, for ever I fear after many days they will chronicle of me that. I was banished out of this land."

Then spoke many noble knights, and said:

"Sir, if you are so disposed to abide in this country we will never fail you, and if you do not choose to abide in this land, not one of the good knights here will fail you. Since it pleased us to take part with your distress and heaviness in this realm, wit you well, it shall equally please us to go into other countries with you, and there to take such part as you do."

"My fair lords," said Lancelot, "I well understand you, and as I can, thank you. And you shall understand that such livelihood as I am born to, I will give up to you, in this manner— namely, I will share all my livelihood and all my lands freely among you, and I myself will have as little as any of you; and I trust to God to maintain you as well as ever were maintained any knights."

Then spoke all the knights at once:

"Shame on him that will leave you! For we all understand

that in this realm will now be no quiet, but always strife and debate, now the fellowship of the Round Table is broken. For by the noble fellowship of the Round Table was King Arthur upborne, and by their nobleness the King and all his realm were in quiet and in rest. And a great part, every one said, was because of your nobleness."

"Truly," said Sir Lancelot, "I thank you all for your good words, though I know well all the stability of this realm was not due to me. But as far as I could I did my duty, and some rebellions in my days were appeased by me. And I trow we shall soon hear of them again and that is what grieves me sorely. For ever I dread me that Sir Mordred will make trouble, for he is passing envious, and applies himself to mischief."

So all the knights were agreed to go with Sir Lancelot, and quite a hundred departed with him, and made their vows they would never leave him, for weal nor woe.

So they shipped at Cardiff, and sailed to Bayonne, in France, where Sir Lancelot was lord of many lands.

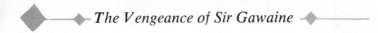 *The Vengeance of Sir Gawaine*

Not content with having banished Sir Lancelot, King Arthur and Sir Gawaine made a great host ready, and prepared to follow him, taking ship at Cardiff. During his absence King Arthur appointed his nephew Sir Mordred to be chief ruler of all England, and put Queen Guinevere under his charge. So he passed over the sea and landed on Sir Lancelot's lands, and there, through the vengeance of Sir Gawaine, he burnt and wasted all that they could over-run.

When word was brought to Sir Lancelot that King Arthur and Sir Gawaine were landed and destroying all his possessions, his knights urged him to go forth to battle, but he replied that he was full loath to ride out to shed Christian blood, so first he would send a message to King Arthur, to see if a treaty could be made, for peace was always better than war. So Lancelot sent forth a damsel to King Arthur, demanding that he should cease warring against his lands.

The damsel started on her palfrey, and when she came to the pavilion of King Arthur she alighted; and there met her a gentle knight, Sir Lucan the butler.

"Fair damsel, do you come from Sir Lancelot of the Lake?"

"Yea, sir," she said, "I come hither to speak with my lord the King."

"Alas," said Sir Lucan, "my lord would love Lancelot, but Sir Gawaine will not let him." And then he added, "I pray to God, damsel, ye may speed well, for all we that are about the King would that Sir Lancelot did best of any knight living."

With this, Lucan led the damsel to King Arthur, where he sat with Sir Gawaine, to hear what she would say. When she had told her tale, tears filled the King's eyes, and all the lords were full glad to advise the King to be reconciled with Sir Lancelot, save only Sir Gawaine.

"My lord, my uncle, what will you do?" he said. "Will you turn back again, now that you have come thus far on this journey? All the world will speak scorn of you."

"Nay," said King Arthur, "you know well, Sir Gawaine, I will do as you advise me; and yet it seems to me it were not good to refuse his fair proffers. But since I am come so far upon this journey, I will that you give the damsel her answer, for I cannot speak to her for pity, her proffers are so generous."

Then Sir Gawaine said to the damsel thus:

"Damsel, say you to Sir Lancelot, that it is waste labour now to sue to my uncle. For tell him if he would have made any attempt at peace, he should have made it before this time, for tell him now it is too late. And say that I, Sir Gawaine, so send him word that I promise him by the faith I owe to God and to knighthood, I shall never leave Sir Lancelot till he have slain me, or I him."

So the damsel wept and departed, and there were many weeping eyes. She came back to Sir Lancelot, where he was among all his knights, and when Sir Lancelot heard this answer, then the tears ran down his cheeks.

Then his noble knights strode about him, and said, "Sir Lancelot, wherefore make you such cheer? Think what you are, and what men we are, and let us noble men match them in midst of the field."

"That may easily be done," said Lancelot, "but I was never so loath to do battle, for I will always avoid that noble King who made me knight. When I can keep quiet no longer, I must needs defend myself, and that will be more honour for me, and for us all, than to strive with that noble King whom we have all served."

Then they spoke no more, and as it was night, went to rest.

On the morrow early, in the dawning of the day, as the knights looked out, they saw the city of Bayonne besieged round about, and ladders were fast being set up. Then from the town they defied King Arthur's host, and beat them from the walls mightily. So the siege went on for six months, and there was much slaughter of people on both sides. Then it befell on a day that Sir Gawaine came before the gates, armed at all points, on a noble horse, with a great spear in his hand.

"Where art thou now, thou false traitor, Sir Lancelot?" he cried with a loud voice. "Why hidest thou thyself within holes and walls, like a coward? Look out, now, thou false traitor knight, and here I shall revenge upon thy body the death of my two brethren."

Every word of this was heard by Sir Lancelot, and all his knights, and now there was nothing to be done but for Sir Lancelot to defend himself, or else to be recreant for ever. Sir Lancelot bade saddle his strongest horse, and fetch his arms, and bring them all to the gate of the tower, and then he spoke aloud to King Arthur:

"My lord Arthur, and noble King who made me knight, wit you well I am right heavy for your sake that you pursue me thus, and always I forbear you, for if I had been revengeful, I might have met you in open field, there to have made your boldest knights full tame. Now I have forborne half a year, and suffered you and Sir Gawaine to do what you would do, and now I can endure it no longer. Now I must needs defend myself, inasmuch as Sir Gawaine hath accused me of treason. It is greatly against my will that ever I should fight against any of your blood. But now I cannot resist it, I am driven to it, as a beast to bay."

"Sir Lancelot," cried Gawaine, "if thou darest do battle, leave thy babbling, and come away, and let us ease our hearts."

King Arthur's host outside the city stood still, all apart, and Lancelot's noble knights came out in a great number, insomuch that when King Arthur saw the multitude of men and knights he marvelled, and said to himself:

"Alas, that ever Sir Lancelot was against me, for now I see he hath borne with me!"

So the covenant was made that no man should go near Lancelot and Gawaine, or have anything to do with them, till the one was dead or yielden.

Now, years ago, a holy man had given a strange gift and favour to Sir Gawaine, which no one knew of except King Arthur. Every day in the year, from nine o'clock in the morning till high noon, his might increased three times its usual strength. The King appointed most trials of arms to take place at this time of day, which caused Sir Gawaine to win great honour.

Thus Sir Lancelot fought with Sir Gawaine, and when he felt his strength evermore increase, Lancelot wondered, and sorely dreaded to be shamed. But when it was past noon Sir Gawaine had nothing but his own strength to rely on, and then Lancelot felt him grow weaker. Then he doubled his strokes, and gave Sir Gawaine such a buffet on the helm that he fell down on his side, and Sir Lancelot withdrew himself from him.

"Why withdrawest thou?" said Sir Gawaine. "Now turn again, false traitor knight, and slay me. For if thou leave me thus, when I am whole I shall do battle with thee again."

"I shall endure you, sir, by God's grace," replied Sir Lancelot, "but wit you well, Sir Gawaine, I will never smite a felled knight."

So Sir Lancelot went back into the city, and Sir Gawaine was borne into one of King Arthur's pavilions, where doctors came to him and dressed his wounds.

Then King Arthur fell sick for sorrow because Sir Gawaine was so sorely hurt, and because of the war betwixt him and Sir Lancelot. Those of King Arthur's party kept the siege with little fighting outside, and those within guarded their walls and defended them when need was.

Sir Gawaine lay sick in his tent for about three weeks, and as soon as he could ride he once more came before the chief gate of Bayonne, and challenged Lancelot to fight. And once more Lancelot wounded him sorely and smote him down.

"Traitor knight," cried Sir Gawaine, "wit thou well, I am not yet slain; come thou near me, and perform this battle to the uttermost."

"I will do no more than I have done," said Sir Lancelot; "for when I see you on foot, I will do battle against you all the while I see you stand on your feet; but to smite a wounded man that cannot stand, God defend me from such a shame!" And then he turned, and went his way towards the city.

"Sir Lancelot, when I am whole, I shall do battle with thee again," Sir Gawaine called out after him, "for I shall never leave thee till one of us be slain."

So the siege went on, and Sir Gawaine lay sick nearly a month. And when he was well recovered and ready within three days to do battle again with Sir Lancelot, tidings came to King Arthur from England, which made the King and all his host remove.

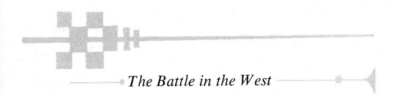

The Battle in the West

While King Arthur was away in France, Mordred, who had been appointed ruler of England, was busy about his own wicked. plots. He now forged letters, as though they came from beyond the sea, and the letters specified that King Arthur had been slain in battle with Sir Lancelot. Mordred thereupon summoned a

Parliament, and calling the lords together, he made them choose him King; so he was crowned at Canterbury, and held a feast there fifteen days. Afterwards he withdrew to Camelot, and sent for Queen Guinevere, and told her plainly that he wished to marry her. Everything was made ready for the feast, and the day for the wedding was fixed.

Queen Guinevere was in great distress, but she did not dare oppose Sir Mordred openly, and therefore she pretended to agree. Then she asked leave to go to London, to buy all manner of things necessary for the wedding. Because of her fair words Sir Mordred trusted her well enough and gave her leave to go.

Directly she reached London, Queen Guinevere at once seized the Tower, and in all haste possible stuffed it with all manner of victuals, and well garrisoned it with men, and so kept it.

When Mordred found he had been out-witted he was wroth beyond measure. He went and laid a mighty siege to the Tower of London, and assaulted it with great engines and guns, but he could not prevail. He tried in all ways, by letters and messages, to make Queen Guinevere come out of the Tower, but it availed nothing; neither for fair words nor foul would the Queen trust herself again in the traitor's hands. She answered shortly that she would rather slay herself than marry him.

Then word came to Mordred that King Arthur had raised the siege on Sir Lancelot, and was coming homeward with a great host to be avenged on his nephew. Mordred accordingly sent writs to all the barony of England, and numbers of people flocked to him. For it was a common report among them that with Arthur was no other life but war and strife, and with Mordred was great joy and bliss. Thus was King Arthur maligned, and evil spoken of. Many whom King Arthur had raised up from nothing, and given lands to, could not now say of him a good word.

So Sir Mordred marched with a large host to Dover, and there came King Arthur with a great navy of ships and galleys, while Mordred waited ready to prevent his landing. Then there was launching of big boats and small, full of noble men of arms, and there was much slaughter of gentle knights, and many a bold baron on both sides was laid low. But King Arthur was so courageous, no manner of men could prevent his landing, and his knights fiercely followed him. They drove Mordred back, and he fled, and all his army.

After the battle was over, King Arthur buried his people that were slain, and then the knight Sir Gawaine was found in a boat, more than half-dead. He had been hurt on the wound which Lancelot had given him at Bayonne, and now he must die.

"Alas, Sir Gawaine," said the King, "here now thou liest, the man in the world whom I loved the most! In Sir Lancelot and thee I had most joy, and now have I lost you both."

"Mine uncle, King Arthur," said Gawaine, "wit you well, my death day is come, and all is through my own hastiness and wilfulness. Had Sir Lancelot been with you as he used to be, this unhappy war had never begun, and of all this am I the cause. For Sir Lancelot and his kindred through their prowess held all your enemies in subjection and danger, and now ye shall miss Sir Lancelot. But alas, I would not agree with him and therefore I pray you let me have paper, pen, and ink, that I may write to Sir Lancelot a letter with my own hand."

Then Sir Gawaine wrote a letter to Sir Lancelot, "flower of all noble knights," telling him all that had happened, and how he had brought his death on himself, because he was hurt on the same wound that Lancelot had given him at Bayonne.

"Also, Sir Lancelot," he went on, "for all the love that ever was betwixt us, make no tarrying, but come over the sea in all haste, that thou mayst with thy gallant knights rescue the noble King who made thee knight, that is my lord Arthur, for he is full straitly bested with a false traitor, my half-brother, Sir Mordred."

Then Gawaine bade King Arthur send for Lancelot, and cherish him above other knights; and so he yielded up the spirit.

After this, King Arthur fought again with Sir Mordred, and drove him westward across England, towards Salisbury, where a day was appointed for the King to meet Sir Mordred in a battle on a down near Salisbury, not far from the sea.

The night before the battle King Arthur dreamed a wonderful dream. It seemed to him he sat on a platform, in a chair, clad in the richest cloth of gold that could be made; and the chair was fast to a wheel. And the King thought that under him, far from him, was a hideous deep black water, and therein were all manner of serpents, and worms, and wild beasts, foul and horrible. And suddenly, the King thought, the wheel turned upside down, and he fell among the serpents, and every beast seized him by a limb.

Then the King cried as he lay in his bed—"Help!" And Knights, squires, and yeomen ran to the King and wakened him, and he was so amazed he did not know where he was.

Then he fell slumbering again, not sleeping, nor thoroughly wakening. And it seemed to him that Sir Gawaine came to him, and warned him not to fight with Sir Mordred on the morrow, for if he did so he would certainly die. Sir Gawaine counselled him to make a treaty for a month, for within that time Sir Lancelot would come, with all his noble knights, and would rescue King Arthur, and slay Sir Mordred. Then Sir Gawaine vanished.

Directly King Arthur awoke he sent for all his wise lords and bishops, and told them his vision, and of Sir Gawaine's warning. They went at once to Sir Mordred, and made a treaty, promising him that while King Arthur lived he should have Cornwall and Kent, and after the King's death, the whole of England. It was further agreed that a meeting between King Arthur and Mordred should take place betwixt the two armies, and each of them should take fourteen persons.

King Arthur, on starting for this meeting, warned all his army that if they saw any sword drawn they were to come on fiercely, and slay the traitor Mordred, for he in no wise trusted him. And in like manner Sir Mordred also warned his host.

So they met, as had been appointed, and they were agreed. Wine was fetched, and they drank.

Just at that moment came an adder out of a little heath-bush, and it stung a knight on the foot. When the knight felt himself stung, he looked down, and saw the adder. Then he drew his sword to slay the adder, and thought of no other harm.

When the host on both sides saw that sword drawn, they blew bugles, and trumpets and horns, and shouted grimly. Both the armies rushed to arms, and never was seen a more doleful battle.

All that day long they fought without ceasing, and when night came, of all King Arthur's noble knights there were none left alive but Sir Lucan the butler, and his brother Sir Bedivere, and both were sorely wounded. Then was King Arthur wroth out of measure when he saw his people so slain from him.

"Alas, that ever I should see this doleful day! For now I am come to my end," said Arthur. "But would to God I knew where that traitor Sir Mordred is, who hath caused all this mischief."

Then was King Arthur aware where Sir Mordred leaned on his sword among a great heap of dead men. Sir Lucan tried to persuade Arthur not to fight, reminding him of Gawaine's warning.

"Blessed be God, ye have won the field," he said; "for here we are three alive, and with Sir Mordred there are none living. And if you leave off now, this wicked day of destiny is past."

"Tide me death, betide me life," said the King, "now I see him yonder alone, he shall never escape my hands, for at a better advantage I shall never have him."

"God speed you well!" said Sir Bedivere.

Then King Arthur took his spear in both hands, and ran towards Mordred, crying: "Traitor, now is thy death day come!"

When Sir Mordred heard King Arthur he ran at him with his sword drawn. Then King Arthur thrust Mordred through the body with his spear, so that he fell dead; but Mordred's sword pierced the helmet and brain-pan of King Arthur, so that he fell in a swoon to the earth.

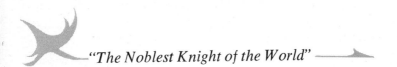

"The Noblest Knight of the World"

Sir Lucan and Sir Bedivere lifted up King Arthur and carried him to a little chapel not far from the sea-shore, but Sir Lucan was so grievously wounded that he fell dead before they could go to a further place of safety. Sir Bedivere wept for the death of his brother, but the King bade him stay his mourning, for his own life was hurrying fast away.

"Therefore," said Arthur, "take thou Excalibur, my good sword, and go with it to yonder water-side; and when thou gettest there I charge thee throw my sword in that water, and come again, and tell me what thou there seest."

"My lord," said Bedivere, "your commandment shall be done, and I will quickly bring you word again."

So Bedivere departed, and by the way he beheld that noble sword, how that the pommel and the hilt were all of precious stones. Then he said to himself, "If I throw this rich sword in the water, good will never come of it, but harm and loss."

So Sir Bedivere hid Excalibur under a tree, and went back to the King quickly, and said he had thrown in the sword.

"What saw thou there?" said the King.

"Sir," he said, "I saw nothing but waves and winds."

"That is untruly said," spoke the King. "Therefore go thou quickly again, and do my command as thou art lief and dear to me; spare not, but throw it in."

Then Bedivere went back and took the sword in his hand; and then it seemed a sin and shame to throw away that noble sword; so again he hid the sword, and returned to Arthur, and told him he had done his command.

"What saw thou there?" said the King.

"Sir," he said, "I saw nothing but the ripple of water, and the lapping of the waves."

"Ah, traitor, untrue!" cried King Arthur, "now hast thou betrayed me twice. Who would have thought that thou who hast been to me so lief and dear, and thou who art named a noble knight, would betray me for the riches of the sword! But now go again quickly, for thy long tarrying putteth me in great jeopardy of my life."

Then Sir Bedivere departed, and fetched the sword, and taking it to the water-side, he bound the girdle about the hilt, and threw the sword as far into the water as he could. There came an arm and a hand above the water, and met it, and caught it, and so shook it thrice and brandished it, and then the hand with the sword vanished away in the water. So Sir Bedivere came again to the King, and told him what he had seen.

"Alas," said the King, "help me hence, for I dread me I have tarried over long."

Then Sir Bedivere took the King upon his back, and so carried him to the water-side. And when they reached it, a barge drifted in quite close to the bank, with many fair ladies in it; they had all black hoods, and they wept and cried.

"Now put me into the barge," said the King, and Sir Bedivere did so, softly.

And there received him three Queens, with great mourning, and so they set him down, and King Arthur laid his head in the lap of one of the Queens.

"Ah, dear brother," she said, "why have ye tarried so long?"

Thus, they rowed from the land, and Sir Bedivere beheld them.

"Ah, my lord Arthur," he cried, "what shall become of me now ye go from me, and leave me here alone among my enemies?"

"Comfort thyself," said the King, "and do as well as thou canst, for in me is no trust to trust in. For I go to the vale of Avalon, to heal me of my grievous wound. And if thou hear never more of me, pray for my soul."

Thus King Arthur was borne away in the barge with the three Queens. The one was King Arthur's sister, Morgan le Fay, another was the Queen of North Wales, the third was the Queen of the Waste Lands. Also in the barge was Nimue, the chief Lady of the Lake, and this lady had done much for King Arthur.

And some people say that King Arthur died, and that the three Queens took his body to a little hermitage near Glastonbury, where it was buried in a chapel. But many men think that King Arthur never died at all, but dwells now in some beautiful valley of rest, and that one day he will come again to rule over England. For on his tomb this verse is written:

"Here lies Arthur,
King that was, and King that shall be."

When news came to Queen Guinevere that King Arthur was slain, and all the noble knights, and Sir Mordred, she stole away with five ladies to Amesbury. There she took refuge in a convent, and spent the rest of her days in fasting, prayers, and alms-deeds.

In the meanwhile, Sir Lancelot had received Sir Gawaine's letter, and with all the haste he could hurried back to England with his company of noble knights. But when they arrived they found they were too late, King Arthur and Sir Mordred were both slain. Sir Lancelot thereupon rode in search of Queen Guinevere, and at last he found her in the nunnery at Amesbury. The Queen told him that she intended never to come out again into the world, and when Lancelot heard this, he determined also to retire to a hermitage.

Taking his horse he rode away into a great forest, and so it chanced he came to the little chapel near Glastonbury, where the body of King Arthur had been buried. Sir Bedivere was still there, and Sir Lancelot asked the good Bishop who was hermit, if he might remain. Here Sir Bors followed him, and others of his noble knights, who when they found Sir Lancelot had betaken himself to such holiness, had no desire to depart. Thus for six years they lived a life of penance, paying no regard to worldly riches, and caring nothing what pain they endured, when they saw the noblest knight of the world suffer such hardship.

Sir Lancelot had lived in the hermitage about seven years when one night a vision came to him, bidding him hasten to Amesbury, for there he would find Queen Guinevere dead. And Lancelot was told to take a horse-bier, and go with his fellow-knights to fetch the body of Queen Guinevere, and bury her by her husband, the noble King Arthur.

So all was done as the vision commanded, and Queen Guinevere was brought from Amesbury to Glastonbury with much sorrow and splendour. A hundred torches were kept burning round the bier, and Lancelot and seven of his knights walked always round it, singing, and saying holy prayers, and strewing frankincense. Thus they came from Amesbury to Glastonbury, and on the morrow Queen Guinevere was buried in the little chapel, in the tomb of King Arthur.

When the coffin was put into the earth Sir Lancelot swooned, and lay for a long time still, till the good Bishop, who was hermit came out and awaked him.

"Ye be to blame," he said, "for ye displease God with such manner of sorrow making."

"Truly," said Sir Lancelot, "I trust I do not displease God, for he knoweth my intent. My sorrow was not, and is not, from any sinful cause, but my sorrow can never have an end. For when I remember the beauty of the Queen, and the nobleness that was with her and the King—and when I saw them thus lie here together dead—truly my heart would not serve to sustain me. Also, when I remember me, how by my fault, my arrogance and my pride, they were both laid full low, who were peerless of any Christian people, wit you well," said Sir Lancelot, "this remembrance of their kindness and my unkindness sank so to my heart, that I could not sustain myself."

After this, Sir Lancelot fell ill, eating and drinking little, and gradually pining away, for there was nothing any one could do to comfort him. Evermore, day and night he prayed, but sometimes he slumbered a broken sleep, and often he was found lying on the tomb of King Arthur and Queen Guinevere. At last he grew so weak that he could no longer rise from bed, and then he sent for the good Bishop and all his faithful companions, and begged that he might receive the last sacred rites of religion. When all had been done in due order, he prayed the Bishop that when he was dead his comrades might bear his body to his own Castle of Joyous Gard, for there he had sworn a vow he would be buried.

Then there was weeping and wringing of hands among his fellow knights.

That night, while all lay asleep, the good Bishop had a beautiful dream. He thought he saw Sir Lancelot surrounded with a great throng of angels, and they carried him up to heaven, and the gates of heaven were opened, and they entered within.

"It is but a dream," said Sir Bors. "I doubt not nothing but good aileth Sir Lancelot."

"That may well be," said the Bishop. "But go ye to his bed, and then we shall prove the truth."

When Sir Bors and the other knights came to Sir Lancelot's bed, they found him stark dead, and he lay as if he smiled, and all around him there was the sweetest fragrance that ever they felt.

On the morrow, after chanting the Requiem Mass, the Bishop

and the knights put Sir Lancelot in the same horse-bier in which Queen Guinevere had been brought to Glastonbury, and took him to his own Castle of Joyous Gard, and they had always a hundred torches burning about him; and so within fifteen days they came to Joyous Gard. There they laid him in the body of the choir, and sang and read many prayers and psalms over him; and his face was left uncovered, that all folk might see him, for such was the custom in those days.

And right thus, as they were at their service, came Sir Ector de Maris, who for seven years had sought all England, Scotland, and Wales for his brother Lancelot. When he heard the noise, and saw the choir of Joyous Gard all lighted up, he dismounted from his horse, and came into the choir, and there he saw men singing and weeping. And they all knew Sir Ector, but he did not know them. Then Sir Bors went to Sir Ector, and told him how there lay his brother, Sir Lancelot, dead. Sir Ector threw his shield, sword, and helm from him, and when he beheld Sir Lancelot's face, it was hard for any tongue to tell the doleful complaints that he made for his brother.

"Ah, Lancelot," he said, "thou wert head of all Christian knights. And now, I dare say," said Sir Ector, "thou, Sir Lancelot, there thou liest, that thou wert never matched of earthly knight's hand; and thou wert the courtliest knight that ever bare shield; and thou wert the truest friend to thy lover that ever bestrode horse; and thou wert the truest lover of any sinful man that ever loved woman; and thou wert the kindest man that ever struck with sword; and thou wert the goodliest person that ever came among press of knights; and thou wert the meekest man and the gentlest that ever ate in hall among ladies; and the sternest knight to thy mortal foe that ever put spear in the rest."

Then there was weeping and grief out of measure.

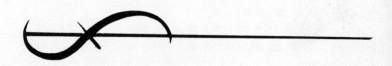

Reading, Writing, and Discussion of
MORTE D'ARTHUR

1. Try to follow the action of the romance chronologically. Notice how the narrator shifts from present to past with little transition. Read with the character of the romance in mind. What elements of style and structure can you attribute to the oral tradition? **2.** Notice the frequent use of *so . . . so then . . . after . . . meanwhile . . .* What reasons can you give for such transition? **3.** Decide on the most dramatic scene in the opening section. Read this aloud to the class. **4.** Identify the villain and the hero. How does the author describe them? List the adjectives used. **5.** Make a list of all characters who appear in the first part. Identify them. Separate the evil characters from the good. **6.** Trace the genealogy of King Arthur. **7.** Make a list of qualities the author attributes to knights. Make a list of qualities the author attributes to women. **8.** Is there a climax in each chapter of this first section? Is there a climax in the section itself? What is the unifying theme in this first section? **9.** You may some day study chemistry; then you will learn about base metals and noble metals. Gold is a noble metal. Malory uses *gold* over and over; e.g.

K. Thomsen
304

cloth of *gold*
    letters written in *gold*
        in every seat letters of *gold*
           his shoulders shone as *gold*
           claws of *gold*   *golden heart*

Find other uses of this word. Why does the author make use of this word. Should he have used synonyms? **10.** Cite examples of the preternatural used either symbolically or realistically.

SIR LANCELOT OF THE LAKE

1. From your study of medieval history or from research draw up a code of chivalry. Does Lancelot, *who excelled all other knights,* measure up to this set of rules? **2.** What motivation stirs Lancelot to go abroad for adventure? How does this show the spirit of romance? **3.** Make a list of Lancelot's adventures. How does he overcome his foes? **4.** What part does disguise play in the movement of the story? Recall instances of disguise in other narratives you have studied. Is this a good technique for developing plot? **5.** Is Lancelot a believable hero? Justify your opinion. **6.** Take note of the author's creation of setting. How does it differ from description in the ILIAD? **7.** What is the most interesting chapter in this section? Write a series of sentences giving your reasons.

THE BOY OF THE KITCHEN

1. What part does coincidence play in the movement of this section? **2.** Is there an element of medieval life in this section that was not presented before? **3.** Examine the verbs that carry the action. Make a list of the general verbs and specific verbs. Take several sentences that have general verbs and rewrite, using vital, specific verbs. Notice what happens to the tone of the sentence. **4.** Make a list of words and phrases which are definitely medieval in feeling; e.g., *twelvemonth, plighted troth, truncheon*. Know the meaning and spelling of each. **5.** Make a list of the uses of color in this section. What does color contribute? **6.** Is there any foreshadowing of the eventual outcome of the story in *The Boy of the Kitchen*? **7.** What is the incident that reveals his true identity?

THE QUEST OF THE HOLY GRAIL

1. How does the author create a transition to this section? How does the author bring the listener up to date concerning the past? **2.** Show how the outcome of the Quest is foreshadowed. **3.** Notice the repetition of incidents in this section. **4.** Make a list of all the inscriptions. What is the purpose of these in the story? **5.** Galahad is privileged to see the Holy Grail. Why is he and not his father so privileged? **6.** Show what part surprise and trickery play in the movement of the story? **7.** Identify the climactic incidents in this section. Should the narrator have ended the story here? Discuss.

THE DEATH OF ARTHUR

1. Is this section anticlimactic? Trace back to the last mention of Arthur. Who is the true hero of the romance—Arthur or ancelot? Explain. **2.** How does the author bring together all the varied strands of the story? **3.** Discuss the ending. Is this satisfactory? Are there any persons or objects left unaccounted for at the end of the story? **4.** Reread the tribute to Lancelot at the end. Is it true? Does it sound sincere? Why does the tale of Arthur end with Lancelot's death? **5.** What effect does the passing of time have on the story? How does the author help the reader to be conscious of time? **6.** Discuss the appeal of characters: Arthur and Lancelot; Elaine and Guinevere. **7.** Does the character of Lancelot change essentially in the course of the story?

811   S
Sargent, E. N.
The African boy.

91483-

The
African
Boy

E . N . SARGENT

The

African

Boy

The Macmillan Company, New York

Collier-Macmillan Limited, London

A section of this book, under the
title "Santos: Tempo Rumba," first
appeared in *The New Yorker*.

First Printing
Printed in the United States of America

The Macmillan Company, New York
Collier-Macmillan Canada, Ltd., Toronto, Ontario

Library of Congress catalog card number: 63-14531

Designed by Andrew Roberts

*If a man does not keep pace with his
companions, perhaps . . . he hears a different
drummer. Let him step to the music
which he hears however measured or far away. . . .*

HENRY DAVID THOREAU

African Boy
give me my first soul, find the clay for my body

give my second soul,
    shape the form in which I am to appear
give then my third soul, the great one
    let me feel danger
    and let me return

When I have been ransomed at slave=sell
When I have made sixteen voyages under ground
When I have become a shadow
            when I have gone into a tree
give me my fourth soul
    Sékpólí
        sépkólí

F Á
F Á
LÉGBÁ
DÁ

The
African
Boy

Part 1

$\bar{A} K B \bar{A} L \bar{A} ' S \ \ S O N G$

or The Joining-of-Ways

From a legend of Dahomey

A strong-minded girl will make every effort to support the pain of the full series of ritual cuts . . . whose purpose is erotic and aesthetic enhancement . . . at one sitting. The fiancé or lover of such a girl is exceedingly proud of her bravery. . . ."

MELVILLE J. HERSKOVITS

The Dahomey, Vol. I

I think of the West African woman——

D. H. LAWRENCE

Bring me the sword death carries, the knife that lives in the eyes
The pain that enters the sight, the blade that lives in the rains
I thought about you all night, my eyes wept red stains
The knife went deep where the old cuts were;   no cries
Disgraced you, my brother, whose old cut is greatest of all.

The long grass waits for us, softly uncut,
Bending like green fire in the eye of the rains
How good it would be to lie down under these green skies
O! the knife went deep all the same
I shall never let you forget the place of seeing
Or the tears of blood that rise at your touch and fall

Nor will I forget you, my brother, whose old cut is greatest of all.

* Ritual Cut.

The cut of rain-wet straw, the longest cut, so that you will abandon
                                        yourself to my long hair
Above the mark of those who eat the night
Above the sign of those who drum the roads
   And the head=word
   Slanting
       aching

As when you talk to me the lightest talk, your playful voice drews me
                                        in its snare
These cuts become livid and pulse like the heart
And there is nothing you need be told
   I have bled words
   Silently
       straitly

You can see above ghosts and ancestors the deep-cut swelling
                                        of my exposed desire
Where the shy brain joins love's second sight
Eyes and mind humble to a double goad
   Your dread words
   Granting
       taking

Let me entangle you forever in the rain of my hair, in the lines of
                                        my transfigured hair
I already know the knife's burning art
I already know the power you hold
   Over my cuts
   Violent
       fateful

(6)

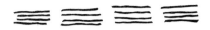

I need these ornaments to move you, my lover
The face has masks but I show reckless lines
When I leave you to return to my house

And you, going your way, look back at me
You see these extreme patterns;   strong
As the knife itself they drive your sated heart

Forward over the sinuous third vertebra of my spine
Old wounds are in flower more than the others wear,
Do not call me vain for each flayed opening

More than is usual costs unusual pain
Or in a dry season may drain the soul-shape
Leaving only formless dust of beginnings

Be glad I seek the strength to make your Being turn
No dancer moves to an unmoved drummer;   let the drum fall
I need these wounds to move you, my brother,
                              whose old wound is gravest of all

O

You seek a rock=deep source in fury of water
The face of maelstrom ways yielding as mine
Among shattered parts a known, simple design,
Seek there on the left cheek white at partings
But dark now once more with memory
Like the parakeet feather, like the sea-lily
A mark no larger than the tip of the index finger
A cut no smaller than the whole of farewell
The ragged, round circle will not be still
It is here that a man kisses a girl
He sucks with his mouth, seeking, and cries,   "Seek
Me, red circle, drop within whirling drink."

```
‗‗   ‗
‗‗   ‗
‗‗   ‗
```

Neck good to touch
Stays in the hut
Stiff as a bird

    flying away
    over a gray
    oracle tray

Neck good to grip
Slides in the shade
Marked like a snake

    twisting a note
    high at the throat
    passion has caught

Note of The Boa
One note over
The note heard

    coiling the nest
    crushing the breast
    rising possessed

Chord on echo
Forward the bright
Unbearable flight

    over the neck
    where a caress
    shivers to rest

I can undergo additional pain now
I will not wait another year for my full beauty
I will not delay the bringer of my full strength
The god of iron will not let evil result from these cuts
I have offered food to Fate's Trickster, the first guide
And he has eaten the seed within the seed
(Half for him and half for my watching lover)
They have given me money to heal earlier wounds,
An adept, the expert of many paths will work on me
I am not afraid   yet
Forward!   the knife is freedom as well as love;

Presence of my lover, friends, and of my kin
You challenge me   I seek the enduring honor
Of one who will not leave a thing half-done
Whether it be pattern or freedom or self
Go on with the knife, go on with the festival
I celebrate, and I am the celebration
I choose and I am the choice and I am the one;

A staff points downwards to the base of my spine
Of all possible patterns I choose this mark
My lover lights a fire with his slow, warm pressing
He kindles the place with his hands
The place is called pass=over *
Because in play he passes his hands over it—
Go away old people, I choose my lover
I choose his male beauty, I choose the sword;
I choose the staff with the sharpened head.

* *glimē:* literally, pass=over.

My own hidden staff draws him up
Do you think I am a pit of ghosts, a hole?
Alertness and conscious form be the price of freedom
Not the voice which says   "later—tonight"
Take the hand which caresses now
The friend of the inward staff
Point upwards from darkness, bury the carcass of lies
Cut, if you like, the hill of small pleasure
But let the creature come to know itself

    For a living, feeling thrust of stem well-rooted

    For a sentient flower on a long stem

    For an upward leap from grasslands as the lightning

    Gather your strength from the red inward dance

    For a point of flesh meeting a point of flesh

    Meet here and we shall meet forever again

    As when the drum begins over and over

    The single pass called   Joining-of-Ways

    Even under ground we shall meet,

    Make war against the shallow unburied death

    The dry death, the death by wind=voices;

    As in a green grove after hurricane the burned boughs
                              show tender buds at will

    Distilling even from salt spray a marvelous sweet liquor in deep still

    Or as wan morning winds these most vulnerable buds
                             with leaf of faintest rose

    Or as one road begins to resemble another and is ever so faintly all roads

As the water-bearer prints his heel on all dust
                         and at once bites all luscious, reddening plants

African Boy

Move forward in my joys and tap the beat of my laments

Distil the sweetness at the core of being
As you distil the heart of the growing yam
(only the knife knows the heart of the yam)
Until the time of great deeds, of art and of feasting
Lift swords!
                    our infinitesimal liquid=flashing essence
Patterns the living skin of the world
                         DRUM

   eighty-one times on the inside of each thigh
      nine rows of nine horizontal cuts of push me *

   if I tire now hold me down   show no mercy
      if I cower   wish me

   covered with coldness   cease now and I shall
      never hold a man's love   bold master

   fearless of blood   these terrible marks remain
      forever   to scourge the coward

   out from the soft love=flesh   from the tender
      inner fold of iridescent, incised thighs

   I want all things at once   first ecstatic flesh
      with its tall deep freedom

   never mind the cost if it means melting
      down every brass bracelet

   cherish the rebel voice   I want to make
      love   and guard these joyful patterns

   the living water of love starts all beautiful free seeds
      and grows   all human intuitions—those sweet
        plants with their idea=flowers

* "zido" cuts: literally, "push me."

DRUM

the living water of lovers   of fighters against
        chains   of free pattern-makers

push me into the fire   if I dance to any other
            beat   he who has the drum is master

And this day makes the drummer mine   he shares
        the heat of the knife   he knows how the cuts burn

he offers   his chest, his arms and the cups of his knees
            in sharing

he   laughs when the others try to drive him away
        he speaks sex=words   into the cuts;
        jokes! stories of the baboon's ass, and
        of how the elephant—

        no one loves pain for its own sake!

ah   the cuts are made to excite, they
                are made for the fingers of fishermen
                and for hunters' thighs

whose great staff rises to meet my
        womb=hook, *Zeuzo* * held within but always held

                                                high

hold me, friends, that I may hold my brother
hard for the sword that releases from bondage
hard for the knife that releases patterns

behold!

I open my eyes and
he of the house=roof   of the forest path and   of the boat
he has brought gifts

many=patterned cloths
each more richly dyed
(as the knife knows) than the one before.

* *Zeuzo:* a hooked staff, sign of nobility among the Dahomeans.

(13)

In the mysterious dawn under house=roof, or white twilight
I mix a pale liquid awakening from water as milk,
My hour-glass left hand stirs in the calabash,
I will give my beloved, who comes as a visitor, a love=sign
Despite mother and father, despite curious children,
                                        sweet secrecy clouds between

As I stir

Akasa * and sugar
Whiten my hand, hourglass patterns blanch, he has seen
How I remember uncovered, serene long-singing times
And though we may not embrace at the moment, he feels the past
He bends down and kisses the cuts of my left hand now soft as silk
In the presence of all, I give him sweetened drink;   mildly;   with the right.

* *akasa:* a white herbal essence.

When I was a small woman enlarging the lips of my sex, they gave me
                                                             a dancing-wand
And told me the story of Ākbala the strong girl
Who saw with eyes of desire the "chameleon's mate"
In the cult house
    praying
        chastely

The Chosen One tried to drive her away: I am pledged to the god
                           of this house for eight years and
Joining of flesh is a sin in sacred places!
But she seduced him, enticing him with songs,
So he lay down
    obeying her
        fatefully

While they mingled, the jealous god grasped the boy by the neck and he died;
Ākbāla, though, would not be driven from his body,
She defied the angry priests: He will awaken,
Here I stay
    today
      and
        always

Then they built a great fire of bitter leaves and placed the empty boy upon it
Pouring palm oil over him to burn away her love;
The spirit of the boy watched from a tree how his body
Turned ashy gray
    painfully,
        hatefully

If I do not enter the fire with him I shall live in loathing of myself,
                                                    said Ākbālā;
She began to sing, and when she had finished her song
She threw herself into the flames. O
Fear-full parts
    belly and heart
        be brave

Remember the beautiful vodu boy and the strong girl who loved him
                                                    even in the fire
Remember how they walked forth hand in hand
Unharmed, their bodies moving in harmony
Remember that
    when you faint
        or fail

Remember how the villagers danced, and how the King ordered them to
                                    gather and hear his command:
"I, Metonifi, the first King of all the world, I who rule the gods,
                                    destiny, the animals and man,
I tell you, every child, even one called by a god to the cult house,
                    must be allowed to play with women and see the sun—"

Dance, my heart, to Ākbālā
                    her story has power,
If you break the rule it changes;   this pattern has power;
Therefore knife, upon my belly blaze the chameleon
Subtler than the leopard, swifter than the crocodile, one
        mutable way
            daring
                and
                    graceful
(16)

I need your deep cut to move me, my lover
No ornament would ever turn these limbs
Quick to your fancy   passing and repassing

Over the same ground unashamedly
You cease to be ashamed of your love=hurt
Lost, buried in sand there will be songs

You least expect of prophecy and desire
To follow the burden of the drum you bear

Instinct and intellect are and do the same
As lovers' fluids   they rouse the core and shape
With living flow each uninformed beginning

They wake the sleeping drum, the dancers call,
And I   –
                I need your dangerous wound my brother,
Your grave ordeal, your ancient burn and scald,
I need your loss, your cised song to move me,
                        whose burden is greatest of all.

Africa, with the sun spread out on her breast,   pride

Of many ornaments; arms, forehead, perpendicular lines between the eyes

On temple, on the cheeks, on the neck

On the chest, at the back of the neck, at the base of the spine

On the lower abdomen and finally   on the thighs!

I praise these variations

Both in the number of cuts given at any one time and the order in which
                                designs are placed upon the body,

Africa, with her limbs stretched to the sun

And her Children of the Hunter, who-are-poor-people—

> "We have come

> If it is well you shall see

> If it is not well you shall see"

Mother who will not let them forget the place of seeing

Within the mask   sing   who has sent her child to deliver me.

I feared to be carried off by the dark, out of mind,

My whole life borne apart as or in a dream farther and farther

Then desperate farthest;   but not by death;

Not death does this nor madness nor crossing water, nor the gods
with their signs

But separate ways within too low or too high

For one nature;

I feared my own person, with its sexual powers, its reckless
leaping   –   forward! and the patterned
marks of experience on its soul=shape;

Captured, each one chained, hungering and alone,

These separate selves were slaves to an impure master;

      We have come

      If it is well you shall see

      If it is not well you shall see

Song limned in the dark to hold back fear

Join us, silver-eyed, who are blindly gathered here.

(19)

He who partakes of all offerings but who is not a god

He who feeds the children of the serpent and the bird=children living
in-a-hole, and the pig=

Children-stubborn-people;   those of the word which causes laughter
—and those of the river of blood

Also people of the route of the sun, and children=iron=within;

And also swamp waders;

He who keeps the leopard, the crocodile and the boa and the dog,

Who leaps with the chameleon but who is not he:

       We have come

       If it is well you shall see

       If it is not well you shall see

Let him come forth at last to the place of seeing

The naked stranger with his male beauty

Men of force, impotent men of impure fancies   haughty
Givers of bad counsel,   you wanted me pale and helpless to serve your ends
You offered me brass bracelets to deny my sex, and I listened
Ashamed of my leaping fancies of man and mask
Among the impotent nations   –
How the wheat-field is gold=dark like a strong man
And how the strong lover is like the rippling wheat

>We have come

>If it is well you shall see

>If it is not well you shall see

Daily bread to the children of prophecy and desire!
Towards the end self blossoms into self,

>>flowing into ether and fire.

Brothers, do not forget the mother who gave us food   warmed

By her fire or cool and fresh from gardens known to us or unknown,

Remember her reckless games with staff and snake

And sword and dancing-wand!   her fanciful times,

Remember her voice which is a wild yet perfect drum

Praise her variations

Her changing tempo and tone, the numbers of patterns worked in
                                    line and color upon her body, and
                                    always within

The power that moves the dancers
            "We have come
            If it is well you shall see
            If it is not well, you shall see—"
Children whose song is limbed with fire like the planets at her knee

Lovers and heroes, masquers come darkly yet with her infinite eyes
                                    and bear forth me.

IN THE BOAT

Chants from the Yoruba

"We bring sweet honey"
Fisherman's song, Traditional

I

Unwinder of free
Tidal journey
Glider to sea
By sea-lily
I will not be
Tied to a tree
They buy the body
For five brass bracelets

      Strike with your ranging iron axe
      Eight dancers bending down in their tracks
      Eight dancers upright as lances
      Shaking their iron bells like chances
      And two other secret ones in trances
      With blood and ashes on their backs;
      Loose the possessed ones lying in stacks,
      The true secret is the awakening!

They take the dream-soul
And break his double
A slave's children
Remain slaves
No day is as sweet
As the day a tree falls
Speak with your hand
Inside me

      They cut the sex of maiden kind
      They make a cannibal of the bride
      They show where the young man is tied
      With no lover to hear his cry,
      The maiden must pierce her lips or die,
      She might tell dangerous secrets, I
      Speak to you, knower of grass
      Rower in the race
                bringer of sweet honey.

On each side the gold=green land moves filled with endless desire
A sparkle of creatures undimmed by day and unquenched by night
Who with their kernels, like palm nuts, of ceaselessly sharpening life
Turn to each other though linked and murmur and clasp and bite
With a splendor of spending the boatman, under no roof, takes for a Sign
Witness of fate, his orbit averting the long envious tide
If we could know thee in full we might safely bathe in thy smile
And the seeing into all creatures that is thine eye,
Sign burned into the riverside tree on the right side
Letters buried in bark at the recurring mysterious site
Forgotten script of termite and the larger poets who work in the light
Birds, rodents, antler-shedders and man two-legged with his pouch of fire
Who told him how to strike flint subtly and take fire to wife
Man, intent on his artful, individual, unconsidering design
Man is there and the hunter hunts him with a great silent cry.

III

Not but there is something fitting about all this:
Who can string the frog's beads about his child's wrist
Or pull the thread of a spider to mend his wind
Or bandage his head with bees, or tie his tongue with nits?
You cannot avoid the everlasting, inward-breathing kiss
Or fail to return outward if you do not wish to be killed.
The young man never hears the death of his pointed stick
The young woman never hears the death of her woven shift.
Who looks at beauty and does not see it will never be skilled
Who looks at beauty and will not see it loses his wits
Who looks at beauty and cannot see it will soon be kissed.
The gold-tipped arrow of beauty is often shot to miss.
The patterned green beads of beauty are often loosely pinned.
The infinite winding beauty may turn on the arm and hiss,
Who looks at beauty and sees may heal the claw-fingered sick;
Ecstatic bended river-arm,* open your living gift!

* Root of sound, vocalized breath of one
swinging an axe.

Honey was the first measure of when you knelt
Voiceless as a bent fledgling before a snake
Will-less as the furry place hawk delves
How much honey do you carry over the waves

Summer in a gourd, treasure in store I brought
Coming at a word to spend the hoarded pay
Comb-sweet honey, the share of times lost
All the honey I could carry out of the grave
All the honey I, the soft unborn
Could carry away in unimagined hands

And then you felt how choosing shape began
And sang
          You winds,
              Carry me along!
Honey of the first, formless, desiring choice
Uttered in the fast flow of a rising stream
How shall we sing the darkly clouded joy?
How much honey to win the mouth of the sea?

Boatman's song: "You winds, Carry me along."

V

Hunters and fishermen sing of the plants and animals
They find on their lonely walks or at night gatherings;
They sing the earth=sound green-gold and sexual,
The E sound on the drum and in language:
The red feathers are the pride of the parakeet
The white flowers are the pride of the green leaves
Two tiny birds jump over two hundred trees *
Our mascot delights women and the barren seas
He is strong and patient, he does everything to please,
He leads the male to the female when floods recede;
A great staff guides the bee on his aching track
A green staff guides the flesh on his pilgrimage
A belled staff guards the self on his fatherings,
He knows where the enemy mates and where he feeds,
He keeps the keel of the boat deep in the stream,
He has songs for the deceived and herbs for those who bleed,
He can understand the crocodile's cold shadow.

* Riddle—(the eyes).

Lullaby, lullaby
Watcher over my child
Who knows the crocodile
Hungry, gray-eyed

Armored crocodile
Hating the unseined stars
Where the great snake
Ripples endlessly

The sky is immense, crocodile
Jealous of warm blood
Yours is not the only law
"deliver the truth and die"

We have seen the Sea=lily
Riding with her red bud
To keep the cold crocodile
From gnawing down the sky.

VII

You winding shape
Of rivers ocean bound
Nakedness of waves
Flowing into sound=
Shape of floating flower,
Help me to escape
Crocodile power,
Ride the planet's back
With staff and song
—*You winds of space*

              Carry me along
Climb the sky rack
Seek The Boa

Call him poet
Who is born in a boat
By sixteen oil lamps

VIII

Lover of wildness, remember the youth who went into the leopard's lair
When your desire journeys up the ocean-river to an unimagined shore;
The leopard's eyeballs burn without sense, his cave is a rank house of fear
The tail of the leopard is never at rest, birds and rabbits are not in his stews
Power and pride are his claws—the hidden ones—men fear him everywhere
When the drums awaken him people cover their ears and close their doors
Nobody goes outside, the leopard's wild friends would eat them alive,
They glower, with shrieks of a fury not hunger they tear their shameful food;
  Yes, I know the leopard, but a strong lover may touch the leopard
                                      and live

  I am of the race who of old threw away their dead-stroking wooden oars
  Of those who used their live hands for paddles, I am of the
                                  *Unexpected People

  Whose Queen, **Sungbo made a great voyage northward seeking her
                                        clews,

  I am of the singing people who built the great wall   of Ilē-Ifē I am heir,
  I am owner of four thousand six hundred and ninety six oracle
                              poems of Ōdū ***

  When I know the tone, my iron-blooded   flesh-hooded song may stroke
                                   the untamed air

  Covering its wildness with caresses until the whole creature trembles
                              like a soft, spotted ear.

* *Yorūba:* literally translated.
** *"Sūngbō":* the Queen of Sheba.
*** *Ōdū:* verb, "you exert."

(34)

spirits of the east
spirits of the west
spirits of the sea
spirits of the north

You come from Ilē-Ifē, land of love;
as you do there so do here; if in truth
you come from the land of heroes
tell the secrets of this man's heart

This man's heart feels change, he becomes
soft as the unborn; he chooses his second shape;
he has two names; as they do in Ilē-Ifē,
land of song, so do here

> he is driven forth
> knives cut him free
> *how much honey*
> *will you carry to the feast?*

With his staff between my breasts
With his great staff between my fingers
With his mild guiding staff sharpened
                        and his eyes sparkling like fire,
With the green beads of infinity
                        wound about his left wrist;

Hunter of secrets
Mender of nets   mender of heads
      mender of the mating of plants and animals
Driver of the first desiring choice
Watcher over my child;

Glider to sea by sea=lily
Lover of wildness but not of the leopard
                        save his soft, spotted ear
Owner of the knife
Sharer of the feast

Our boat is frail
I feel the underswell
My honey=offering trembles in the hold
The waves of time beat against the gunwales!

Call them heroes who go forward without ceasing
Call him poet who goes forth to return
Call him a sacred king of Ilẹ̄-Ifẹ̄
Who passes through famine and the cities of death
Call him poet who rejoices in the staff
Who rejoices in the race to deliver sweet honey;
   You know the cold eye of the crocodile
   You know the warm red of the sea=lily
   You feel the outward-pouring, sinuous current
   Bringing you and taking you away
   Shaken, do not call The Unshaken Tone
   On open water or beneath low leaves
   'Offspring of The Boa wearing-the-crown,
   Changeless-in-changing-tide, Untiring One—'
   Let flow sweet freedom, terrible to slaves!

How much honey do you carry over the waves?

XII

We do not sing a mourning song without death
We do not sing a boating song under house=roof
Or a racing song without honey

We do not call on the one who is nameless
There are no praise-names for the unknown one
We bring a calabash of sweet honey

It is sacrilegious to sing when feelings have not been aroused
It is death to sing without the tone of the heart
Such song is the spoiling of a secret

Let me not sing the spoiling of a secret
Let them not say I kept death under my cloth
As the gods arrive, unexpectedly, let me sing

Joy to the hunter and boatman, joy to the guide
Joy to the Staff which brings me this far
Joy to the voyage, joy to the streaming waters

    Winds, you winds carry me along
    With golden-streaming honey, sweet-to-worship.

Part I I I

A W A K E N I N G   O F   A   D R U M

In the ceremony of awakening a drum,
there will be the refrain 'I am
learning, Let me succeed' or alternatively
'I am listening, Let me understand' . . .

''VOICES OF GHANA''

The great human serpent over everything——

WILLIAM JAMES

Let there be an awakening!

—Some say a man and a woman descended from the sky
They held hands
(the dead hold hands while crossing rivers)
They passed through the four magically protected entrances
They passed over the mountain that separates the two worlds

—Take away the songs sung in your honor but not the voice of the singer

Take the drum rhythms but not the drummer!

—The dancer throws his body from side to side

—Now at last there is time
                    to tell the resilient life
                              of sacred things

—Some say everything that happens has already happened in the sky
These do not wear masks, do not pierce their ears
(what is said will not go inside one ear and out the other)
They do not cicatrize their bodies, saying, man cannot improve
                              upon the creation of the gods
They do not celebrate the earth;   their vodu is a shining mirror
                              called Dark=Bright

But these allow human sacrifice . . .

—Some say in the beginning was a sacred cage=
Dwelling for patterned serpent-life
(if the center is alert no harm can come)

                    I am listening
                    Let me understand

We know a gigantic tree in the depths of a vast forest
A great snake hanging down, reaching and reaching
Down to the center of the earth, always downward
When it touches the earth it is long enough and strong enough
                                        to reach the sky

—Protect us as you protected the first woman and man
Against ourselves, against each other
                            against human sacrifice

Against what will not let a thing be born
Against "we do not know what we do not wish to know"

—Ever since the manifold creator created things
The drummer is treated gently and kindly
(he drums so that he may get something to eat)

                    I am learning
                    Let me succeed

—Wisdom and earth=joy, twisted iron and a bell
You who opened a man's and a woman's eyes   (for we were born blind)
If you are gods speak now and defend yourselves
Or you will be disemboweled, roasted and eaten

What may be called the serpent, what may be called children of the serpent
Born with royal patterns of nerve-cells
Full of serpent=life   prophetic craft and skill

Awaken!

—Deep in the bush   deep in the inmost tree
All things flexible, sinuous and moist
Are
    All things that fold and refold and do not move on feet
                            though sometimes they go through the air
The rainbow has these qualities   plant=roots   the umbilical cord
And the life of man, the one who is asked to explain;

Listen to the drummer:

If the gods are called they come;   in whatever tone they are called
                            they come, but larger
Therefore wisdom says it is better to make masks
Ritual and form and memory
The things the gods love in man
                the dangerous and disproportionate gods
For himself man has the unseen serpent=life

            I am listening
            Let me understand

Drums and shadows tell us where we are
                    where we have been
                        and where we shall be

In the vast forest that opens like a fan
                        with many ribs

Or a cage of sacred staves

One of our members bears the unbearable
Feels on his cheek the forbidden insult
And we who drum feel with him
His mark appears upon us with its pain
We rise as one spirit
                    brothers
                        whatever our vodun

Come
Running-at-once from horned Togoland to the worm of Whydah
From Ghana's Ēwē hills and perhaps even farther (who knows
                                how far they come)

straight-as-a-spear

running-mad-through-the-villages-until-insult-is-avenged

Nothing stops them   they set fire on fire
No chief or chief's wife remains   no palace or temple

            The sacred cage is carried aloft
            Poets, singers dancers all run mad
            The living drum and the dead answer

            They drum and the living reply

            Heroes awaken   single perilous exploits

            Act   without ancestors or procession

            (if-the-center-is-alert-no-harm-can-come)

            Inside the cage the serpent=life moves

            Far away a pale shadow comes
            Through hills and waters moving to my drum
            Echoing my beat with a pulse small as grass
            Listen to the white shadow:

(46)

In the long night of awakening my eyes began to be wet with tears

    We answer, Fire eats grass until it comes to a fast runner

I ask, why was I given a green life?

    No need to fear
    You will only be as many others are

And if the breast shrivels and the babe hides his face
Hides his face in his hands like an old man

    No need to fear
    You will only be as others are

And if I watch him die, if he shrivels in my arms like a leaf—leaf of my
                                           bough
If we lie down on the earth and the earth withers
If men come with seed and there is no longer lust for planting
And then if we eat the seed—how shall I make them see it?

    No need to fear
    You will only be as many others are

Now I must make them see him, now or never again
Our little brother withered, his blood fouled with hunger,
                               no moisture for his tears
His mother with her stretched grin of grief beyond grief
Look! they are there and we are here, eating,
All must die;   those two will die sooner   but we shall die forever
                              if we do not see them

    No need to fear
    You will only be as others are

What if the war comes and we go as they go
Alone to the festival, alone yet not alone
But with a babe at breast and unspeakable death drifting down,
The green greyed from our land, the thousand-year delights of
craft and skill
Gone in an instant—what of the dry river-bed we shall know
And the stone upon stone   the fire upon ashen fire?

No need to fear
You will only be as others are

My cord is buried under a secret tree
If a figure is carved from the wood am I that figure?
If a mask is fashioned from the bark am I that mask?

My tree is a sanctuary for serpent=life
The snake likes to be there with a long reaching
With a long touching, until it is time, of every thing

What if they take my cord
What if they take my tree
What if they take my reaching?

No need to fear
You will only be as many others are

Listen:

The serpent goes free where there is water
Needs mingling of male and female fluids
Needs the living water of voyages
In silent mornings

I am learning
Let me succeed

The serpent's sign is an ear like an eye
Double flower   open to the word and the tone=

Color   I have a daughter
She is a white lily, a white rose, cyclamen white=
Blooming in the time of great snows, at a sunny window
Let her not wait for a lover drunk with carnage
Let her not wait for a soldier back from the wars
                    who smells of death in the morning doorway
Changed by the western star, she was formed of disasters overcome
Caress this lovely head of Europe lifted by the breathing wind
                                    and planted here

Give her milk and sweet water, and a supple, knowing body
Give her the African heaven of dancing ghosts,
                    of palm trees and yams
                    of the long, warm evening sun

Talk to her from Madagascar
Serpent=wise through the jungle
                    sing to her
From the Ēwē mountain that separates the two worlds

Snake=wise
        rainbow=wise
                    along the ocean=river
Your tone comes   in the blood
                    hold her as a friend
The shape of your tone is litheness intertwined

                    I am listening
                    Let me understand

Enfold her once or infinite twice
Before you coil away to touch the Indian strand . . .

(49)

I know a small room in a vast city
Deep in a maze of tangled, living stone
The serpent is there with a strong reaching
Downwards, ever down to the center of the stone
Touching the life of man   gone
                                        far to the last darkness

Flowers grow there darker than last years
The red gone purple, the purple gone to black
By some subterranean stream
I am only a leaf of grass
Come to dip in your waters   alone
And not with secret strength or hidden friends
                                        wan   in your darkness

From the pass that separates the two worlds
From the joining of ways
Even from the boat I have come
Do not be afraid   I have not come to drink
I have not come to take
I am only a leaf of grass
                        dipping in the stream

Of the great snake
Who ripples and reaches and tenses
Touching the center of the earth and the bright-dark sky
Who ripples and reaches

—I thought I heard the voice of a white woman
Singing our songs beside an Ēwē stream
I thought I heard the tone of the white woman
Across the mountain that separates the two worlds

Let her look upon the farthest eyes of darkness . . .

(5 0)

I am only a single blade of grass dipping,
                              dipping in the stream
Do not be angry, I have not come to drink
I have not come to take   but only to wash
To lave myself in living rippling waters

To freshen   to strengthen   to redden my pale root

I went to read my poems in the Capitol

There were vultures circling over the Library of Congress,

The fountains with their green dolphins and humans
                    were drained dry that day

An oriental prince drew a crowd in the domed marble hall
                         with its turquoise and scarlet
                         and carnelian

   There were no new words in my poems;

High in the mosaicked dome Dante   Shakespeare   and others
                    appeared   letters of gold

I went down to the cellar and read in a sound-proof room

The lines I had written   they choked me;   I thought I heard a drum
                    shadow of darkness

Calling across the hills and the many waters;   I thought
                    of my self

And how I, a woman, was reading poems into those crypts
                    to hold so long as the capitol stands,

   There were no new words in my poems;

Where is a word touching woman-and-man

How do you tell the live touch=root with ever-changing flowers?

We have a way of saying wound and a way of wounding

If we could speak the opposite we might know our next knowledge
                    that dark dimension of greatness
                    sensed, sometimes, at the end
                    of a life=time   or at nightfall

    There were no new words in my poems;

What is the opposite of a wound?   I asked myself that,

The tears flowed over my cheeks   against a blow

I thought   what is the word . . . closer and closer . . .
                    I thought I heard a drum

From a land where the women, even without bread, are poets

I thought I heard of soul=health woman-and-man

    There were no new words in my poems;

We went up to a high chamber overlooking the green

Trees, roofs of the town all verdigris in the white spring light
                    yet golden with approaching summer

From a wide balcony I could view the blanched limestone
                    and marble splendor

My tears ran down over the dry water-sculpture and the many tombs

    There was no new word in my poems;

An ancient silence held me   chain of a word
                                     held back too long in a dry throat
My freedom was too new, my fancy leapt half-formed
                                     and disproportionate
The serpent fed from my hand   from behind bars
                                     his head came through
I feared those ambiguous fangs (drawn or withdrawn?)
                                     where death may yet take all
    There was no true word in my poems

The world is a spacious place yet how narrow is our room

—I would not call the great goddess
                                     whose hand is as large as the dark
                                     side of the world
    I would not call upon her son and mate

    The wise do not call upon the gods
—Shadow of darkness I am calling, calling

Far away
            borne on by streams of ocean
The African Boy came
He wore no glass beads, cowrie shells or gold

Sent forth from his mother, who knows the lost truth of the night
With many sayings and many a vodu
To give him power over the blind, who must have something to touch

The forest people carved an image of him, but not frightful like a god
They made him human, of soft brown wood of the Serpent's Tree
And then, because he was afraid, they limned his eyes with silver
            so that he might see into all
                        and be seen by all
                                     who fear the dark

Human they made him and human they made his mother   with her
                        heavy bracelets   and her large limbs
                        scarred from the birth-hut how many hands
                        have clawed her frenziedly?

He mourned his dark mother on the alien shore;
She too has silver eyes   to reflect firelit festivals
                              but her face is charred
        how many times has she gone with bare-breasted terror
                              through deserted streets?

In a pale land   cold   among the unseeing
I saw the figure of a boy stand up for sale
Carved form   motionless on a block,
Brave knees of a four-year-old   he was like my son
And that look   of knowing a task for the first time.
People of the forest, what is the errand you sent him on,
                              the young hunter?
Why did the African Boy cross the water?

Ah   you have made him well with his vulnerable loins and his
                        clenched fists from which the staff was torn
Sign of nobility he might not carry among strangers
You made him well
But there are nails in his hands where the staff was, and
                        the mark of tears on his cheeks
Old tears   child's tears   run over and over and down;
Shadows of the forest, you taught him well—the game finds the hunter!

But why did you send him naked across the water?

—There is a bird who when she soars her daughter does not grieve
There is a bird who when she sings her son does not die
Perhaps he has come to hunt that bird
Or perhaps he has only come to change and grow
To strengthen   to freshen   to redden his dark root
Throw off your old slavery, white woman, and hear a word
From a land where the women even without bread are poets:

(5 4)

He comes   BIA: to strengthen
            with drum-beats
            with horns of eerie sweetness
            and with the streaming honey in his hands

bia   he comes   to freshen
            with life=color
            and with a long vine

            to redden: *bia*
            with serpent=life
                  that ripples and reaches
                                and tenses

            I redden
            my self *bia*

            you redden

                  you become red
                        you grow vivid inside-and-out

bia   takes on earth-power
                  serpent=life
                        nerve=life loose in the world

we kiss   we caress
              sexually we know
                  esthetically we know

you join   in knowing
              you plant joy
                  you nourish individual roots

they redden man-and-woman if both be free
they redden dark-and-light freely
they redden all, if all be free

                BIA: *to redden*

to allow a thing to be born
to travel from open town to opening town
with chant and festival and drum

to-be-and-to-know   the inward wreathing

color   and   line

I say wait for the next arrival

If you call a thing it comes
renewed
in
human
touch

bia   *Let those who seek the hunter find the hunter*

Let those who see love=freedom join ways

I am learning
Let me succeed

Let those who seek the serpent touch the serpent

I am listening
Let me understand.

(5 6)

TEMPO RUMBA

"We Are Reborn"

Who is it speaks to me among the dancers?
It is the god Dámbálla
riding fast
    riding far
    riding all the way from Africa

Dance the colors of life   and I shall watch
Dance the deep unfathomable night sky
Darker than purple, darker than dark black
Dance the white beads of the sun and stars
Paler than pale amid the shadow=worlds

Who is it touches me among the dancers?
It is the god Dámbálla
he who is so tall
    with long fingers
    and the five-beat

Dance the gold of honey, the green=gold
Of the gods' strong names   one of them is so strong
That if I say it the whole world disappears from view
"Aidō-Husū - - - - - - - - -"
"I-speak-in-my-own-voice-and-I-am-understood"

Who is it reaches down among the dancers?
It is the god Dámbálla
the great traveler
    rainbow rider
    dark=bright

Dance the blue of thunder   for seven days it will storm
With wild and terrible rage like that of the newly born
Dance the brass blade which carries the serpent on both sides
And whose candidate comes forth from the dark shrine alone
—   Softly, softly, it is only your father

BA BA LU

Who is it holds the serpent by the neck?
It is the god Dámbálla
stranger on the shore
        riding fast
        riding without fear

Dance the red color of the three-day madness
(There is a bird who when she sings her child does not die)
A child, a child does not quarrel with its mother

MA MA LU

But if I cut the bird's throat and the blood runs
Over and down?

Blood cries for blood
I am your child says the drop of blood on the stair
I am your dear child says the red place on the floor
I am your own dear child says the dark place in the bed
A child, a child does not need to fear its mother

BA BA LU
MA MA LU

Sweep the house and all about it
For a friend comes from afar
yield, keepers of the door
    it is the god Dámbálla
    who rides here

It is He
The dark traveler
with the rainbow between his knees
    bright horseman on the shore
    and the birth=cord   long liana

Wild-grape vine   free
Holding-us-together
    serpent leaping in his hand
    he is near
    he is quite near

    Living hand   hold my hand!
A cry is heard)
    Gésú - - - - - - - - -
    Gésú=
    Dámbállá

        DAMBALLA LU

FIVE LYRICS

African Violet

tender leaves, full of life's fluid
light=red blossom
whatever delicate is given to this hand
whatever needs the morning sun
and succulent springs to drink
and warm nights
give grace to touch
give quiet breath
give conscious flesh
give tender mind
                    Light red
let me cut your leaf
listen to things sometimes rather than beings
or wait for you to double and part

African darkness, yield   midnight art
let him come forth at last to the place of seeing
figure cut from a tree
silver-eyed
conscious of death
carved by the lash
his warm thoughts
frozen in hard rivers
I hate to see that evening sun
go down in this child's untouching land
Blossom of red light
let our touch be renewed.

The White Cyclamen

the palest flower
keeps red stems
downy as an infant's ear
or the sunny side of a pear
and her petals, even in the white
light of noon
give back glow
give live vein
in the hush
of a loving mind.
          Who tends
her has loveliness all year long
This is a good plant, and strong
I see him standing above her

His hands unsteady yet ready to love her
his face still green with self reddening a bit;
he trembles but touches her, with lucky wit
parts the flowers to see red stems
heavy and lush
his own vein
grows heavy to know
her scentless swoon
his face reflects her softness day and night
she has him in her snare
She draws him near
and he comes
each day truer, a tightening drum.

Woman And Man

this way
that way
where is the way

Let it come to you like rain on house=roof,
beating, like drums to the dancers,
the tight red skin of a drum, the
                    plucked string of a harp
the flute
holding a stop
be always there like the rainbeat
the light tapping on taut skin
to the dark female nerve
be the flute=bird
in me

in you
by true touch
I feel a sharp swerve
to my song, male and taut
I am there like the rainbeat
holding a stop
I suit
your bright red skein of inward muscles,
                    these I draw
streaming, like dancers to the drums
let it come to you   like rain on the roof
there is the way
that way
This way

Dark=Bright

what a way to look at the morning
what a day
when the rainbow of the brain
flashes red rays
of interior sunrise   all scarlet
in the sun's gaze
the ghostly flowers wake
Thirsty calling, take my heart and slake
your mouth all day long
here is black bread and strong
crimson wine

Take the experienced one, bear him forth out of mind
You farthest god, make me more delicate . . .
but this altar of morning says nothing is offered yet
What does he care for wine whose staff is free
or for bread who tastes of flowers
or for any praise
or mortal shade who is dark=bright
forever   Stranger   slay
our death and raise the murdered flesh of love
                                        O rainbeat ray
of darkness yet arrayed with radiant morning.

Story from the Old Country

In a quiet place let us learn.
"*Bā-Oulē*"—these are not merely letters, as some have claimed:
Beloved son, Once upon a time
There was a queen whose people fled the enemy;
A nameless tribe, poor in war,
They came to a deep river
They could not cross
They felt the enemy's spear
They felt his arrow,
Rich only in songs
And images,
   they wept.

From the center of weeping an ashy priest crept,
"Send a little boy
Weighted with heavy fear
And his mother's sorrow
And his sisters' loss
Into the deep river."
None would give, although the fierce shore
Bled; at last the queen lifted her own four-year-old gently
And offered him to the waters; Once-upon-a-time
They say, a river parted and our people were named:
"*Bā-Oulē!*" the queen cried *We-Are-Reborn*.

THE RITUAL CUTS

("there-one-sees-place")   The first cuts are placed over the bridge of the nose and beneath the eyes.

("rain-wet-straw")   Straw, signifying hair. The long lines are made near the hair to emphasize its beauty; following them are two very fine cuts called "head-word."

("you-seek" or "kiss me")   It is here, on the left cheek, that a man kisses a girl.

("the cuts that, at parting, cause the man to turn and look back")   This series is marked on the third vertebra of the spine.

("neck-good-to-touch")   When a man embraces a woman he caresses these scars.

("loins-place-cicatrizations" or "pass-over")   The choice of this design rests with the individual. E. N. Sargent chooses "the sword."

("push me")   A series of nine rows of nine horizontal cuts, placed on the inside of each thigh.

("water-drink-milk")   An hourglass design, placed on the left hand.

This design is placed under the navel, and is often a representation of a lizard or some other animal.

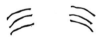

("shoulder-cuts")

The last design is placed between the breasts, and often takes the form of a series of links or of straight lines radiating from a central point. "Children of a hunter, who are poor."

The preceding material is to be found in Volume One of Melville J. Herskovits' definitive study, *The Dahomey*, J. J. Augustin, Publisher. Glückstadt, Hamburg and New York.

Bibliography

Beier, Ulli, *Bashonga Music*

Ellis, A. B., *The Yoruba-speaking Peoples*

————, *Ēwē Language*

Epega, Rev. D. Onadele, *The Mystery of the Yoruba Gods*

Forde, Daryll, *The Yoruba-speaking Peoples of S.W. Nigeria*

Herskovits, Melville J., *The Dahomey*

Manoukian, *Ēwē-speaking People of Togoland and The Gold Coast*

Phillips, Ekundayo, *Yoruba Music*

Rutherford, Peggy, *Darkness and Light*

Westerman, Diedrich, *A Study of the Ēwē Language*

Black Orpheus, Nos. 7, 6 (special editions), 3.

ODU, Nos. 2,3,4,5,7, General Publications Section, Minister of Education, Ibadan, Niger.